Vinegrowing in Britain

Vinegrowing in Britain

GILLIAN PEARKES

With illustrations by the author

J. M. Dent & Sons Ltd · London

First published 1982
Second fully revised edition 1989
© Gillian Pearkes 1989

This book is set in 11 on 12pt Monophoto Sabon

Printed in Great Britain by Butler & Tanner Ltd,
Frome and London

British Library Cataloguing in Publication Data

Pearkes, Gillian
Vinegrowing in Britain. Rev. ed.
1. England. Vineyards. Grapes. Cultivation
I. Title
634′.8′0942

ISBN 0–460–04771–X

Contents

Illustrations

To Geoff and Janet

Preface

There is today a need for a new book on viticulture in England, the emphasis here being on the word 'new' – a book covering the more up-to-date practices and thinking on all aspects of this wide field, rather than a reworking of existing books, full of facts which we already know.

The drawback with all books on practical and technical subjects is that they can soon become out of date. This is unavoidable, and if writers allowed such a problem to inhibit them, no books would be written. There comes a time when one has to take the plunge.

Therefore, I would ask experienced growers to bear with me while I explain certain simple basic procedures which they already understand, and remember that many readers are either totally or partially new to the winegrowing scene and will need to know all the facts.

This book offers a treatise on the choice and preparation of a site, the vines to plant, the planting, training, pruning and annual maintenance of a vineyard, with references to nutrition and health, followed by suggested ways of making fine wines.

The many superb standard works on the wines of the different fine wine areas of France and Germany invariably omit real information on viticultural practices and details of winemaking techniques. One is treated to in-depth studies of the geographical and topographical or visual location, histories of wine towns and châteaux, the growers and their family histories, the food of the area, the output and marketing of the wine, vintage charts and so on, but no facts or details to satisfy the aspiring winegrower who searches in vain for clues on how fine wines are grown, blended, made and bottled.

In desperation one realizes that the only way to gain this knowledge is to go and study in the winefields that have an association or link with practices that could relate directly with our own embryonic wine industry. In this way we might improve our methods in the field and in the winery and lead more of us, in time, to create fine wines that can hold their own against their European contemporaries.

The opportunity came for me to further my studies with the backing of a Nuffield Association travelling scholarship. Having submitted an application, and been summoned for an interview, with the belief firmly fixed in my mind that this very professional and august body would not consider a mere woman in a man's world, particularly on such a 'way out' and, perhaps, almost frivolous subject as wine growing, I was more delighted than words can express to learn in due course that my application had been accepted.

This came for me at a vitally important time in my life. I had decided, after ten or more years of trial work on vines, to grow wine commercially – a big decision for me. After planting a vineyard, there followed two years of dedication. One's effort is devoted to the training of the young vines and incessant weed control, two years of work with no reward, no harvest to show for the hundreds of hours of toil. If ever one suffers self-doubt, it is during these first two years of sheer slogging to maintain the *status quo*. The decisions have been made; on row width, on vine varieties, on the eventual wines that one will have to offer to one's customers. These decisions initially involve days, weeks, months of planning, and the result of a vast shedding of vines with cultural problems, of studying the existing vineyards, noting the few that were really successful, pin-pointing the factors that made them thus, and fathoming how these élite vineyards managed to harvest a crop in years that saw total failure in other vineyards.

And so it was not without misgivings that I set sail for France and Germany, more than half expecting to discover that we eccentric English growers were more foolish than we had allowed ourselves to believe, and that we were chasing in vain after the elusive crock of gold at the foot of the rainbow.

But gradually, it dawned on me that the very opposite was the case, the further I went, the more I saw, and the more experts to whom I spoke, the more convinced I became of the very real future that English wine could enjoy – an excellent future, but with certain very real reservations. Too few take the trouble to find *a really fine site* or realize how vital this is when attempting to grow a crop on its northernmost periphery. *The choice of site is even more important in Britain than it is on the Continent.* Very few take the trouble to ally the right vine variety with their site, all tending to grow one or both of the two most popular vines, Müller Thurgau and Seyval. Müller Thurgau has severe culture defects, particularly in poor summers; the other is a hybrid, and produces an acceptable wine in large quantities, but is a wine of moderate quality and style, and that only in a good year, for in a cool, wet year the Seyval also tends to bear few, if any, grapes.

With a definite trend towards longer colder winters, cold late springs and, consequently, a shorter growing season, we should look towards vines that require a shorter ripening season, vines that will ripen their grapes in a moderate or even poor summer so that productivity and income is fully maintained. With the new improved chemicals to assist vine health, mildew and botrytis should be less troublesome.

I returned full of optimism and high enthusiasm for the future of the English wine industry as a whole, and my confidence in my own project was restored; I was also full of gratitude for the opportunity to travel and to be able to absorb the atmosphere and viticulture of all the areas I visited.

I have written two reports for the Nuffield Association on my travels; the first a précis which was included in the booklet combining the reports of the nine scholars of my year, the second a fuller report on the facts, figures and findings assimilated during my journeys in France and Germany.

This book contains a fuller appreciation of the Continental comparison, a means whereby we may perhaps improve our own approach toward the growing and making of wine, and, perhaps, a clearer, less woolly set of guidelines for the grower of the future.

One must not be too rigid in one's philosophy. Be prepared to be flexible enough to change methods of training and choice of vine if either should prove to be wrong. We have several leading growers who have been sufficiently far-seeing to grub and replant. Major-General Sir Guy Salisbury-Jones at Hambledon grubbed ageing and unsuitable vines, and replanted and extended with high-quality champagne vines, which has upped the style and depth of his wine remarkably. The Paget brothers at Singleton, faced with acres of Chardonnay on an unproductive rootstock, at the best of times a vine of low yield in England, replaced this with Seyval to boost their output, and to complement the quality vines occupying the remainder of their 13-acre site. Ken Barlow at Adgestone on the Isle of Wight also took the same brave decision to replant a section of Reichensteiner to improve the quality of his blend.

New growers in particular should spend longer studying the local conditions and idiosyncracies of their site and microclimate, studying the sites, training systems and vines grown in other vineyards in their own and in other areas, and the successes and failures in other vine-growing projects – and try to discover why the less effective ventures have failed. All this research helps a plan for one's own vineyard enterprise to develop in one's mind, and will help to eliminate failure and wrong decisions. Thousands of pounds spent on making wrong decisions can be averted by employing the service of a vineyard consultant who will help by pointing out the pitfalls to avoid, and will assist in forming a plan of action to be followed in assessing the site, soil, planting and training programme, linking suitable vine varieties to the soil and site, providing names and addresses of suppliers of essential equipment, and follow this up with on-site advice during the formative stages of the young vineyard.

While pointing out that even now we are absolute beginners in this form of husbandry, still pioneers in a new field, we have so much to learn which is exciting, a very real challenge, particularly in a difficult growing season. However the new grower today is indeed fortunate in that he is able to avoid many of the mistakes of the earlier growers, and can, therefore, plant with a greater expectation of success.

Having briefly summed up the field I aim to cover in this book, may I leave you, dear reader, in the sincere hope that my efforts will include some new ideas in one or another of the many facets of the fate we choose to follow; may I raise my glass to our common bond, the Vine!

1988   Gillian Pearkes
                                               Yearlstone Vineyard,
                                               Bickleigh, Tiverton, Devon

1
Winegrowing in Britain Today

Soon after the Second World War, two men began, by sheer coincidence, growing vines for wine in southern England, quite independently of one another. They imported many vine varieties from the Continent, planting ancient noble varieties, some of the Vinifera crosses and several French-American crosses, known to us as hybrids, and grew these vines on a trial basis. The vines that succeeded in their respective vineyards were propagated and in due course they both wrote quite extensively on the results of their work.

Little did these early pioneers realize the size of the cult they had unwittingly begun. Very slowly the interest they generated began to impress fertile minds and all over southern Britain small vineyards began to be planted by enthusiastic growers anxious to try to grow their own wine.

As more books were published by these two remarkable men, so practical participation multiplied, and in 1952 the first really professional commercial vineyard was planted by Major-General Sir Guy Salisbury-Jones, at Hambledon in Hampshire. The site was ideal, a south-facing slope on chalk soil, perhaps a little high, but otherwise good, with adequate shelter and excellent drainage.

The subsequent success of Hambledon wine did much to fire the imagination, and one by one, slowly at first, then with gathering momentum, others followed suit. In 1960 Colonel and Mrs Gore-Brown planted England's second commercial vineyard at Beaulieu in Hampshire, a five-acre south-facing slope below their house. Here a variety of vines were planted to produce a rosé wine, using Seibel and Wrotham Pinot grapes to provide the colour in the wine.

Two or three years later Mr Jack Ward of the Merrydown Wine Company planted two vineyards near Horam in Sussex to provide grapes to process into wine at Merrydown. The performance and yield of these two sites varies widely, due to one having fairly adequate protection against the elements, and the other having very little. The wine, Horam Manor, is attractive, fresh and has some style.

In the mid-1960s, the enthusiasm began to spread and take hold, and slowly but surely vineyards were planted elsewhere, in Somerset, Devon, Essex and in Surrey. This gradual participation blossomed by 1970 into a veritable maelstrom of activity countrywide, a considerable percentage of the new vineyards being planted in East Anglia.

In 1967 all the then growers arranged a meeting, the result of which was the formation of the English Vineyards Association. This association has to a degree recorded, in the increase in its membership figures, the meteoric rate at which vineyards were, and indeed still are, being planted, since it is in the best interests of all growers to join.

Today about one half of the 500 members have vineyards of half an acre or more, an area which would indicate a minimum commercial planting, the total commercial commitment being estimated at well over 1000 acres.

Apart from the actual area devoted to vines, the rate of increase of vineyard planting is significant. There are sceptics and critics who still maintain that wine production in England is not a viable or profitable occupation. To put the Doubting Thomas out of court one only has to look at the calibre of the people planting vineyards. A very fair percentage are hardheaded farmers, who see wine production as a means of further diversifying their interests within their farming scheme, perhaps as a means of putting an area of steep land to good profitable use, but no farmer worth his salt goes into any new venture without first examining the capital outlay, the running costs, when a return on the investment may be expected, and examining the cash flow and the marketing angle very, very thoroughly. There is also, of course, the very considerable interest factor, for winegrowing is a fascinating, if sometimes fickle, occupation. The farmer realizes better than anyone just how dependent any crop is on the weather, be the crop hay, corn, roots, potatoes or maize – grapes are no exception.

Another group of people who tend to look at viticulture very seriously as a retirement interest and, hopefully, an income, are men who have served in Her Majesty's Forces, and are looking for a really absorbing and challenging occupation to stretch their initiative and energy, for many retire comparatively young and look for an interesting new way of life.

Others who may lead a very stressful and demanding professional life, may turn to viticulture as a way to escape at weekends, for vinegrowing is mentally a very therapeutic occupation, and allows the grower to lose himself, to great effect, in the annual cycle of growth, harvest and dormancy. A good many doctors grow vines.

Some comparatively young people see vinegrowing as a means of opting out of the rat race. Accepting a lower standard of living, perhaps, to gain a life in the open air, a life of honest toil has its own reward and especially when cultivating a most attractive crop – and escaping the stress and obligations of a commuting existence. The sensible approach to this could be to plant the vineyard and strive to maintain it at weekends until the fourth year, when one has some wine to sell, so that one eliminates the problem of cash flow or lack of income during the establishment period.

People from every walk of life are drawn to grow vines, which contributes to the considerable richness of talent and qualities to be found in the winegrowing fraternity. Therefore, apart from the bond we all share, all are interesting individuals in their own right. The wide collection of fertile minds has done much to foster a varied approach to ways and means of growing vines, and many philosophies on the aims and rewards of viticulture. Some look to yield as the one and only goal, and are quite satisfied to produce a large quantity of moderate wine. Others seek quality above all else, and are gaining a very considerable name for their beautifully made high-quality wines, their customers knowing they can expect a reliable, sound and fragrant wine with which they can both interest and impress their guests during a meal.

So much for the individuals, whose vineyards are shown on the accompanying map. How has the English Vineyards Association kept up with its fast-growing membership, how does it serve these members, and are there any achievements to date?

At the beginning, when growers then numbered perhaps 20 or so, the aim of the Association was little more than that of a friendly society and meetings were get-togethers where ideas and problems might be exchanged. Membership increased alongside a growing thirst for expert knowledge and advice and the Association began to take care of the educational demands by staging seminars, and annual winetastings where members' wines could be compared, different grape varieties appraised or otherwise; these events proved to be invaluable to the discerning.

The south-east of England was the birthplace and cradle of the new winegrowing, East Anglia became the next centre of activity, with a few outposts in other areas. As time went on, vineyards were planted fairly widely throughout all southern Britain, as far north as Lincoln,

1 Map of English vineyards.

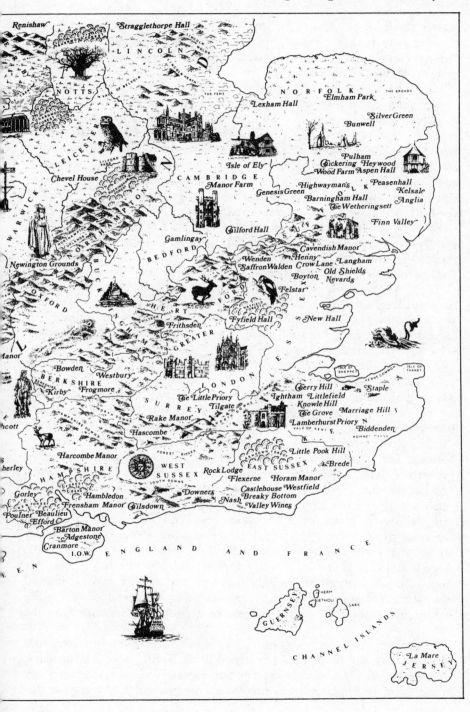

Renishaw · Stragglethorpe Hall

LINCOLN

THE WOLDS

LINCOLN HEATH

THE FENS

NOTTS

NORFOLK

THE BROADS

Elmham Park

Lexham Hall

Silver Green

Bunwell

LEICESTER

LILFORD PARK

Chevel House

Isle of Ely

Pulham

Dickering Heywood
Wood Farm Aspen Hall

Peasenhall
Kelsale
Anglia

CAMBRIDGE

Manor Farm

Highwayman's
Genesis Green

Barningham Hall
The Wetheringsett

NORTHAMPTON

UPLANDS

Newington Grounds

BEDFORD

Gamlingay

Guilford Hall

Cavendish Manor

Henny
Wenden
Saffron Walden Crow Lane Langham
Boyton Old Shields
Nevards

Finn Valley

SUFFOLK

OXFORD

BUCKINGHAM

HERTFORD

HATFIELD

CHILTERN HILLS

Frithsden

Felstar

Fyfield Hall

New Hall

GREATER

LONDON

ISLE OF
SHEPPEY

HERNE COMMON

ISLE OF
THANET

Bowden Westbury

BERKSHIRE
Kirby Frogmore

SURREY

The Little Priory
Tilgate

Rake Manor

Hascombe

NORTH DOWNS

Cherry Hill Staple
Ightham Littlefield
Knowle Hill
The Grove Marriage Hill
Lamberhurst Priory

Biddenden

VALE OF KENT

ROMNEY MARSH

HAMPSHIRE DOWNS

Harcombe Manor

FOREST RIDGES

WEST
SUSSEX Rock Lodge

SOUTH DOWNS

Little Pook Hill

Brede

EAST SUSSEX

Gorley Hambledon
Frensham Manor Guilsdown

Downers

Flexerne Horam Manor
Castlehouse Westfield
Nash Breaky Bottom
Valley Wines

Poulner Beaulieu
Efford

Barton Manor
Adgestone
Cranmore
I.O.W.

ENGLAND AND FRANCE

GUERNSEY HERM
JETHOU SARK

CHANNEL ISLANDS

La Mare
JERSEY

Worcestershire, Herefordshire, into Monmouth, Glamorgan and even Cardigan (as it was then was), in Gloucestershire, Somerset, Hampshire, Dorset, Devon and even in Cornwall. The south-west now proves to be a very well represented area.

Finding themselves cut off from the other centres of growers, the growers in the south-west formed their own Association in 1970, so that growers from this vast area could have the chance to meet, see each other's vineyards, and visit the Research Station at Long Ashton near Bristol where a vineyard was maintained and detailed studies are done on a wide range of subjects within the viticultural and winemaking spectrum. The Association also enjoys visiting experts from the Continent from time to time. Some four to six events are arranged annually for both professional and private growers.

In 1977 an Association was formed in East Anglia to cater for the interests of the commercial growers in the area, and in 1978 The Weald and Downland Association was formed to encompass both private and commercial growers in Hampshire, Kent, Surrey and Sussex.

These Associations do not in any way serve to compete or replace the national English Vineyards Association, but merely to provide growers in the more rural and far-flung areas of the country with a chance to meet and talk with kindred spirits from time to time, and to enjoy educational lectures and visits.

The south-west growers stage their own regional wine contest each year, inviting Masters of Wine, wine merchants and restaurateurs to judge their keenly fought classes of wine produced within the area.

The English Vineyards Association now occupies itself in striving to obtain certain rights and privileges for its members from Parliament, the Ministry of Agriculture, the Customs and Excise, and the European Community. Many minor, and several major concessions have been granted to date, the more important being the right of growers to retain 120 gallons per annum for their own use, duty free, and the right of growers to pay duty a month after selling their wine, instead of paying duty before the wine leaves the premises. We have also been granted the right to attach a seal of quality to our wine if it passes a series of stringent organoleptical and chemical tests, which will prove that the wine is sound and stable and of a certain standard. In due course it is hoped that the duty we pay will be lowered, and that we may be granted a structured framework whereby, according to the standard of quality our many wines achieve, this degree of quality may be stated on the label.

In France all wines are sold under one of four different categories. Starting with the least first they are, Vin de Table, next Vin de Pays, followed by Vin Delimité de Qualité Supérieure (V.d.q.S.), the top wines being granted Appellation Controlée status, the rules and regulations under which the latter are produced being very strict indeed. The consumer is, therefore, offered a choice of quality of wine for each area, the status being reflected in the contents and the price.

Germany has a similar system whereby her wines are categorized, the lowest denomination being Tafelwein (table wine), next Landwein (wine of the country designated), next Qualitatswein bestimmter Anbaugebiete (quality wine of designated regions, Q.b.a.) and the top-grade wines are classified as Qualitatswein mit Pradikat (quality wines with special attributes). There are five categories within this top classification. They are as follows: Kabinett (wine made from grapes with a minimum Oechsle of 70–75), Spaetlese (late-picked grapes), Auslese (selected bunches), Beerenauslese (selected berries), Trockenbeerenauslese (berries infected with Edelfäule, the noble rot or *Botrytis cinerea*). The latter two wines are of immense weight, with a high residual sugar content, honeyed and rich with an overpowering bouquet, more like a rich nectar than a wine. They are vastly expensive wines for very special occasions.

The Germans make yet another wine, Eiswein, the grapes being left on the vine until they are frozen. They are picked at dawn during a sharp frost of a minimum of $-5°$ Centigrade, rushed to the wine press, the water in the grapes remaining frozen, and an intensely sweet juice of about $150°$ Oechsle is extracted. This must, if fermented, creates an immensely rich wine, a honeyed nectar with an unbelievable depth of flavour with much residual sugar.

These categories are reached by the grapes attaining higher and higher sugar assimilation, each grade demanding a minimum Oechsle reading which differs slightly in each of the many German winegrowing areas, lowest in the cooler northern areas, and higher in the warmer southern winefields.

In Britain the present law demands that we call our wine Table Wine, whether the quality is less, equal to, or better than Table Wine standard. We have been told that when we have been marketing wine for ten years, we should re-apply to the EEC Commission for Wine, but for the time being all English labels have to carry the words 'Table Wine'.

The aforegoing paragraphs sum up some of the problems we still face, and some of the concessions that we have achieved to date. Today we see still more vineyards being planted; the pace at which new sites are established continues unabated, many are already being planned for next year, and the grand total of 1000 acres under the vine in Britain will very soon be achieved, if it has not already. The sum of two million pounds paid into the Treasury annually as duty on wine sales was probably reached with the 1983 and 1984 vintages: English wine has really arrived.

The Future

How will the future treat the English winegrower? He will be hoping for a lowered duty levy, a structured category system for different qualities of wine that can be stated on the wine label, and realistic grants in line with other fields of horticulture and agriculture, perhaps towards the planting of a vineyard, the setting up of the winery and the processing equipment in the winery.

As more and more growers reach the stage where they actually have wine to sell, a more professional marketing approach will be needed. To date there is little or no problem in placing wine with local hotels and restaurants, or for growers to sell a good proportion from their own premises, which is the most profitable method, in that one can sell at full market value and not at the wholesale price.

Obviously, as new growers' wines appear, they will have to look to a wider field in which to find outlets should they have planted near another vineyard. One or two large growers sell their entire crop to a massive wine marketing concern, thus eliminating the worries in trying to move one vintage before the other comes in, but it does mean that the wine is sold with a very limited profit margin, as such an outlet would cut one-third off the retail value. Others look to export.

Maybe the time will come when each region could employ a sales manager to sell the wines of a wide collection of growers, a person with a sound marketing experience who is willing to take the wine further afield than the busy winegrower can manage.

At present most growers find they have to don at least three different hats: primarily he or she is a viticulturist, a grower of vines; secondly he is a winemaker, two *very* different arts; and finally he has to be a wine seller, usually the most difficult of the three. One rarely finds a grower, usually a sensitive, gentle person, able to adapt him or herself to push his wares, to practise the hard sell in the tough outside world of hoteliers, restaurateurs and shopkeepers. And if he runs his vineyard and winery efficiently, he will have little or no time for the business of selling the wine.

The new grower also has the problem that establishment costs rise annually, each year it becomes more costly to plant a vineyard and equip a winery, not to mention the expense of buying land.

But the carrot to dangle in front of the donkey, the ultimate attraction, is the knowledge that, given a good site, early ripening and consistent vines and, of course, a moderate to good growing season, the rewards for one's toil can be a profit of £1,000–£3,000 per acre, a figure that few other growing enterprises can match. With a really first-class site and a carefully chosen high-yielding high-quality grape of a really consistent habit, this income could be doubled.

One last point worth raising is the area to plant. Bearing in mind the high cost of labour, one has to decide whether to plant an area that can be managed by the grower and his family without employing outside help – this area would be dependent upon the age group and degree of commitment of the grower and his family, the ease or difficulty of the site and the level of mechanization one proposes to put into the establishment. The size of the family unit tends to vary, but it is usually within the four to six acres bracket.

If the vineyard is to be much larger and it is necessary to employ part-time or permanent help, then the vineyard must be sufficiently large so that the wages or salary can be covered by outgoings and still leave a viable profit for the owner, even in a poor year with adverse weather. The jump in size, therefore, from a one-man or one-woman unit, or slightly larger for a family unit, to a vineyard capable of supporting two or more families comfortably is quite considerable – a serious step that needs much careful thought and planning. In this situation one must be considering a ten-acre planting, maybe larger. And the profits from the larger unit will not necessarily be greater than those from the smaller family unit – it may well be more work and more of a worry to have to find the wages each week. Perhaps today the answer to this problem might be, 'small is beautiful'.

2

Our Winegrowing Past

England has enjoyed a long, interesting and varied courtship of the vine. Originally vines were introduced by the Romans, no doubt to ensure a sustained supply of wine rather than relying on an erratic seaborne supply from Italy, and their existence has been adequately confirmed by archeological evidence. One may suppose that many villas and Roman towns had their vineyards – probably planted with the Pinot Noir vine.

Viticulture was maintained at a low key, a small but recognized part of the agricultural scene here after the Romans left, until winegrowing gained greatly by the arrival of the Normans, who brought their obvious skills in this craft with them, and in a mere 20 years established 40 to 50 recorded vineyards in southern England. The Domesday Book, a most remarkable record of property and people of the era, provides an illuminating picture of the life and times of the Norman takeover of Saxon England.

We may assume that viticulture enjoyed some three hundred or so years of success – due in no small part to a period of warmer weather that coincided with this first flowering of vinegrowing. The vine, still the Pinot Noir, no doubt flourished under the prevailing conditions, and produced wines of a style similar to a Burgundy or a still Champagne, according to whether a red or white wine was made, without, of course, the modern skills of sterile bottling, corks and storage life.

A wealth of stone carving and decoration in old English churches and other surviving buildings supplies additional evidence of the importance of the vine in English life; grape bunches and vine leaves were a favourite

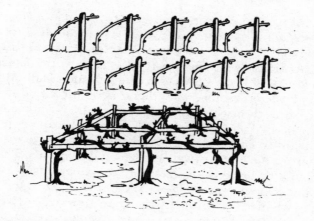

2 Ways in which vines were trained in medieval times. The trellis below is part of a living demonstration of early monastic methods of viticulture at Kloster Eberbach in the Rheingau area of the German winefield.

subject for embossing stone columns and friezes, also parge work and woodcarving.

This early participation in vine production was at first severely checked and then finally practically eliminated.

It has been discovered that in or about 1350 the Gulf Stream changed course and the 300-year warmer spell of weather came to an end. The Pinot Noir quickly found the cooler shorter summers not to its liking and the grapes failed to ripen. The Black Death, or Bubonic Plague, decimated the population. Henry II's marriage to Eleanor of Aquitaine brought all the Bordeaux winelands under English rule, with the result that the dwindling home-grown product was ousted by the fine fullbodied Bordeaux wines, which must have warmed the English during the colder winters. Many of the Norman vineyards belonged to monasteries, and, obviously, the sacking of the monasteries by Henry VIII's henchmen tolled the final death knell for widespread winegrowing in England.

A handful of enthusiasts kept the art of vinegrowing alive through the following centuries, so that at no time in our history were we without vineyards – some were small, others formed a part of the fruit gardens of vast country mansions, and a few produced wine to sell, and were, by all accounts, remarkably successful.

Also many cottages and houses had vines planted against a south wall, as they have today, and one can imagine that offspring of vines introduced by the Normans may have been planted on dwelling walls, cuttings taken from time to time and given to friends, allowing, in such a way, the vine to live for ever.

During the past two centuries the more tender indoor vines have been grown under glass – again propagated and multiplied, many of the indoor species being chance seedlings which grew from pips and formed varietal variations from their parents. Vines with names such as Madresfield Court, Lady Downe's seedling, Canon Hall, Mrs Pearson, Mrs Pince, Foster's seedling and others, were discovered by gardeners and named after themselves, the house where they worked or after the lady of the house. The culture of indoor vines became a fine art, and with heating then cheap the cold, cool and hot-house grapes became a great feature of the larger private garden establishments. The only time one can find little or no evidence of any real vineyards in England was between the 1914–18 and 1939–45 wars, but in 1945 and 1946, two pioneers, to whom all of us today remain greatly indebted, began serious trials on a considerable number of outdoor wine and eating grape vines in their gardens at their own expense and with massive enthusiasm, their work and results being the foundation of the viticultural scene in Britain today. Both these men, Edward Hyams and Ray Barrington-Brock, wrote extensively on their work with vines and it was the discovery of these books that originally fired me, and I suspect many others, to take up the challenge and prove that winegrowing was still a very real possibility in England today.

Ray Barrington-Brock's open days in September were the greatest possible draw, magical days – to see grapes actually ripening on vines in the open and to be given a glass of wine from these many separate varieties while talking to the handful of people then actually growing vines in England was a great experience.

The seeds were sown, the enthusiasm aroused, and slowly but surely today's winegrowing renaissance gathered momentum and vineyards were planted in England once again. The wine revolution had begun again in Britain.

For a more detailed account of our winegrowing past read *Growing Grapes in Britain* by Gillian Pearkes published by the Amateur Wine-maker, Andover, and for a marvellous in-depth study read Hugh Barty-King's remarkable book *A Tradition of English Wine* published in 1977 by the Oxford Illustrated Press.

3

The European Comparison

The purpose of this chapter is to discuss the philosophies behind the different approaches and methods of vinegrowing in different regions and countries, and the aims and results achieved in comparison one with another, particularly where there is some point that might be of use to the British grower.

We tend to become too involved with our own national vine-growing venture, and those of us with our own vineyard become totally immersed in the day-to-day problems and the annual cycle of events. To look at the viticultural scene in Europe, in France, Luxembourg, and Germany in particular, might be thought to be depressing in that the wonderful winefield sites and better climate would tend to prove that winegrowing in Britain has no future. But this is not the case. To visit the winegrowing areas of northern Europe is little short of pure inspiration, and instead of returning home full of gloom about our future prospects, the feeling is one of very considerable confidence, that with a commonsense approach we may forge ahead towards really solid achievement.

France

France seems at first a vast country. It is big and square, and the various regions are totally different in appearance one from another, in soil, terrain, plant life, architecture, people and, of course, wine.

At first one wonders why all northern France is not devoted to the vine; there appears at first sight to be hundreds if not thousands of ideal slopes on glorious liver and white soil – calves' liver-coloured loam over limestone right across northern France from Bayeaux in Normandy to the Champagne region. But, on reflection, in France wine is grown on *superbly* suitable land, and then in vast blocks, with few other crops grown within that area at all. The demarcation line which decrees where crops begin and where vines end, is laid down by the law of that area, and thus the winefields are limited to the area they now occupy. This has two very solid reasons behind it; firstly, the areas of suitable geographical sites and soils are naturally limited, and the generic vines of any area would not be true to type if grown outside the confines of that area; secondly, if supply of a particular wine were to exceed demand, both the status and price would drop dramatically below a viable return, therefore it benefits the growers of an area that demand should exceed supply, this being desirable and a very healthy situation for trade.

There is already a surplus of wine being produced in Europe, hence the so called 'Wine Lake'. This surplus is created by certain areas mass-producing low-grade wines from high-yielding grapes, wines of the Midi, Provence, Roussillon, and also the lesser wines of Italy. Steps are being taken to relieve this situation by the EEC levying a planting ban which dictates that no new vineyards may be planted anywhere, whether in the lower or the very finest wine-producing regions; that in the areas making the low-grade wines, no son may inherit a vineyard on the death of a parent or relation, the vineyard must be grubbed up; and, thirdly, a scheme exists for paying older winegrowers adequate compensation for grubbing up their vineyards.

These restrictions will, in time, bring about the desired effect of lowering the output of poor cheap wines that no one wants to buy in such vast amounts, and returning the market to an even keel, at which time we hope the ban will be rescinded, and allow at least the fine wine areas to replant or even expand at a controlled rate should they so wish.

This planting ban does not restrict private planting. Indeed from well north of Poitiers down to Bordeaux, most of the farmers have a strip of vines to produce sufficient wine for the family. I saw this in the Dordogne Valley from Bergerac almost up to where the deciduous trees declined in favour of conifers, also in the foothills behind the great Rhône Valley, in certain areas of the high Auvergne, and high up the hillsides bordering the Beaujolais region. Doubtless the same applies to many other areas. These vine plantations varied from a quarter to half a hectare, sometimes more.

The major winefields of France vary greatly one from another, and yet share great similarities. It would be most useful at this stage to go

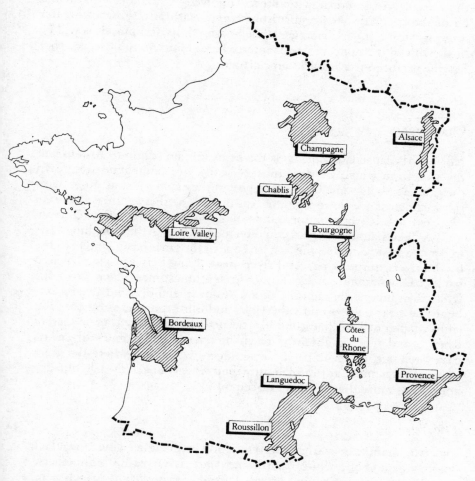

3 The main winegrowing areas of France. The classic fine wine areas are mostly alongside great rivers.

through each region in turn, giving a brief description of the geology, the site, the vines and the viticulture, followed by any ideas that could be of direct interest to the British grower. Naturally those of greater interest merit a fuller coverage. Winemaking skills and practices will be dealt with in the appropriate chapter where points were observed that may be useful to the English wine grower.

Champagne

Not only because Champagne is the nearest wine region to Britain is it the area from which we have most to learn. In Champagne are grown the same vines as some of us attempt and they suffer just as much with the weather as we do, even more so, in fact, as the weather is always more extreme on the Continent than in our more equable island climate.

The Champagne winefield could be likened to a giant mole hill in the midst of a vast flat plain, the eastern edge of the Paris basin, and bisected by the river Marne, a peaceful river meandering between vine-covered banks. This Champagne area is Tertiary limestone, which gives the wines their unique character. The soil drains splendidly, and also reflects light and heat back up into the vines and onto the grapes by day, but chills at night. The limestone has been tunnelled beneath the city of Rheims and the neighbouring town of Epernay, and miles of cellars have been cut, often up to six layers deep, which are where the great Champagne houses store and mature their wines. One of the Champagne houses has more than 13 miles of cellars.

The Vines

The two main vine varieties grown for Champagne wine, the black Pinot Noir and the white Chardonnay, are at virtually the northern-most limit of their ripening at this latitude. That they do ripen here, and this only in good years, is by virtue of the hot air rising off the surrounding plain up the vineyard slopes. Any fruit, ripening at the extreme edge of its viable existence, attains the highest possible quality and, given a good pollination and set, and good weather during the final month of ripening on the vine, the Champagne is of superb quality. This may only occur in one or two years in ten.

The two vines will only create superb quality grapes on the Tertiary limestone of Champagne and the Jurassic limestone of the Côte d'Or, elsewhere the wines fail to show more than an elusive shadow of their true potential. The Chardonnay is also grown in the Chablis area, which is situated on Kimmeridgian clay soil, an area situated almost midway between the Côte d'Or and Paris. We find an outcrop of Kimmeridge clay on the English Dorset coast, at Kimmeridge Bay, and occurring again in similar form as Blue Lias further west at Lyme Regis and Charmouth. It would be interesting to plant Chardonnay on this soil in Britain to see if a good wine could be made. Good Chablis is a most noble elegant wine.

The vines are not heavy croppers, but produce an adequate crop per vine and per hectare. Yield is controlled by local law to preserve the great quality and good sugar/acid balance in the grapes for the highest quality wines, slightly higher acids are allowed for wines of progressively lesser denomination.

Champagne is made from a blend of the two grapes, the Pinot Noir and the Chardonnay, also a smattering of grapes of the early ripening Pinot Meunier are added. The black Pinot Noir, grown mainly on the Montagne de Rheims and in the Vallée de la Marne, contributes two-thirds of the grapes to one-third of Chardonnay for Champagne wine. Providing the black grapes are pressed immediately after milling, the skins have no chance to colour the must. The white Chardonnay are mostly grown on the Côte de Blancs, stretching south in a narrowing triangle to Vertus from the Marne Valley in the north.

Viticulture

Successful training and management of vines in the particular local climate and on the existing soils and subsoils of an area took many centuries to evolve. In this field the French winegrower reigns supreme, being sensitive to the needs and capabilities of the vine variety he grows, as well as the regular production of well-ripened quality grapes. Therefore, we see in each French wine area this adaptation of training methods to the area and prevailing conditions of climate, latitude and soil.

In Champagne the majority of vines are trained by the Chablis method, evolved in the Chablis region some miles south-west of Champagne, tried by the Champenois at some time, found to be beneficial in yield and quality, and gradually generally adopted. Obversely, the method used in the Chablis region is called 'Vallée de la Marne' and is a training system that must have originated in the Champagne winefield, and been found to be better suited in the Chablis area than other systems. In places the Guyot and the Cordon de Royat methods are used in Champagne.

The principle is that the vine is allowed three, four or five branches, each pruned in winter to leave just one shoot at the furthermost extremity, each shoot with four buds for the Pinot, and five for the Chardonnay – on the latter the buds nearest the main branch are fertile.

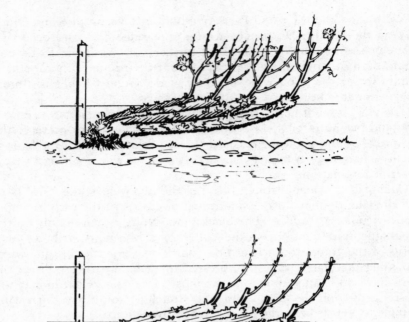

4 In Champagne, vines are trained leaving 4 short replacement canes each year on the
end of ever lengthening old wood.
When a vine reaches its neighbour, the lowest and longest length of old wood is
removed and a new young cane is trained down at the top, in the place of the shortest
length of old wood. Vines shown before and after pruning. This system is known as
the 'Chablis' method, with vines planted 0.6 m × 0.6 m (2 ft × 2 ft) or 1 m × 1 m (3 ft × 3 ft)
apart.

This is the case with many ancient Vinifera varieties.

During the growing season each of these buds develops into canes,
many bearing fruit. In the following winter all these new shoots are
removed except the lowest, which is pruned back to four or five buds.

Obviously the branches will advance towards neighbouring vines,
and in time will reach them. When this occurs the longest branch is
removed and a new branch is trained in from the head or crown of the
vine. It follows that on older mature vines in most years an old branch
is removed and a replacement tied in.

With the Guyot system, rods which have borne fruiting laterals are totally removed each year, and one new replacement rod (for Guyot simple), or two new replacement rods (Guyot double) are tied down onto the bottom wire – in the case of the double Guyot one rod is tied each side of the stem or head of the vine.

The Cordon de Royat vine has a permanent rod which is trained at about 0.7 metres (2ft 4in) horizontally above the ground, spurs are retained at 15-cm (6in) intervals, pruned to two buds on the Pinot Noir and Pinot Meunier, and three for the Chardonnay – on the latter two extra long six-bud spurs are allowed, and on all a six-bud spur is allowed on the farthest spur from the stem of the vine.

Spacing

Vines in the Champagne region are trained close together and low to the ground, with the exception of Royat vines. This is due to the latitude of the area, being nearer the northernmost limit of the wine vine. Though the white soil reflects the sun and heat well, there is no shelter from the elements here, Champagne being a virtually treeless series of gentle slopes and, therefore, the nearer the ground and the closer together the vines are trained, the warmer the climate for the vines and subsequently for the grapes. The vines, when in full leaf, thus create their own micro-climate within the vineyard, by virtue of their numbers and close proximity one to another, which has the effect of bettering the climate of the area within the actual vineyard.

By planting the vines at such a high density, each vine plant and its root system are asked to produce a lesser poundage of fruit than if the vines were planted at much wider stations. The result is that the grower of close-planted vines can match or surpass the yield per hectare of wider spaced vines, but each vine, in being asked to carry a lesser crop, will produce a crop with a better balance of sugars and acids and other components, and thus in a northerly situation, produce better wine.

The basic viticultural principle will crop up again in sections dealing with other wine regions, and is a fact which we British newcomers to this ancient art might well take note. There are one or two British growers who dispute these facts frequently and vociferously, but the facts speak for themselves. After two thousand years of uninterrupted tending and cropping vines, would we still find the French and German growers spending half their lives bending to prune, and then bending to harvest their grapes, if they could achieve the same results in yield and quality with the working area of the vine at, say, waist or chest level?

The French and German growers must be interested to read of the perverse British, with 15 to 30 years, at the most, experience in viticulture, adopting high-training systems used no further north than Austria, in the hot and humid New York State, and in New Zealand (where I gather the high system is fast losing favour), when we are situated further north by 100–200 miles from the Loire, Champagne and Luxembourg winefields. I shall discuss this matter later, giving some sound reasons for and against this system.

Pruning

In Champagne a late pruning is advised, in March rather than January or February, to avoid the severe February frosts which can cause considerable die-back to newly-pruned vines. This practice is acceptable when a large work force can descend on the vines, but where a vineyard is a one- or two-man operation, pruning has to be started early and continued daily regardless of weather, in order to be finished in time.

When the pruning is finished, and the prunings burned, the next job is to tie down the replacement canes to the wires. In the depth of winter, wood is inclined to snap if bent, whereas, if left until late March or early April when the sap is rising, the canes are more pliant and bend easily.

Conclusions

The training method for the Champagne vines is interesting, and must be worth the extra effort involved in comparison with the neat, quick Guyot replacement system.

The Champagne vine is not cropped until the fourth or fifth year, so it has a chance to become really established and vigorous, a totally different approach to the Germans who demand that a vine crops in the third year otherwise it is not a commercially viable variety. Again, we can see that the two races have totally different approaches towards their viticulture.

Due to the high cost of producing Champagne today (each bottle is handled on no less than 80 different occasions before being sold) the Champagne grower has become very cost conscious. Due to the high cost of natural manure, the Champenois has turned to a by-product of the Paris waste system, which is dried, has all ferrous metal removed by magnetism, then the mass is powdered, and delivered to the growers as a semi-organic manure. This most unattractive substance, of a dull grey colour, is then spread throughout the vineyards. Certain plastic and metal objects resist the processing, and one sees dolls' heads and legs, plastic and non-ferrous metal waste of all descriptions and colours decorating the vineyard floor. It is no doubt a good idea to utilize waste products, and beneficial to the vines, but the appearance of the vineyard floor is somewhat besmirched, and there is always a possibility of tainting the wine with noxious substances remaining in the waste.

The Champagne winefield is the only major wine-producing area, together with that of Beaujolais, to have adopted total herbicide weed control, and to have dropped all cultivation. This is due in part to the soaring costs of Champagne production, materials and equipment, and, of course, by far the greatest burden, labour costs. The price of the end product has also risen.

The chemical Round-up has largely replaced Simazine and Gramoxone with many growers in Champagne, being especially effective in controlling the more pernicious perennial weeds. This practice also contributes towards the unhealthy dull grey soil colour, which seems not to worry the wine grower, nor his advisers. The soil is solid and impacted due to man and his vehicles constantly passing up and down the rows, and develops a deep fissured crust in dry weather. There will be further discussion of cultivation versus non-cultivation in the chapter dealing with weed control.

The Loire Valley

A great variety of wines are produced from the Loire valley, vineyards being planted on the river valley sides from the mouth, where the salty Muscadet is grown, and thence up river for many, many miles through Anjou, Touraine, Sancerre to Pouilly-sur-Loire.

The middle section of the Loire is on cretaceous soils which tend to produce rather undistinguished vines, like Anjou Rosé. Further east sparkling Vouvray is grown on chalk, in a manner similar to Champagne, and, like Champagne, is stored in deep cellars cut into the chalk banks of the Loire in the Azay-le-Rideau. The resultant wine is not dissimilar from a very cheap wedding Champagne.

Trellis and Training

Anjou is a veritable garden of Eden and, more prosaically, could be likened to the Vale of Evesham; nurseries raising all manner of plants, shrubs and trees abound in the area. The greater majority of vineyards are head trained, most with a one- or two-wire low trellis, the remainer with no trellis. Some vineyards are Guyot simple (single) trained, and all vines are 1 m apart in the rows, the rows 1 m to 1.5 m apart. The Guyot vines are on a low trellis with a single bottom wire and a double upper wire. The two low systems, the head and Guyot, are used in 99 per cent of vineyards in the middle Loire area. The trellis is so low that one can bend over and lay the palm of one's hand on the ground on the far side.

The Vines

Of the vine varieties planted here, perhaps only the Chenin Blanc (or Pineau de la Loire) would be of any value to the British grower. This grape is so adaptable that several different types of wine can be made from the one grape by different methods of vinification, ranging from sweet to dry, and all are wines of good standard and balance. This vine is on trial in Devon now, and results are awaited with interest.

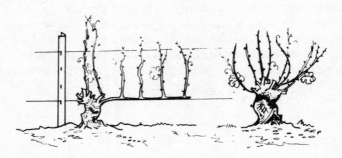

5 In the Loire valley, vines are either Guyot simple (single Guyot) on a low trellis, or they are head or goblet pruned in low free-standing bushes.
Vines are about 1 m × 1 m (3 ft × 3 ft) apart, with the top about 0.75 m (2 ft) above ground level.

There are many clones of Gamay, and a trial of the Loire Gamays might be worthwhile in Britain, whereas the Beaujolais Gamays would tend to be selected from later ripening clones. This also applies to the Sauvignon Blanc from the Loire, which would be those with earlier ripening tendencies than those grown for Sauternes so much further south of Bordeaux. This principle of planting clones of vines from as far north as possible is important; it follows that to grow Chardonnay and Pinot Noir from the Champagne region rather than from Burgundy or Alsace would give the British grower a greater chance of success.

The vines are kept to a great age in this area. There is little or no evidence of the old vines being replaced, as in Alsace and in Germany, where a regular programme of replanting is practised when vines reach 15, 20 or 25 years of age and their yield declines.

To sum up here, note that in this northerly winefield the vines are close together in a row, and trained close to the ground; every possible action is taken to attract as much warmth as possible up onto the ripening grapes. A faint possibility for use in England is the Chenin Blanc grape, which would add a new facet to the range of English wines available to date – a fresh, dry, clean French-style wine would be a welcome addition to the predominantly German-style wines grown in Britain so far.

Chablis

Chablis may be likened to the Champagne area in that it is a mound rising out of the plain of northern France, not so dramatic nor so famous, but producing the most attractive dry, flinty green-gold wines on Kimmeridgian Marls. In the Vaudesir vineyards the soil has the appearance of limestone, so perhaps the Kimmeridge Marl is a subsoil, or occurs on the surface in other vineyard areas.

This area is very exposed and so comparatively cool that, on average, only five out of every ten years produce vintage-quality wines, probably no less than any other winefield in a given decade but grown under more hazardous conditions. Chablis is particularly vulnerable to spring frost which can devastate an entire vintage in one night.

The Chablis winegrower goes to immense trouble to set up an adequate protection system to combat spring frost. The old method was to use smudge pots into which oil was poured and, when frost theatened, the oil was ignited and the thick smoke created kept the temperature up by a degree or two and so prevented damage. The modern method consists of a series of either gas or paraffin burners set in rows up the vineyard, connected by supply pipes from an oil tank or vast gas cylinders. In spring these burners look like ranks of daleks marching through the vineyards as far as one can see – the growers certainly deserve to make a good wine when they go to such expense and effort to ensure that their crop avoids the frost.

Of all areas, Chablis is probably the coolest – which indicates that the grapes ripen really slowly. It follows that if the season is kind enough to allow the grapes to achieve full ripeness, then they demonstrate most dramatically the golden rule that a fruit that ripens slowly and in a cool rather than a hot climate achieves added nuances of bouquet and depth of flavour that endow the Chablis wines with exquisite and aristocratic qualities, a fresh acidity, a glorious fruity flavour with great depth and length in the mouth. Good Chablis is a glorious wine.

The Vines

The Chardonnay is the main grape grown in the Chablis region, locally called Beaunois. Other permitted grapes are the Sacy and Aligote, which can only be sold as Bourgogne Grand Ordinaire and Bourgogne Aligote.

Trellis and training

The vines are trained to a low three-wire trellis, spaced 1.28 m square to allow the vineyard tractor to fly up and down the rows to cultivate the soil and spray the wines. The life cycle of vines here is 40 years, as opposed to 20 to 25 years in Alsace and Germany.

The training of the vines, a system called Vallée de la Marne, is unique to the region, and involves keeping a short length of two-year-old wood at pruning, and retaining a one-year cane on the end of this older wood, which is arched up and back onto the bottom wire and secured. A further replacement cane is kept from the head of the vine, and this is arched up and down to be secured where the older wood ends and the other replacement cane begins. A look at the explanatory drawing would help to explain the principles of Vallée de la Marne pruning.

It has been proved that in *this* area the Chardonnay vine crops better and produces higher quality fruit from this method. This system, merely a variation on the Guyot theme, is a different way of pruning the Chardonnay vine from the straightforward Guyot system practised in Burgundy, in the Côte de Beaune area.

The Germans condemn the Chardonnay vine on the ground of low productivity. They train the vine to a 0.7 bottom wire, and use a uniform Guyot simple pruning.

On discussing the German opinion of the Chardonnay with a French Chablis or Champagne grower, one is told that one cannot expect the best from this vine unless it is pruned to one of these two methods for adequate productivity – note that in both the Vallée de la Marne (in Chablis) and the Chablis (in Champagne) systems of pruning, old wood is incorporated instead of the usual Guyot total annual renewal.

The Classification System used in Chablis

Chablis Grand Cru
Consists of a mere 11 vineyards, the very best in the area
Minimum alcoholic strength   11°
Maximum yield   311 gallons per acre
Average harvest   27,200 gallons
Declassified   Chablis Premier cru, Chablis, Bourgogne or Bourgogne Grand Ordinaire

Chablis Premier Cru – (2500 acres including Chablis area)
Minimum alcoholic strength   10.5°
Maximum yield   356 gallons per acre
Average harvest   203,500 gallons
Declassified   Chablis, Bourgogne or Bourgogne Grand Ordinaire

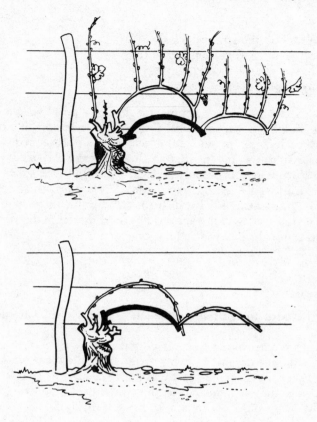

6 In the Chablis region, the Chardonnay vines are trained by the Vallée de la Marne system, which is virtually a double Guyot, but with a section of 2-year wood being retained each year, and using the end cane from this 2-year wood as a fruiting lateral. A second replacement cane is grown from the crown each year. The 2 fruiting canes are bent in one direction. The vines are planted 1 m × 1 m (3 ft × 3 ft) apart, trained low to the ground to gain a maximum quality field and maintain the best microclimate possible.

The Classification System used in Chablis (*cont.*)

Chablis
Minimum alchoholic strength   10°
Maximum yield   356 gallons per acre
Average harvest   1,250,000 gallons
Declassified   Bourgogne Grand Ordinaire

Petit Chablis
Minimum alchoholic strength   10°
Maximum yield   356 gallons per acre
Average harvest   1,250,000 gallons
Declassified   Bourgogne Grand Ordinaire

From this chart you will appreciate that in a good year the wines of each classified area are sold under their area heading; if however the quality of a harvest is poor, the wines are declassified to a lower denomination, the worse the quality the lower the classification. Should a vineyard produce more than the legal yield limit the excess has to be declassified and sold as a lesser wine. The same principles apply in Burgundy (and also in Bordeaux). Minimum alcoholic strength, maximum yield and average harvest figures differ from district to district according to local rules and regulations.

Conclusions

What is there for the British grower to learn from his Chablis counterpart?

Certainly we are no worse off climatically – in fact, providing we choose good hillside slopes away from frost pockets, we are far less likely to suffer from spring-frost damage. We have available to us early ripening vines that give more ripening consistency than the Chardonnay in Chablis. We could perhaps adopt a self-discipline in demoting our own wines from a bad year to a lesser name and label; English wine varies dramatically from year to year. We could perhaps create a second lower category for any wines we feel are not fit to bear our top label – perhaps bearing the name of our village or town if the top label bears the vineyard name, or a district or even county name.

The buyer would then begin to appreciate the streaming of the two qualities we would offer, with a price differential. In this way the reputation of our better wine would not suffer from a poor, acid vintage.

We can also learn adaptability from the Chablis grower. He goes to tremendous lengths to protect his precious crop from the spring frost. He adapts his training system to his site to assist his vines to produce a viable crop in a difficult climate, and he achieves success by keeping his vines low to the ground and the rows close together to maintain a climate within the vineyard. He uses a variation on the Guyot system having discovered that this practice suits the site and the particular vine variety he grows, and his whole winemaking process is geared towards capturing the tremendous charm and quality of that wine in the bottle. The creation of fine Chablis is an affair of the heart, no less.

Alsace

The Alsace winefield is situated on the south-east-by-east-facing lower slopes of the magnificent and dramatic afforested Vosges mountains that divide Alsace from Lorraine in eastern France. With the high range of mountains protecting the vineyards from any rough weather, Alsace is a garden of Eden, a winegrower's paradise – and stretches across the river plain to the great Rhine some 20 miles to the east, with the German Black Forest in the far distance. The soil of the foothills is a friable limestone, and that of the Harth, the plain below the mountains, varies widely from granites to various sands and silts. The lesser quality grapes tend to be grown on the Harth.

The approach to winegrowing in Alsace is one of total naturalness – this principle is followed through the production of the wine. The Alsatian grower has the ideal climate, soil and site – conditions are perfect and this is reflected in the wines of Alsace, which are full-flavoured, generous with a rich harmony of fruit and acidity, and a glorious length or after taste – one can smell and taste the sun-drenched grapes in every bottle.

Alsace is not so far south that the climate is too hot, which would tend to produce very strong alcoholic, coarse-flavoured wines, nor too far north, where the grower has a constant struggle, in years other than heatwaves, to encourage enough sugar into his grapes, and has to battle with excess acidity, has to use masses of sugar or sweet reserve to create a palatable beverage, and produce a wine created by a clever wine chemist rather than the vine alone.

The Vines

Most Alsatian growers produce seven wines, all single grape wines. There are in order of quality, starting with the best, Riesling, Gewurz-traminer, Pinot, Tokay (or Pinot Gris/Rulander), Muscat, Sylvaner and Pinot Noir, the latter as a red wine.

There are a few other varieties grown for the creation of lesser wines, the Chasselas which was phased out in 1980, Knipperle – an old Alsatian variety, little grown today – and Müller Thurgau. These lesser quality grapes are used for the production of Zwicker, a cheap, honest and refreshing carafe wine sold in cafés and restaurants, a vin du pays. Edelzwicker is also a blend, but must be made of a blend of the quality grapes only.

In a rare sunless wet summer, should any of the better grape varieties not meet the required quality by harvest, these are blended and sold as Edelzwicker, so that again the grower does not lower his or his country's standards by selling inferior wine under his quality label, but declassifies his wine automatically.

Therefore, it follows in a poor vintage the Edelzwicker and Zwicker wines will be better than in a good year, for they will have been made of a higher percentage of better grapes.

Hugels of Riquewhir market the full range of quality single-grape wines, and call their lesser quality blend by different names for different countries, for example Chevalier d'Alsace, Couronne d'Alsace and Flambeau d'Alsace.

Riesling

As in Germany, an Alsatian grower may own quite a few vineyard plots in different places within his locality, and he will grow the Riesling vines in the hottest and most favourable of all his vineyards, these being situated on the lower slopes of the foothills of the Vosges mountains. The Riesling is the highest quality wine, demands the highest price, and requires a long ripening period to attain full maturity. These higher sites can be very steep indeed, and unless one is born to working on such a severe slope, remaining upright, let alone moving up or down, is a perilous if not impossible task to the uninitiated.

Gewurztraminer

This clone of the older Traminer, bred by Oberlin in the last century, has totally ousted the Traminer, and is also planted on the best sites and makes a heady spicy wine, redolent of roses and violets with muscat undertones. Fermented out almost dry with just a gramme or two of residual sugar, this wine is very popular with the tourists, and indeed the export trade, and is probably the best known wine of Alsace.

One finds, however, the locals do not drink the wine; Gewurztraminer is too rich and flavoured for their taste. For the special occasion the Alsatian will drink Riesling, and his everyday wine is the Pinot, a lovely dry, balanced harmonious wine that goes so well with a meal. It is probably too late in ripening for Britain.

Pinot

Today the Auxerrois is being planted heavily and replacing discontinued varieties as they are grubbed up, as it raises the quality of the Pinot wines which are very popular in Alsace. Auxerrois ripens earlier than the Pinot Blanc, produces a higher quality grape, and is a more consistent cropper. Pinot wines can be a single-grape wine of any of the above varieties, or a blend of two or three of the Pinots. Being early-ripening, the Auxerrois can be grown in the lesser sites in Alsace, but would require only the best sites in Britain. The Pinot Gris needs a hot hillside site to ripen to perfection, and is grown to produce Tokay wine.

Muscat

The muscat wine has a very individual nose, and fermented out dry makes a strong earthy-flavoured wine. The muscat is often blended with Pinot to make Edelzwicker. It is a later-ripening grape and requires a hot hillside site in Alsace. It is a very vigorous and highly yielding vine, but ripens too late for Britain.

Sylvaner

As in Germany, the Sylvaner, a heavy cropper, is a bread-and-butter wine, a soft bland wine of little quality, a quaffing everyday wine; too late for Britain except on an exceptional site.

Chasselas

The white and red Chasselas grapes are destined either for zwicker wines, or are sold at the roadside to tourists as dessert grapes, just as strawberries are sold in England. It is too late for Britain when grown in the open, though the grape will ripen when grown on a hot south wall.

Vine Training

The illustrations demonstrate the form of trellis more ably than mere words. The training is still Guyot, the double Guyot, the only difference being that it is strung on a higher trellis. This system is universal throughout Alsace – on the Harth, the plain, should a spring frost roll down from the mountains, the vines would be above the worst effects. In these valley vineyards the air would tend to be more still in summer than on the hillsides, and keeping room underneath for air circulation would do much to prevent mildew and botrytis attack.

The trellis is, therefore, higher in the plain and lower on the steep hillside vineyards. The trellis consists of a tall outward sloping brace post beside the end posts of each row, from which a wire is braced onto a stone sunk well into the earth. There are four single wires, the replacement cane is arched over the second wire and back to the bottom wire. The fruiting laterals grow above the top wire, where they may be left to hang over; most growers, however, cut the top growth back some five or six times in the summer to allow freedom of access for the spraying and cultivation machinery.

In an exceptionally good summer, growers arrange for a helicopter to spray their vineyards, and thus do not summer prune as there is not the need for access – though they would prune before harvest. I would have thought that if a vine were *not* pruned, the spray from the helicopter, being sprayed from above, would fall on the *upper* side of the mass of leaves and the grapes, which is not where the spray is needed.

1975 Alsatian Vine Statistics

Varieties	Hectares	1975 Price Per Kilo (2.2 lb)
Sylvaner	2600	1f.40
Gewurztraminer	2300	2f.10
Riesling	1400	1f.95
Pinot Blanc & Auxerrois	1300	1f.45
Chasselas	800	1f.35
Tokay (Pinot Gris)	450	
Muscat	400	
Pinot Noir	300	1f.90
Total	10,200	(600 hectares planted since)

Yield limit of 78 hectolitres per hectare
Average yield 70–74 hectolitres per hectare
(Average yield 1560 gallons per 2.2 acres)
Average temperature 11° Centigrade (52° Fahrenheit)

Noble Vine Varieties (with local names)

Riesling
Gewurztraminer (Spicy Traminer)
Pinot (Clevner/Burgunder)
   Pinot Blanc d'Alsace (Weiss/Clevner/Weiss-Burgunder)
   Pinot Gris (petits Grains) = Tokay d'Alsace
   Auxerrois Blanc = Weisser Auxerrois
   Morillon Blanc = Pinot Blanc = Pinot Morillon
   Chardonnay = Chardonnay Blanc
   Pinot Noir = Roter Burgunder = Blauer Burgunder
Muscat Muscat Ottonel (poor set in cool weather)
   Muscat Blanc d'Alsace (the best variety)
   Muscat Rose d'Alsace

Ordinary Mass-produced Vine Varieties

Sylvaner = Oesterreicher = Grunling
Chasselas = Gutedal = Sussling = Frauentraube – (phased out in 1980)
(Chasselas Blanc, rose, de Fontaine bleau, Fendant rose)
Knipperle = Kleiner Rauschling = Gelber Ortlieber
Goldriesling = Riesling dore (Riesling × Courtillier Musque)
Müller Thurgau = (Riesling × Sylvaner)

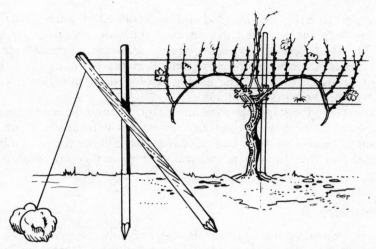

7 The trellis as used universally throughout Alsace. Note the method of anchoring the end post, the high trellis and the double Guyot training with exaggerated bend to the year-old fruiting wood.

Rovral and Ronilan are in use in Alsace against botrytis, which is not such a problem as in Britain because in Alsace the rainfall and humidity are lower. The Vosges Mountains, being so high, relieve the rain clouds from the west of their rain, most of which falls in Lorraine, the department to the west of the Vosges range, the climate of which is degrees colder and far wetter than Alsace.

Most of the growers I spoke to in Alsace were in favour of weed control by cultivation, and were against chemical weed-killing, believing that the poisons must build up in the soil, and cause trouble in the future. Again they demonstrate the natural approach.

Nowhere is the past history of France more poignant than in Alsace. One notices when travelling to France the total absence of farmhouses and cottage smallholdings such as are dotted over the entire length and breadth of England, Scotland and Wales. Europe in the past has suffered so many internal wars, with battles raging over the countryside time and again down through the centuries, that people living in lonely farmhouses and cottages would be defenceless against invaders. Thus the entire population lives either in the towns, or farming and country people live in tight village communities, houses close together, and those that own or work on the land go out from the village to work each day. The only area in France where there are country houses and farms such as in England are in Brittany and Normandy, and to a lesser degree in the Dordogne Valley in south-west France. The former area is in general too far west to have been invaded and has retained the early pattern of rural development that the Normans brought with them to England in 1066. The Dordogne Valley, in Aquitaine, was under English rule for some three hundred years from the time of Henry II's marriage to Fair Eleanor of Aquitaine. and the area was obviously influenced by the English manner of ordering affairs.

Alsace, being the stepping stone into France from southern Germany, has suffered more cruelly than any other region from the effects of constant strife and warfare, and has indeed been under the rule of both countries one after the other, and was only quite recently returned to France.

Conclusions

In Alsace we again note the use of the Guyot training system, which has been adapted to suit the particular climate and geographical situations within the winegrowing area; the quality vines on the better hillside sites, and the mass-production lower-quality wines grown on the valley floor. Concern is expressed about an excessive use of herbicides with the possibility of a long-term build-up of poison in the soil.

None of the Alsatian vines, with the exception of the Auxerrois, are of much interest to the British grower. In Alsace the low-quality grapes have been, or will be, phased out – the vineyards rest after vine grubbing for three years before being replanted. The Pinot Noir is also being phased out as the vines need grubbing; there was a great vogue for the Pinot Noir wine some years ago, so everyone planted this grape. The popularity of this light, thin red wine is waning, and the growers are gratefully replanting with more attractive commercial vine varieties.

An Alsatian vine yields effectively for 30 years and, after grubbing, vetches and clovers are sown, and the ground fallowed for three years to recover before being replanted. Alsace was the only area where I noticed such a degree of replanting.

Newly-planted vines are enclosed by plastic mesh cylinders to protect the young plants from rabbits. These are left on for three or four years, until the trunk of the vine is sufficiently large in circumference for rabbits to cause it no harm. The cylinders are also used in Germany, where they are sometimes made from thick-gauge polythene sheet with holes punched all round to allow air circulation.

In the large French and German winefields, individual vineyards are divided from one another by track. There is no protective fencing surrounding the whole, or surrounding plots belonging to different owners, so rabbits and hares have free access.

The firm belief in the benefits of ground cultivation by about 90 per cent of Alsatian growers even extends into their apple and cherry orchards, where small vineyard tractors, with a cultivator on the rear, fly back and forth between the trees. These belts of fruit trees are planted at fairly regular intervals on the Harth, presumably initially as shelter belts, and to provide fruit for the family as a secondary consideration.

The best quality vineyards in Alsace lie between Colmar in the south, and Ribeauville in the north, roughly the middle section of the 70-mile long winefield. Alsace is an area of outstanding natural beauty. The dramatic Vosges mountains to the west form a backdrop to a land of soft beauty, of plenty – and the people are friendly and outgoing, generous to a degree, and combine the very best of France and of Germany in their culture, their food and their attractive life, not forgetting their very attractive wines.

One last point. The Alsatian winegrowers producing their six or seven different wines can offer a wine to suit all tastes, wines for highdays, everyday drinking, wines for the locals, for visitors, and wines for export. Surely there is a lesson for all here – while one would not recommend the British grower to produce seven different wines, I do feel that to produce a minimum of two, preferably four, means that one can cater for all tastes; a dry white wine with body, depth and character, a sweeter wine and, perhaps, a dessert wine. In this manner you have a wine to suit all customers.

Cognac

When travelling south from the Loire Valley towards Cognac, the fast French traffic and the endless colonnades of tree trunks have a mesmerizing effect on the mind – sunlight and shade flash across one's eyes and it comes as something of a shock to realize suddenly that the architecture is changing. The roof outlines of northern France, which, with fairly sharp roof angles to shoot off rain and snow more readily, are similar to those of Britain, give way to the southern orange clay Roman tiles. The rooves are much flatter, and project further; the village houses are lower, with thicker walls, smaller windows, and, with some excitement, the realization dawns that one is in a different world, where the house is built to protect the inhabitants as much against heat as against cold.

This has a very definite effect on the senses and, now fully awake, the slightly exotic and definitely southern villages and landscapes captivate the interest.

The Cognac winefield is divided into districts, radiating outwards much like a target, with the area in the centre producing the highest quality wines of all, the next area producing slightly lesser wines, and so on. The style of the wines of each area is dictated by the soil and the climate. The top quality area in the centre is on very chalky soil, and includes the two main towns of the area, Cognac and Jarnac. This district is known as Grand Champagne and produces wines which, when distilled, are the most delicate and fragrant of Cognacs, the most suitable for ageing, taking longer to mature, but, once mature, staying at their peak for longer.

The next area is known as Petite Champagne, which is followed down the scale by Borderies, Fins Bois, Bon Bois and lastly Bois Ordinaires. Most Cognacs are made from a blend of spirits from several of these areas in order to produce a balanced product. Each area has a progressively less chalky soil.

Viticulture

The region is extraordinarily flat, with the slow-flowing muddy Charentes river running right through the area from east to west. The soil is a glorious 'calves' liver' brown with a very chalky appearance, perfect for vines.

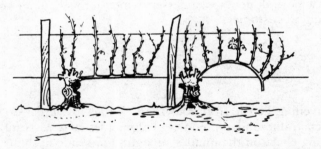

8 In Cognac, most vines are trained by the Guyot simple or double system on a low trellis with 2 single wires, with vines about 1 m (3 ft) apart and rows about 1 m (3 ft) from each other, and the top wire about 0.75 m (2 ft) above ground level. Also the goblet or head system is used. Vines are Columbard, St Emilion and Folle Blanche.

The vines in the Grand Champagne district are supported on a low post and wire trellis, and are either single or double Guyot, with the bottom wires from 15–45 cm (6–18 in) above the ground. New plantings have been trained with a long outward angled end in order to give added strength, and have intermediate posts every four vines.

Driving south from Cognac to Barbezieux, in the Petite Champagne district, I noticed two forms of high trellis, firstly the arched high Guyot double like the system used in Alsace, and also a method whereby two replacement canes were trained, one out each side along the top wire, from the top of a strong five-foot stem. The laterals would hang down, much like a single Geneva double curtain. The high systems are much more popular with the grape pickers! Some chemical weed control was in evidence, but most vineyards are also cultivated mechanically, at least twice a year, probably more in the better areas.

Vines

The three Cognac vines are the St Emilion, the Folle Blanche and the Columbard, though all Cognac is now made from 95 per cent St Emilion. Pre-phylloxera the Folle Blanche was the dominant grape, but it does not take well to being grafted, so the higher yielding but less fragrant St Emilion now dominates the planting.

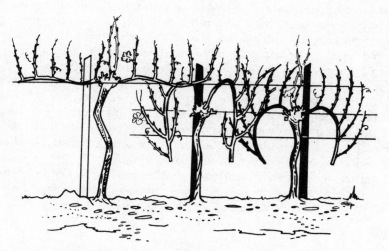

9 In an area to the south of the Grande Champagne district the high trellis is used, and vines are trained in one of the three ways illustrated here. The middle method is reminiscent of the American umbrella training, and on the right the system is not too dissimilar from the Alsatian method. Note the first of the three methods uses a single wire and the second and third use three wires.

There is no yield restriction in the Cognac area, as the grapes are best when harvested prior to full ripeness – Cognac needs to be made from thin acid wine and, therefore, a high sugar content is not important.

Vines appear to be allowed to live to a considerable age to judge by the old vines in some vineyards, and there was little evidence of replanting.

Distilling

The name 'Brandy' comes from 'Burnt' wine; much Cognac (Brandy from the Cognac area) is pressed, fermented and distilled by the wine farmers themselves, and the famous, and not so famous, Cognac firms from Cognac and Jarnac buy young spirits from growers in various districts, to make up a balanced blend of young Cognac on their own premises. Some of these companies have large vineyards of their own in several districts, and also buy in from the winegrowers; others, such as Delamain, have no vineyards of their own, but buy in only the best from their regular suppliers. There is a great art in buying fine brandies, which will, when blended, create a masterpiece, smooth, fragrant and gentle on the mind after years of maturing in casks of Troncais oak.

Although none of the Cognac wines would ripen their grapes in Britain, and we have nothing to learn from the viticulture of the area, could we not follow the French example and, in a poor cold year, when we have a low sugar/high acid must, which is an essential for a good grape spirit, apply for a licence to distill our wine? This practice is adopted in many areas; in Champagne all the grape skins and debris are taken from the press to be distilled into Marc (pronounced Mar) the local brandy. We British growers throw away tons of pulp each year. If one of us in each region were to apply for, and press for a licence to distill, the pulp could either be bought in and quite a considerable amount of spirit made and the matured end product eventually sold, or the pulp could be distilled by the licensee and then redistributed to the supplier growers to mature on their own premises.

I gather one British winegrower applied for and has been granted a licence to distill a small amount daily, so this is definitely a field that should be explored if we are to widen our present enterprise.

Bordeaux

Obviously we cannot expect to ripen Bordeaux grapes in the open vineyard in Britain, and to make good – even passable – red wine grapes must be ripe. But the philosophy in their viticulture and wine-making, the creation of the finest red wines in the world, has much to commend it to all who aspire to grow wine.

The Medoc is a narrow riverside strip of land stretching north-west from the town of Bordeaux up the southern side of the Gironde estuary. The soils are relatively new, ranging from Tertiary to Quaternary, the vines growing in river silts and sands with a high stone content, which hold and reflect heat up into the ripening grapes. Drainage is therefore good in spite of the Medoc appearing to be virtually flat.

The several districts of the Medoc produce wines of quite widely varying character, the areas producing the best wines being Margaux, St Julien, Pauillac, St Estephe; the wines tending to range from a lighter body and more delicate nose and temperament in Margaux, to the broad-shouldered, deep-coloured, more masculine wines of Pauillac and St Estephe, these areas situated in a north-west direction as one travels out from the town of Bordeaux. The other areas where they follow similar principles are St Emilion and Pomerol on the north bank of the Gironde estuary, and on the Dordogne watershed.

Vines

The grapes grown for red Bordeaux are, firstly, the Cabernet Sauvignon – which gives the wine backbone, hardness, character and long, long bottle life in a good year. Then there is the Merlot, which is the first to ripen and is the grape that offers softness and fullness to the wine, and, lastly, the Petit Verdot – often a mere 2 per cent of the total blend – which gives the wine acidity and a glorious nose or bouquet. Different chateaux use varying percentages of Cabernet Sauvignon and Merlot to create their own particular wine, each with unique weight, character and style, often a closely guarded secret.

The Medoc at first sight is flat, an uninteresting landscape, and has few of the features of other great winefields – for example no range of mountains to the west or the north to throw heat down onto the vines. The vineyards are on the silt beds deposited by the river, and are not planted on the lower slopes of a hill range, and the soil is not the usual limestone or chalk like other great vineyards.

The plus features gradually make themselves obvious – the soil offers good drainage, there is uninterrupted sun access from dawn to dusk. and the area is very hot in summer – and mild in winter – due to its close proximity to the Atlantic and the wide Gironde estuary to the north. The vines find the conditions ideal.

St Emilion is an ancient hilltop town, with steep, narrow, cobbled streets and highly attractive, glowing, golden limestone houses and cottages. It is one of the most beautiful small medieval towns in France – and it is really well cared for, which is unusual in France – a general lack of paint, repair and structural care usually combining to give French towns an air of decayed elegance which for some has its own attraction. St Emilion is surrounded by a rolling sea of sweeping vineyards.

Viticulture

In the Medoc the vines are trained on a low trellis, so low that when the vines are in full leaf one could bend over and touch the ground on the other side. The double top wire is a mere 0.6 m (2 ft) high, the bottom wire 0.33 m (1 ft) from the ground. The vines are planted 0.6–1 m apart, with their heads often no more than a mere 5–15 cm (2–6 in) from the ground. The rows are close, again 0.6–1 m apart, each vine is pruned to carry a fairly light crop, but the high planting density maintains an acceptable yield, and the principle produces grapes of outstanding quality. Guyot simple or double is used.

A glance at the drawing of the training of vines in the Medoc will demonstrate the system more easily. The vines in the St Emilion winefield are trained higher than in the Medoc.

Conclusions

The most important fact to be learned from the viticulture of the Bordeaux area has already been mentioned, namely that, in order to produce wines possessed of noble classic quality, no less than three grape varieties are used to achieve this result, both with red Bordeaux wines and white Bordeaux wines. Sauternes is the best known white wine; and it is made from two grape varieties, the Semillon and the Sauvignon Blanc, the grapes of these vines being left on the vines until they have been partially consumed by Pourriture Noble, or the noble rot. This evaporates the water in the grapes, which has the effect of intensifying the sugars within the grapes, enabling the most luscious white wines with residual sugar to be made. In Britain we tend to adhere mostly to the production of single-grape wines, whereas we could maybe make better rounded, balanced wines by a very careful alliance of two or three grapes, each providing an essential characteristic not found in the others, and thereby producing wines with more depth.

Though few have yet successfully made a really good red wine in Britain, a red wine with a good colour – this is most important – and a good body or substance, several of us are working on this. A red wine must also be attractive commercially and I have a strong feeling that, if this problem is to solved, the answer is to be found in the Bordeaux principle.

Having grown a wide range of vines over the years, including black grapes, most of which have been discarded, I have hit upon the idea of marrying a minimum of two black grapes to make a good wine.

To begin with, the three or four grapes must be of the same breed or type, or at least they must not vie with one another for supremacy.

The first feature to look for is colour. The German vine breeders have

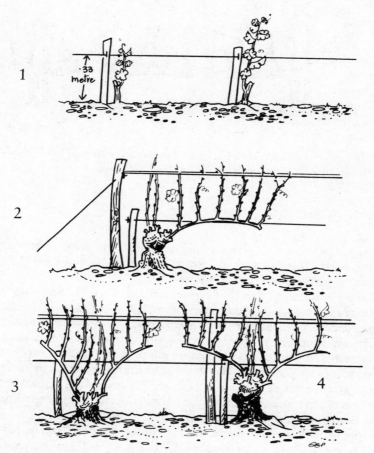

10 In the Medoc region of the Bordeaux area, the vines are trained low and close to the ground. In the first year small single stakes are used, one to each vine, placed 0.6 m (2 ft) apart, and a single wire is stretched from post to post along the rows 0.33 m (1 ft) above the ground. In the third year, longer posts, 0.6 m (2 ft) to 1 m (3 ft) above ground level, are inserted, and a double wire is inserted between them, thus completing the trellis (see diagram 2).

The vines are very dwarfed, planted a mere 0.6 m (2 ft) to 1 m (3 ft) apart both ways. Some stems are a mere 5–15 cm (2–6 in) high (see diagram 3). Here are 3 variations on Guyot pruning seen in the Medoc, leaving only 6–8 fruiting laterals per vine.

produced a fair range of colouring grapes recently, grapes which have dark red juice, which saves one the necessity of extracting colour from the skins. Some are well bred, which will mean that they could add more than just colouring to the wine. Read the chapter on German vine

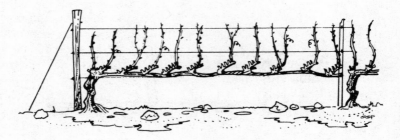

11 In the Bergerac region many vineyards are trained in cordons. The old rod is often 3 m (9 ft) or more in length, and each fruiting lateral is pruned down to 2 buds each winter.

varieties where the colouring grapes are listed, but remember that good setting, early ripening and wood ripening plus adequate yield are also important features to look for.

The second component is flavour – allied to yield and bottle life. A vine that raised a great deal of interest in 1979 and 1980 was the Austrian Zweigeltrebe, a Pinot Noir–St Laurent cross, a grape with classic breeding. It is a generous cropper, ripens on good warm sites, shows good vigour with fair winter wood ripening. Here we had a distinct possibility, but unfortunately time proved that the colour achieved was mere Rosé at best, and the wine tended to be thin, earthy and gritty. The more recent Austrian export, Blauberger, looked to be another likely contender, but sadly both soon faded from interest.

Another vine could well be one or more of the Alsatian Khulman hybrids, mostly bred from the classic Pinot Noir or Gamay crossed with Riperia, Triomphe d'Alsace and Leon Millot being the most interesting. The former requires a high potash and zinc input to help to prevent millerandage if cool and wet during blossoming; quadruple Guyot is an excellent deterrant to this decimating condition since it takes up more of the vine's extra high vigour.

Another grape receiving renewed attention is the Russian Kuibeshevski, an Aurumensis vine, again bred from Pinot Noir. The advantages here are early ripening and loose bunches, which are less mildew prone than tight bunches, plus a good flavour from the Pinot Noir parent. Whether the grapes have a sufficiently high acidity at harvest is questionable, and yield has yet to be recorded over several harvests.

The Pinot Noir might well be tried on old limestone, providing the site is outstanding; on other soils the results are disappointing.

For those with really high, cold, northerly or more exposed sites, the earliest ripening black grapes are the Alsatian Marechal Foch and

Oberlin 595, the German crosses Dunkelfelder and Deckrot, and maybe the French Noir Hatif de Marseilles, the latter requiring spur pruning. The Russian vines Gagarin Blue in particular, and maybe Kuibishevski are also early ripening, and are certainly worthy of trial. There is certainly no lack of choice here.

It is hoped that even if the vines are not the right choice for all soils and situations, at least the principle of using more than one grape to produce a fuller, more generous red wine with a good colour and some degree of character will prove to be useful. I am convinced that using the vines now at our disposal, big strides forward can be made in this particular field, providing the vineyard site is really suitable.

Burgundy

Burgundy, like Champagne, is one of the old Dukedoms of France; and has an atmosphere of ancient settled prosperity, beautiful green river valleys, woods and forests on the hillsides, attractive faded medieval villages, lovely stone manor houses and moated castles. Apart from the sweeping seas of vines, one could almost be in England.

The classic Burgundy winefield is strung along the west side of the wide valley of the river Soane, occupying gentle slopes from the valley floor up to the crest of the hills. Lesser wines are produced in the area beyond, and also on the river plain nearer the river. The Burgundy winefield, the Côte d'Or, is divided into two areas, the Côte de Nuits to the north, situated between Dijon and Beaune, and the Côte de Beaune which begins at Beaune and stretches south towards the Beaujolais region.

The Vines

Both red and white wines are grown in this district. Pinot Noir creates the wonderful deep velvety fruity red wines, and the white Chardonnay grape is grown for the great big full-flavoured golden, grapey white Burgundies. For many these two wines are the greatest in the world. Aligoté is grown to make lesser wines.

These vines are ideally suited to the area: here they are capable of producing, without undue stress, truly magnificent wines in all but abysmal summers, barring the misfortune of natural catastrophies (like hailstorms) wrecking ripening grapes.

Yield is strictly controlled, also spacing and pruning, even to the amount of inches of old wood left on each vine. Quality is all important here.

12 A head or goblet trained vine before and after pruning. Some 12 fruiting canes are allowed to develop each year, and each is pruned down in the winter to leave a spur of 2 buds to provide fruiting canes for the following year.

13 In Burgundy, the vines are trained on a very low trellis of 2 single wires. Vines 1 m × 1 m (3 ft × 3 ft). Guyot simple used universally here. Amount of fruiting wood and buds left on the vines is strictly controlled by local ruling; yield kept low to maintain the highest possible quality.

Viticulture

In Burgundy the Pinot Noir and Chardonnay vines are planted close together in the row, 1 m square, to keep the yield per vine low, which in turn maintains massive quality in the end product. As each vine is only allowed to carry such a small crop, the balance of sugar, acidity and all other elements within the grapes is perfect, ideal for fine wine production. Cropping ratio is restricted to 30 hectolitres per hectare, which is *circa* 264 gallons/acre, 1584 bottles/acre, and a little in excess of $1\frac{1}{2}$ tons per acre.

A low trellis is used to support the vines, the bottom wire often a mere 20–30 cm (8 in-1 ft) from the ground, with metal stakes every five or six vines. Single Guyot training is universal, indeed compulsory, double Guyot is not allowed.

The lesson to be learned here is that in this district where one of the two finest red wines in the world is grown, an enormous yield is not the aim, indeed, it is not allowed. The situation is created by spacing and hard pruning followed by control of the buds and subsequent fruiting canes which are allowed to develop and bear. Indeed, the Pinot Noir and Chardonnay vines are not naturally heavy croppers, and give of their best when they are not overcropped.

Wine

Several houses still tread their red grapes, the wine is then fermented in open casks. In certain instances $\frac{1}{5}$ of the wine is subjected to a hot fermentation at 34–35°C. This might run for eight days and ferment out to dryness after which it is added to the other $\frac{4}{5}$ of the wine.

Other establishments favour a twelve day, cooler fermentation at 25–28°C. Romanée Conti limit their fermentation to 23–25°C. These quick fermentations are designed to speed up the time between vine and bottle, with all modern aids brought in to make the wine ready to sell far earlier. The shorter ferment on the pulp and skin makes for wines of lighter colour and substance, the overall process turning out wines that are ready to drink sooner and with a much reduced bottle life. Indeed many houses, including the most famous, now pasteurize all their wines, which instantly stabilizes and sterilizes them, which eliminates the old fashioned method of achieving the same end by a lengthy slow maturation period in cask and bottle.

Lovers of the older style red Burgundies, great big dark velvety wines that could be laid away for years, and slowly become absolutely magnificent, abhore the modern quick turn-over system. The best establishments still use new casks for their new red and white wines each year as in Bordeaux, others replace some 5–8 per cent each year. They have not yet succumbed to tank fermentation like most of the lesser houses.

White wines are subjected to a malolactic fermentation, a difficult process to induce when the wine has a high acidity following a cold or moderate summer. Most wines are bottled at a year old.

Conclusions

We have to accept that being situated so much further north than the native habitat of the Pinot Noir, we in Britain are unlikely to be able to do justice to red wine production from this grape, except perhaps in years such as 1975 and 1976. The Germans attempt to make red Pinot Noir in the Ahr valley, the northernmost wine growing area in Germany, also around Assmanhausen on the Rhein, but the result is little more than rosé in colour and greatly lacking in body and flavour, a mere shadow of the French Burgundy. Also remember that in Champagne the Pinot Noir is used together with Chardonnay to create the white wine of the area.

Vinified white, Pinot Noir can with care make a crisp, fresh and very French wine of considerable quality, more particularly when blended with Auxerrois grapes. The yield from mature vines can certainly reach 1 bottle per vine, from Guyot-trained vines planted at 2,000 to the acre, a yield in excess of 2 tons to the acre.

14 Beaujolais vines are either trained on a low trellis or as a free-standing bush as shown here. Double Guyot not allowed. Vines are planted 1 m × 1 m (3 ft × 3 ft) apart.

Pinot Noir responds well to traditional Guyot training and pruning, crops well from the fourth year, and thrives on a high lime diet.

The Chardonnay vine on the other hand is really just too late in the open in Britain, again the exception to the rule happened in 1975 and 1976, but these freak years are too rare for this vine to be worthy of a place in the vineyard. Under glass or in a polythene tunnel both Chardonnay and Pinot Noir are absolute winners.

Beaujolais

Whereas the Pinot Noir and Chardonnay vines of Burgundy yield their magic on the old limestones of that area, the Gamay vine of Beaujolais needs granite to thrive, indeed neither will prosper on the soils of the other area.

The Beaujolais area is vast and sprawling, quite flat and gently undulating in the lower regions, but quite mountainous in the middle section. The spine of central France, which begins to the north in Burgundy, continues down through Beaujolais to the west, and indeed is to be found again in the Rhône valley further south; it acts as shelter from the west wind, and throws back and holds the heat in the three winegrowing areas. This feature is repeated to the east in Alsace, where the Vosges mountain range performs a similar function.

The overall impression in this region is of being *much* further south than the Côte d'Or; the nearly flat orange pantile roofs to the low cottages and houses are there to provide protection from the sun as opposed to the steeper, more northern roofs, which are formed to shoot off rain and snow.

The Vines and Viticulture

The vine of the Beaujolais is the Gamay. Most mature vines have no supporting trellis, and are head pruned; a low wire trellis is used in some areas. Newly planted vines are trained to slender chestnut slips of some 75 cm in height to encourage a straight stem or leg.

The vines are spaced 1 m × 1 m in general, often closer in the rows. Some fruiting laterals are allowed to develop from the spurs on the crown of each vine, which in turn bear some 24 bunches of grapes.

Chemical weed control would appear to be universal in the flatter areas and there are few signs of ground cultivation. A percentage of growers use the high straddling vineyard tractor for spraying, though some still use a large tank on a horse drawn trailer, from where the spray is pumped down long rubber pipes to hand lances.

Wine

The Gamay is too late ripening in the open in Britain, but is very dramatic indeed when grown under glass. The wine should be drunk young, not laid away like Bordeaux or Burgundy. The best wines of the area are most attractive, and reflect the soil, terrain and sunshine of the area.

The Rhône Valley

The Rhône valley vineyards are divided into two main areas. To the north the vines begin just south of Vienne, and include Côte Rotie, which produces the most elegant and delicate wines of the whole area. The further south in the area, the bigger and more complex the wines become, Hermitage and Châteauneuf du Pape in particular producing wonderful big, spicy, peppery wines, in which one can smell and taste the baking-hot sunshine.

The Rhône is a very wide, very commercial and very busy dirty brown river. The northern winefield is planted on the hot precipitous rocky hillside rising up to the west of the river. Some terraces are so narrow they can accommodate a mere two or three rows of vines. Vines are grown right up into the foothills of the mountains. The enormous southern area is much flatter as the river flows down towards the Mediterranean.

The Vines and Viticulture

Quite obviously vines from so far south are quite out of the question for Britain, the Sirah and Grenache being two of the several varieties of the area. Of interest is a system noticed in the foothills for supporting vines known as 'échallat'. The vines are all goblet or head trained, every two vines being provided with a pair of narrow split chestnut stakes which are driven in, one on the outside of each of the two vines, and then pulled in above the top of the vines and tied together. The different vine training systems used in the many wine growing areas are perhaps mostly of academic interest to those who are passionately interested in the vine and viticulture, but in fact all have a practical use, and serve to illustrate the adaptability of the vine to a variety of systems, any of which could be tried in Britain.

Summary of Spacing and Training Systems
(More important grapes in italics)

Region	Vine Varieties	Row width	Vine spacing	Training System	Wine
FRANCE					
ALSACE	Riesling, Gewurz, Pinot, Muscat, etc	1.25– 1.50 m	1.25– 1.50 m	High Guyot double	Single-grape wines
BEAUJOLAIS	*Gamay*			Head training	Single-grape wines

15 In the Rhône valley vines are seen trained both by the goblet system, and also a method known as échellat, as illustrated here, whereby two vines are supported by two posts included towards one another and bound where they cross.

Region	Vine Varieties	Row width	Vine spacing	Training System	Wine
BERGERAC	Cabernet Sauvignon, Merlot, Cot etc			Cordon	Similar to but lesser than Red Bordeaux
BORDEAUX	*Cabernet Sauvignon, Merlot,* Cabernet Franc, Petit Verdot	1.30 m	1.30 m	Guyot double	Blend of 3–4 grapes
BURGUNDY	*Pinot Noir, Chardonnay,* Aligote	1.30 m	1.30 m	Guyot single	Single-grape wines
CHABLIS	*Chardonnay,* Aligote	1.28 m	1.28 m	Vallée de la Marne	Single-grape wines
CHAM-PAGNE	*Pinot Noir,* Chardonnay, Pinot Meunier	0.7–1 m	0.7–1 m	Chablis, Guyot and Royat	Blend of 2–3 grapes
COGNAC	Folle Blanche, *St Emilion,* Columbard			Mostly Guyot some Lenz Moser	Blended wine used for distilling
LOIRE	Gamay, Sauvignon Blanc, Chenin Blanc etc			Head and Guyot	Single-grape wines
RHÔNE	Syrah, Grenache, Mourvedre, Cinsault			échallat (Côté Rotie)	Blend of 2–4 different grapes

Germany

The winegrowing areas in West Germany are situated in the south-west of the country. The vineyards are planted on the steep south-facing slopes of the river Rhine and her tributaries in the north of this region, and to the south on the wide, gently undulating river plain down as far as the border with Switzerland by Lake Constance. Germany offers every possible type of site imaginable, from near impossible precipitous slate screes along the Mosel Valley, slightly more gentle hillside sites in the Nahe Valley, majestic south-facing sweeps from the Tanus hills down to the Rhine in the Rheingau, the most classic and perfect of sites producing the biggest, fullest and richest wines in all Germany. The Rheinhessen, Rheinpfalz and Baden are different again, offering open, gently undulating river plain, wider than the eye can see, producing immense yields of more ordinary wine than the northern regions. To the east are the Franconian and Wurtemburg winefields, bordering the rivers Main and Neckar respectively, each producing distinctive and individual wines, different again in style and weight. To the extreme south, adjoining both Austria and Switzerland by the Bodensee, or Lake Constance, are further vineyards, while in the extreme north, vineyards border the river Ahr, producing thin red wines from Pinot Noir grapes.

Naturally there is a dramatic difference in climate between these areas, the austere northern areas occupying the northernmost limit of the vine on the European continent, suffering harsh winters and lower summer temperatures, and the southernmost limit, bordered on the west by Alsace, Switzerland to the south and Austria the east, offering a hotter milder climate, with an added month of growing season. The wines reflect their areas of origin, those from the south tending to be more bland, full-bodied, generous, with a higher alcohol content, compared with the more delicately flavoured, acidic, racy, fine crisp wines of the Mosel and its two main tributaries the Saar and the Ruwer, at the northern periphery of the German winefield. Which wine is preferred is entirely a matter of taste, the range produced is limitless. The German is on the whole fiercely loyal to the wines of his own locality, thus even in the areas such as the Rheinhessen and Baden where yields are as high as 150 hectolitres per hectare, and there are vast co-operative wine factories to cope with the giant harvest, a very considerable percentage of the wine is consumed by the local populace. This home demand could be responsible for the high price of exported German wines; demand exceeds supply, especially of the finer wines. French and Italian wines are imported into Germany, and therefore the Germans seek to raise home production yet further so that imports can be lowered and eventually cease. Germany seeks to be self-sufficient in wine.

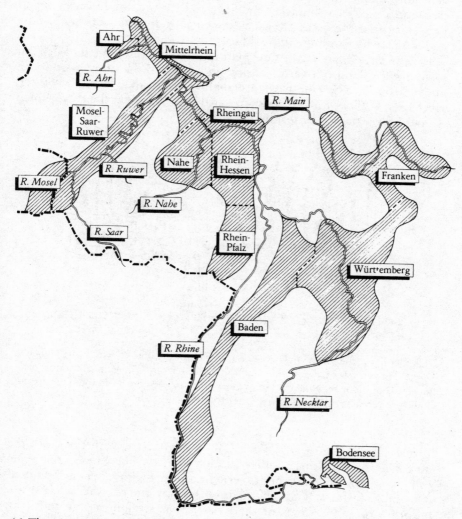

16 The winegrowing areas in W. Germany which are mainly situated in the valleys of the Rhine and its tributaries.

Vine Training

There is little variation in the vine training methods throughout Germany; single Guyot is almost universally adopted. In the valleys of the Mosel and her tributaries, the Saar and Ruwer, the hillsides are so very steep that the vines are each trained to individual stakes – a post and wire trellis would be impossible in these conditions.

In the southern areas, the new plantings tend to resemble the Alsatian system using long outward slanting end posts, the bottom wire 0.7 m above ground. The vine rows are slightly wider than in the northern vineyards to allow for fast modern cultivation between the rows which is possible on the flatter terrain.

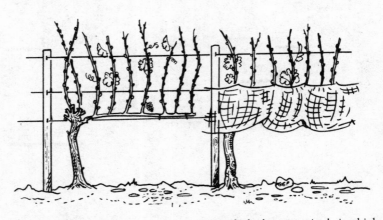

17 In Germany, the single Guyot system is universal, the bottom wire being higher in the more favourable areas, and lower in the cooler regions. The vines are trained flat along the bottom wire. Note the use of fine netting to keep the birds and wasps from spoiling the earliest ripening grapes, i.e. Ortega etc.

In the Rheingau the rows are 1.30–1.50 m apart, with the vines the same distance from one another within the rows. The vines in the Nahe Valley and all other northern German winegrowing areas are planted in a similar fashion. The general impression is one of exact and precise uniform order, the stems of the vines are as straight as ramrods, the fruiting rods taken at right angles from the stem, and tied really neatly straight along the bottom wire. Nowhere in Germany did I see any arched rods.

Neither did I see vines grown on a high or Geneva double curtain system. I was told, however, that one of the top growers in the Nahe Valley, who owns vineyards in the Bad Kreuznach area, had converted his vines to Lenz Moser training. The reputation of his wines had previously been second to none, but has apparently fallen dramatically following this change, the wines no longer being outstanding.

Weeds

In all the German winegrowing areas I visited I saw little or no evidence of chemical weed control, all vineyards being kept impeccably clean by frequent cultivation. Herbicides are sometimes used around the perimeters of vineyards. Professor Becker of the Geisenheim Institute says he likes the air in the soil, and is very against herbicide use. With a non-cultivation system, the soil becomes concrete hard with the frequent passage of mechanical equipment and feet back and forth in the rows.

With frequent application of herbicides the newest root growth of the vine can and does suffer die-back as the herbicide is washed by rain through the soil. This can put undue strain on a vine, more particularly following a very wet winter, when waterlogged soil conditions can also cause root die-back. When we discover vines showing small yellowed leaves, little or stunted spring growth, followed by the leaves browning and dropping off, we can attribute the cause to one or the other of these two elements or possibly a combination of both providing that no insect pest is to blame.

I am told there is a woodland area in south Wales where herbicides have been used for many years to control weed growth between young trees and the situation has now become so acute that no living plant can exist on that ground; everything, including the trees and the weeds have died, and no newly introduced trees can take hold before they too die. It would appear that the fears expressed to me by many vine growers in France, Alsace, Germany and Luxembourg are well founded, in that they suspect that a build-up of poison in the soil will eventually become so great that the vines will die and the land become barren and useless. This opinion is certainly worth serious consideration.

With today's high prices of herbicides, I would calculate that the costings of cultivation as opposed to herbicide control are not very different. A vineyard would not need more than three, or at most four cultivations a year; one in the spring, followed by a second after some three to four weeks to further knock the newly turned spring weeds and a third in July to turn in any weed re-growth. July sees the end of the energetic growth period, the pace lessens in the heat of the summer. A fourth cultivation, just before or just after harvest completes the cycle and leaves the vineyard clean for the winter months.

Vine Age and Yield

Today the German grower demands that his vines begin cropping properly in the third year, and that his vines bear heavily and consistently. Vines are therefore cropped at full capacity throughout their span, and as soon as the yield begins to drop, they are grubbed and replaced. This takes place from 15 to 20 years after planting.

The Viticultural Research Stations in Germany have for many decades spent all their time and effort in satisfying the demands of their growers by painstaking selection of élite clones of different vine varieties, and rejection of those clones that are less than perfect in every respect. Modern research technique has enabled the scientist to recognize and isolate virus in vines, and to supply the top vine nurserymen with selected virus-free material for propagation, with a result that there are now few virus-infected vines in all Germany. Vines with virus function will bear at considerably lower par than virus-free stock, and once all infected material has been eliminated from a country there is little chance of re-inoculation.

Therefore the Germans have created an élite range of vines for their own use, vines that crop in the year, and crop heavily thereafter because they have been propagated from selected heavy-bearing parent plants. These vines do decline earlier because they have been expected to yield to capacity every year, and as soon as they show signs of decline, they are removed. This is very different from the French approach.

A cautionary word here. Having a very wide range of vines planted in a trial area, separate from my commercial vineyard, I am beginning to notice a very wide variation in performance among these vines, some varieties stemming from no less than three original sources. Many Continental nurserymen are not particular about the principles outlined in the previous three paragraphs, particularly when the order comes from English growers or import agents.

There is no doubt that in many cases we are being sold very inferior stock, not only in terms of the quality and the chance of survival of the initial plant, but also in the strains and clones being planted in England. From a reliable source I have learned that the vast majority of the Müller Thurgau planted in England are of discontinued, poorly functioning clones. There are élite clones of Müller Thurgau available if only we took the trouble to run some to earth and book them. These are clones discovered by and distributed from research stations to all German growers.

This failing is particularly noticeable with Müller Thurgau, Riesling, Pinot Blanc, Auxerrois, Pinot Noir, Pinot Gris and Chardonnay from Germany and Alsace. These, you will notice, are all ancient vines, with the exception of the Müller Thurgau, which is the earliest of the modern crosses. Before ordering it would be in the new or expanding grower's interest to make sure from where his vines originate, to check on the clone or strain and, ideally, to make arrangements either to collect those vines himself or to make private arrangements for collection.

Better to order vines from the northernmost area possible; why buy Pinot Noir, Chardonnay, Auxerrois and Müller Thurgau, even Riesling from Alsace when the former could be bought from nurseries in the Champagne region, and the Müller and Riesling from the northernmost area in Germany, where they will be clones selected for their adaptability to the more northerly winefields, and therefore, far more suited to England.

As in every other field of business, there are good and bad vine nurserymen, some men with the highest principles, and others with none whatsoever. Some are little more than vine traders, never turning down an order, however vast, and having to rattle around all other known dealers, however dubious, in order to book and secure the vines they need. This results in vines travelling the length and breadth of Germany and/or France, going from dealer to dealer, travelling several weeks and hundreds of miles before reaching the unfortunate grower in a very jaded and dried out condition.

There is nothing more depressing than discovering in the third or fourth year after planting that one has a clone so inferior that the vines make little or no effort to throw any flower, and never produce a commercial crop. Such a misfortunate is a complete waste of time, money and effort.

The aim of the average German grower is to take the highest yield possible from his vineyard, for such are the levels of cellar skills in Germany that saleable palatable wines can be made from underipe grapes with the aid of plentiful supplies of Sussreserve, which is unfermented sweet grape juice. I shall discuss this process more fully in the chapter on winemaking.

To underline this statement, one only has to compare the yield figures for the different areas of France with those of the German wine regions, bearing in mind that the majority of French quality vines are affected by virus. The maximum yield allowed in each area of France or Germany is levied by a committee of top growers from that particular area; rules and regulations are created to suit the local growing principles, be it lower yield to attain maximum quality, or maximum possible yield to cater for massive demand for relatively cheap wines. In Germany the highest yields are only allowed in the lesser quality mass-production areas – certain districts in the Rheinhessen, Rheinpfalz and in Baden.

One has to admire the German vinegrowers for the immaculate appearance of their vineyards, the precise uniformity of the training of the vines, and the skills in husbandry in attaining such massive crops. The health and vigour of the vines speak for themselves, they are a real example of viticulture at its best, and, as such, we have much to learn here – remembering to temper our enthusiasm for the German skills with the creed of the top French quality wine growers.

The German winegrowing regions vary less than the French wine areas. The trellis, pruning, training and spacing methods are similar throughout Germany – the Mosel, Saar and Ruwer areas being the one exception. Therefore there is little to be gained by describing all the regions in great detail. There is, however, much for the British grower to learn from certain regions, and these will be discussed in some depth.

The Rheingau

The great river Rhine (*Rhein* in German) flows from Switzerland in the south, continues on its northerly course from south to north Germany, is bordered by Alsace in the south-west and finally flows into the North Sea.

During its northern journey the Rhine meanders to east and to west, at times providing quite excellent sites for vineyards when south, south-east and south-west slopes are created. A site of unique proportions, a *perfect* winefield, is formed when the Rhine takes a right-angled turn to the west at Mainz, and flows due west for some 26 miles making the most glorious of sites in the entire Rhine valley. Sheltered to the north by the Tanus hills, the sloping south-facing vineyards enjoy uninterrupted sunshine from dawn to dusk, so that it is little wonder that the Rheingau wines are quite the richest in all Germany. The wonderful combination of perfect site, glorious limestone soil, sunshine, heat and light reflected off the surface of the river and up into the vines to aid ripening, create the special wines of this area, rich in extract, tasting of honey and sun-ripened grapes, with a perfect balance of alcohol and acidity.

The conditions offered by the Rheingau are equal to those of sites 200 miles further south and are unique in such a northerly area.

Vines

The Riesling vine reigns supreme here, a vine ideally suited to the Rheingau vineyards, an area where the geographical location encourages the grapes to ripen to perfection in all but truly abysmal summers. Again an example of allying the right vine to the conditions offered by an area.

Most Rheingau vineyards have one-tenth of their area planted with the Ortega grape, a very early ripening grape of a somewhat bland and undistinguished character, but capable of assimilating a very high sugar percentage even in a poor cool summer. These early ripening grapes are easily recognized as they near ripeness, being covered by fine blue netting to keep the birds and wasps away. The Ortega grapes are naturally harvested first. They are either pressed out and fermented, to be blended later, if necessary, with the Riesling wine, or they are pressed and the resultant juice kept unfermented under pressure to be used as Sussreserve if the Riesling wine, when it has fermented out, is found to be too acid to be marketable.

This practice could usefully be followed by the English growers who are heavily committed to later grapes such as Müller Thurgau and Seyval Blanc, but great care must be taken to choose a grape that will harmonize with the main grapes, a grape that will either blend in with the major grape without making its presence felt at all, or, alternatively, will add to the major wine. A safe move is to choose an early grape with one common parent, or if possible both parents the same as those of the major grape, then the blend is likely to be excellent.

The grower will thus be equipped with a home-grown sweetening agent for his wine, to which he may add up to 15 per cent of the sweet wine or sweet juice, Sussreserve, and still name the wine after the major grape. If more than 15 per cent is used, then the wine label must by law carry the name of both grapes.

To become more self-sufficient in this manner will relieve the grower of the temptation to import sweet reserve from another country within our area of northern France or Germany, or, as one or two growers in England have done, import sweet reserve from the south of France or Italy, juice of grape varieties totally alien both in flavour and style to those we grow here, a practice which completely alters the harmony and balance of the English wine in question. This process tends to debase the very characteristics of English wine we find so attractive and strive to perpetuate, namely the delicate flowery nose, a fresh racy acidic fruity flavour, lessening these qualities to such a degree that the wine takes on a mass-produced bland taste, with a top-heavy sweetness that is not sufficiently supported by the alcohol content or the acidity. We must move towards keeping up our early ideals and standards, and not allow others to debase our product and, by so doing, lower the good name of all our wines in the eyes of our customers.

To return to the Rheingau, the premier winegrowing area of Germany, renowned for its world-famous estates and vineyard sites. The State owns the greatest area of the vineyards in Germany, principal among these being Steinberg (stone hill), 79-acre walled vineyard, magnificently sited on a gentle south-facing slope looking down towards the river Rhine over a sea of vines. Planted with the noble Riesling Vine, the Steinberg Vineyard produces wines of classic proportions with honeyed fragrance and a magnificent balance of fruit and acidity, and as with all great wines, great length in the mouth. It is a sobering thought to realize that this vineyard was originally walled and planted in the twelfth century by Cistercian monks from the nearby monastery, Kloster Eberbach, and has been lovingly tended ever since. Other State vineyards include plantings at Assmannshausen, Rudesheim, Hattenheim, Rauenthal and Hochheim.

It is said that the Emperor Charlemagne noticed that the winter snows first melted on the slopes now occupied by the 85 acres of Schloss Johannisberg, and planted vines there. The vineyards of Schloss Johannisberg spread beneath the mansion house like a vast billowing apron, with magnificent views from the terrace of the length and breadth of the Rheingau. Here again the magical ingredient of soil combines with climate and centuries of experience to create a unique wine, each vintage a masterpiece, a great wine of superb elegance, style and depth and length.

Schloss Volrads is the third great estate of the Rheingau, a castle built in 1300 by Baron Grieffenclau, and owned and lived in continuously by his issue. The great wines have a unique house flavour, unforgettable once tasted, wines of perhaps more substance and depth than either of the foregoing, more inclined to clover honey than the heather honey of Steinberg and Johannisberg.

These three are, rightly or wrongly, the most famous wines of the Rheingau. There are other great wines grown in the area, wines of exquisite flavour and tremendous extract, all the best being carefully fermented, stored in cool underground cellars, the walls festooned with the penicillin mould, *Cladosporium celare*, which can only survive in conjunction with the gases given off by fermenting wines in oak casks.

Also situated on the Rheingau is the world-famous Viticultural and Vinological Institute at Geisenheim, where invaluable research into improving viticulture and winemaking and also extensive vine breeding trials are carried out, resulting in the discovery of many new and improved varieties. Beginning with the first, the Müller Thurgau (1882), the quality of the new vines has been most impressive, for the aim is to produce vines with Riesling parentage, on one side if not both, or at least a Riesling grandparent. Work is also under way on producing some new black grape vines for red wine, the emphasis here being on early ripening and high sugar, with some producing a grape full of blood-red juice and pulp, so that when these vines are released to growers, they will be able to make red wines with a great depth of colour.

At Geisenheim, where the friendly genius Professor Helmut Becker is director, there is a massive collection of vines from all over the world, so they have a vast bank of material to draw on for their breeding programmes; one is shown all the processes in the production of new vines. The vine destined to be the mother of a new vine is grown in a glasshouse, the florets are each enclosed in separate polythene bags before blossoming. When flowering is imminent, the cap is removed, and the stamens are then removed to prevent self-fertilization. When the ovary is in a receptive condition, pollen from the chosen father vine is introduced into the ovary, every care being taken that no other pollen can gain entry into the polybag at this time. The florets then develop into berries. When ripe, the berries are opened, the pips dried and then sown. Offspring is thus obtained in the same year, and the time taken in being able to assess the potential of the new young vine is thus reduced to a minimum. The new vines are first reared under heated glasshouse conditions, then they are removed to outdoor frames, and those with real potential are finally planted out into the main vineyard trial area. They can bear fruit in the third year, so that the decision on whether they have viable commercial promise is quickly reached, and, if they have, they will stay for longer trials but, if not, they will quickly be grubbed to make way for other experimental vines that are always in the Geisenheim pipeline.

At Geisenheim there is also a collection of American rootstock vines, great tall rampant creatures making many metres of stout rod per annum.

Many of the vines bred at the Geisenheim Institute have proved to be highly successful due to the principle that one can only expect new vines of classic style by using noble parent vines. Several of these vines have proven themselves to be highly adaptable to the soils and conditions in Britain. There are similar Institutes in all the different winegrowing areas of Germany, each doing similar work on vines and wines, both white and red, and it is largely due to this modern research on vines that we in Britain have been able to contemplate growing wine with any degree of confidence, and harvesting ripe grapes and making palatable wines.

The present emphasis is on making natural wines at Geisenheim. The location of the vineyards is so good that the grapes ripen to perfection in most years, and superb wines are made without the addition of sugar, so the true nose and full flavour of the grape can be assessed and savoured. These natural wines are more to my liking than the softer sweeter finish of the average German white wines, which are mellowed with sweet reserve. I suspect these natural wines would bring many more English wine drinkers to German wines could they but have the opportunity of trying them, and were they commercially available in Britain. The average British wine lover likes drier wines than the German wine drinker, who likes really sweet smooth wines.

For us, Professor Becker sees a future for Sekt, or sparkling wine. In poor years when we have an over abundance of acid grapes we could well convert our grapes into Sekt. At the Geisenheim Institute they have made Sekt by both the tank method and the 'methode Champenoise', and have produced very superior results indeed as they use sound ripe grapes, but grapes with a high acidity, as this factor is an essential for really fine Sekt, or indeed any sparkling wine.

The Geisenheim Sekt proves that a really first-class product can be made. Using sound fruit and first-class controlled production, the end product is worlds apart from the third-rate Sekt sold in inns and cafés in Germany, a poor thin rough carbonated apology for Sekt, made from grapes sold by the growers to the local Sekt factory as they are too acid, unripe, infected by mildew or botrytis, or generally of too poor a quality for the grower to make a wine to sell under his own label. Therefore as far as the growers are concerned, the Sekt factory has a place in the community because it will buy a product that would otherwise be thrown away. Naturally there are fine Sekts made, refreshing wines of some charm though the finish is always rather sweet for the English palate. Sekt is fine providing one remembers it *is* Sekt and does not attempt to compare it with Champagne – the two are worlds apart. Top-quality Sekt is made from the Riesling grape, run-of-the-mill Sekts from any grape combination thereof, whereas Champagne is always made from the classic Pinot Noir, Chardonnay and Meunier. Good Champagne has great finesse of flavour and a superb length, Sekt tends to lack length; the two wines have few, if any, similarities, and should remain so.

The Nahe

The Nahe, a tributary of the Rhine, entering the Rhine at Bingen (directly opposite Rudesheim), is a considerable wine growing area, particularly near to the lower reaches of the river. The remainder of the area is rather fragmented, with a fair concentration around Bad Kreuznach.

The wines of the Nahe area are bounded to the north by the Rheingau, to the east of the Rheinhessen and to the west by the beautiful Mosel and her tributaries. Wines with a particularly rich honeyed nose and charming balance are made from the Bad Kreuznach vineyards.

Further upstream, the Nahe flows through beautiful wide gentle water meadows, bounded by fairly steep hills to either side, not unlike the reaches of the magnificent Wye Valley near Tintern Abbey in England. Here the State Wine Domain, Staatlichen Weinbandomänen Niederhausen-Schlossbockelheim is situated on a perfect south-facing slope with glorious views of the valley below.

The viticultural scientists here have discovered that the vine ceases to function when the temperature rises above 30°C, about 90°F. The assimilation of sugar stops at such a time, and the leaves become limp. Therefore, when one assumes that during a heatwave the grapes are accumulating vast sugar reserves, that will only take place if the temperature rises no higher than 90°F. This simple fact also explains why wines from tremendously hot countries do not have a massive alcohol content. In such areas, where the temperatures are more likely to be above 90°F in the day, the vines can only assimilate sugar in the evenings and at night when the temperature falls. This would apply to the wines of Algeria, Turkey, Greece, Southern Italy, the South of France, and Spain. The growers in very hot countries tend to grow their vines on high pergolas, so the leaves shade the grapes, and keep them as cool as possible. The opposite of the northern principles!

At Niederhausen overhead irrigation lines have been erected, so that immediately the temperature rises beyond the critical 30°C, water is pumped up from the river Nahe below, and sprayed over the vines and the soil. Within ten minutes the temperature within the vineyard is lowered, the humidity rises and the vines begin to function once more. Even in a heatwave a good ten-minute soaking is not required much more often than once a fortnight. By so doing the maximum oechsle or sugar is achieved each year from the vineyard. Hot days and cool nights help to raise the oechsle level in the autumn, cool nights are apparently essential.

The wines grown in this State Wine Domain are among the most attractive produced in Germany. These are an admirable combination of the flowery nose and elegance of the wines of the Rheingau, and the racy fruity acidity of Mosel wines.

I charge all my readers to try and run to earth some wines of this state-holding; wines of Kabinett Status, Niederhausen and Steinberg in particular. O. W. Loeb of Jermyn Street are English agents.

More of the work of this state wine station is included in the chapter on the making of white wines – their revolutionary work on making wine at extremely low temperatures so that the characteristics of extreme youth are for ever retained in the wine in bottle.

Near the confluence of the Nahe with the Rhine, up the Berg Layen Valley just above a vast volcanic core, a newly planted vineyard had strips of black polythene running up the entire length of each row, neatly tucked into the ground on either side of the vines. This acts in two ways. Firstly all weeds are suppressed between the vines within the rows, a strip of bare earth is left between each strip of polythene which is kept clean cultivated. Secondly, moisture is retained beneath the polythene, preventing the vulnerable young vines from drying out and dying in very hot dry weather.

In a Nahe vineyard above the town of bad Kreuznach, Agrolam is used extensively to keep both birds and, apparently, wasps from attacking the ripening grapes. This product is used a great deal for protecting the grapes that ripen really early. Sold under different names in different countries, Agrolam is also used a great deal in Alsace in the flatter Harth area. I gather it is very efficient; if a bird entangles himself in the rayon mesh just once and lives, he will never do it again! One wonders if our persistent blackbirds would be deterred so easily!

The Mosel, Saar and Ruwer District

The Mosel river rises far away to the south of Germany in the Vosges mountains, the range which divides Alsace from Lorraine. Flowing north, the Mosel (Moselle in France, Mosel in Germany) passes through Trier, the ancient Roman town, capital of the German Mosel, Saar, Ruwer vinegrowing area. The south-facing banks just ask to be planted with vines.

The greatest Mosel wines come from the middle Mosel, the area between the villages of Piesport and Traben-Trarbach, known as the 'great bends'. In this area there are great south-facing sweeps of river bank, hundreds of feet high, often forming a vast basin or bowl effect, suntraps, natural amphitheatres for the production of great wines. One only has to look at a map of the Mosel, aligned with a north-south compass sign, and the great south-facing bends are readily evident. Among the greatest are the vineyards of Piesport, Wintrich, Lieser to Wehlen, Berncastel and Traben-Trarbach. The combination of site, soil and vine somehow reaches magic proportions in this region; the steep (45°) slopes attract and retain every ray of sun and every degree of heat. The soil – which is almost entirely composed of fragmented slate, again conducive to heat retention – provides the unique character of the Mosel wines. The Riesling vine, that *most* noble of white grapes, when given a reasonable summer in the Mosel Valley, creates wines of unique proportions, a glorious full and flowery bouquet, a majestic balance of fruit and acid, and a heavenly length in the mouth – fine delicate, elegant wines.

The growers in the Mosel Valley have adapted the training of the vines to suit the terrain. On the steep slopes each vine is trained to a single stake, each vine having a stem or leg of 1–2 m high (3–6 ft), and from the top of his stem two rods are trained out, downwards and then upwards, forming a pair of large circular loops, and the laterals that issue forth from these rods bear the grapes. Two replacement rods are grown each year, the two fruited rods are entirely removed, and the replacements tied in. This is of course a form of cane pruning, like

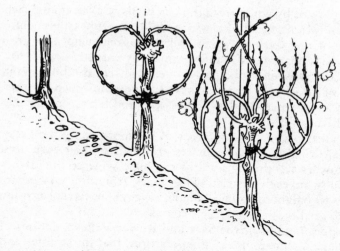

18 On the precipitous sites along the river Mosel and its tributaries, the vines are trained to stakes and no wires are used. The vine on the left shows a newly pruned vine; the vine on the right shows a vine after harvest and leaf fall. The two replacement canes shown in the centre are trained up the post.

Guyot, and is a clever adaptation of a system to suit a particular site and terrain.

The further up river one goes, one notices that the vines are lower and closer together, an adaptation to the greater height above sea level and therefore slightly cooler conditions, and a slightly shorter growing season. This trend is even more noticeable when travelling up the Mosel tributaries, the Saar and Ruwer (pronounced Roo-ver).

The soil in these higher regions is less fertile, so that in the upper reaches of these vinegrowing river valleys, the vines are as close as 0.6 m (2 ft) in both directions in order that a worthwhile crop can be expected.

In areas where wide flat meadows have formed from river silt on the Mosel valley-floor, vines are Guyot-trained on a post and wire trellis.

The chances of a great and classic vintage becomes more unlikely the higher and more remote the vineyard, but so well sited are some of the more famous Saar Valley vineyards, with steep, well-sheltered south facing slopes, that given a good flowering and fine dry weather during ripening and harvest, some wines of unforgettable proportions are made, wines with a blend of an almost heavenly delicacy, combined with a lovely balance of racy acidity and a purity of flavour that is unequalled in the world.

The wines from the great hill of Wiltingen are perhaps the greatest, closely followed by wines from the vineyards of Oberemmel, Scharzhof, Ockfen and Kanzem, all of classic proportions and truly memorable to the lover of fine German wines. All these great vineyards are planted with the Riesling wine, which explains why weather is vital for a good harvest, and why only one or two years in ten, the hot summers, are capable of producing great wines. Lesser vines such as the Müller Thurgau are planted on the lesser slopes and lesser sites in the Mosel, Saar and Ruwer district.

As in all the winegrowing areas of Germany, only the great estates and classic vineyards make, bottle and market their own wines. The small growers sell their grapes to the huge wine co-operatives placed strategically in each district. The wines from the co-operatives are honest, well-balanced and well made, never great, having a certain mass-produced quality.

The upper regions of the Saar and Ruwer Valleys, and also Luxembourg, have a climate, mean temperatures, bud burst dates and length of growing-season on a par with that of the few best vineyard sites in southern Britain. I think this is significant. The truly outstanding wines that are made in these higher cooler districts in magnificent summers are ample proof of a claim that grapes, or any fruit, reach perfection at the northernmost limit of their growing area. Lacking the overblown fullness and flatness of wines grown in hot southern districts in a really good summer, these more northerly wines display facets and nuances of bouquet, flavour and character one would never believe possible in wine. Perhaps my enthusiasm will encourage my readers to seek out wines of great vintages from the Mosel and Saar villages previously mentioned, wines from top growers; 1975 and 1976 are the most recent great years, so I do hope so. Again, consult O. W. Loeb of Jermyn Street, London.

Wines of particular merit are the Bernkasteller Wehlenner Doktor from the Thanish vineyard, and J. J. Prumm's Wehlenner Sonnenhur, both from the Mosel, and Wiltingen Braun Kupp from the Saar. The Bernkasteller Wehlenner Doktor is pure bottled magic, and must be one of the greatest wines in the world.

Luxembourg

A considerable amount of wine is grown in Luxembourg on the suitable slopes of the banks of the Moselle valley. Little is exported; most is consumed within Luxembourg. The Luxembourg winefield is a continuation of the Mosel Valley winefield in Germany; the valley sides are less dramatic, less steep, the wines are less spectacular, but are extremely well made and typical of the grapes from which they are made.

The vines are mostly Guyot-trained, fairly close, and low to the ground to catch all the sun and heat available.

Vines

The Elbling used to be the main grape grown here, but it was phased out due to the quality of the wine leaving much to be desired, also being a very heavy cropper. The Riesling grape has always been grown on the very best sites; the Sylvaner is also quite extensively grown, but as in Germany the Müller Thurgau has gradually become the most widely grown grape.

The Viticultural Research Station at Remich is conducting trials on all the more promising of the new German varieties, plus some older French varieties.

Wine Vines

Under trial are Chardonnay, Gewurztraminer, Gamay Noir, Ehren-felser, Elbling × Siegerrebe, Rulander × Elbling, Elbling 39/639, Rulander × Abondant, Bourdin × Rivaner, Reichensteiner, Kerner, Gutenborner, Schönburger, Optima, a Bourdin cross, Ortega, Wurzer, Osiris, Regner, Fontandara, Findling, Rabaner, Friesamer and Bacchus.

These are vines of interest, but the real station work is on vast clonal trials on Pinot Blanc, Auxerrois, Müller Thurgau and Elbling. The Elbling is being allowed to be grown in Luxembourg once again. It has its uses due to the massive potential yield, and is being crossed with other varieties to attempt to produce an offspring of superior quality.

Professor Huberty of the Remich Institute has some most helpful advice on vines with a future in Britain, recommending Auxerrois most highly, Pinot Blanc for good sites, Pinot Noir, Kerner, Ortega and Osiris, also Huxelrebe – with reservations, due to its habit of overcropping and then resting for a year; severe crop control must be practised otherwise this vine will succumb to winter frost, and fail to crop in the following year.

Flowering usually begins in Luxembourg on 23 June, but in 1978 it did not begin until 15 July, when most varieties in my Devon vineyard were in full flower, the black grapes having already flowered and set here by then, a fair indication that the development of vines in England is on a par with those in Luxembourg, in the Moselle Valley.

Professor Huberty has evolved some interesting techniques on wine-making, developments which would definitely assist us in improving our wines. This will be covered in the relevant chapter.

Maximum Yields Permitted under
Appellation Controlée or Equivalent

	Maximum yield hectolitres per hectare	Average
FRANCE		
ALSACE	78	70–74
BEAUJOLAIS	45	
BORDEAUX		
Bordeaux rouge	50	
Medoc	45	
Haut Medoc	43	
Margaux, Moulis, Listrac, St Julien, Pauillac, St Estephe	40	
Sauternes	25	
St Emilion	42	
BURGUNDY		
Clos de Vougeot	30	
Echezaux	30	
Vosne-Romanee	35	
Macon	50	
CHABLIS		
Grand Cru	35	
Premier Cru	40	
COGNAC		
No limit		
LOIRE VALLEY		
White wines	45	
Red wines	40	

	Average yield hectolitres per hectare 1968–1973
GERMANY	
Ahr	95
Mosel, Saar, Ruwer	110
Rheingau	95
Rheinhessen	144
Nahe	95
Rheinpfalz	105

	Average yield hectolitres per hectare 1968–1973
Hessische Bergstrasse	95
Franken	70
Wurttemburg	90
Baden	85

34 hectolitres per hectare = 300 gallons per acre
2.5 tonnes per hectare = 1 ton per acre

4

Vine Varieties for Outdoor Culture

There are some three thousand vine varieties in the world, but it is only the European vine, *Vitis vinifera*, that concerns the British grower, plus perhaps a few of the native American and Russian vines, and certain of the crosses between American and European vines known to us as 'hybrids' and to the Continental Europeans as 'producteurs directs'.

There are a great many vine varieties grown in France. Each vine growing area has a completely separate selection of vines that suit the local soil and climatic conditions and are, of course, the vines from which the local breed of wine is created, vines which have evolved through the centuries by tradition, trial and error and clonal selection.

In Germany far fewer vines are grown, principally because the basic range of quality vines are grown in each and every region, with a few regional variations. There is also a lesser quality group of vines that are grown in the areas that are not capable of fine wine production.

I do not propose to list the vines of Spain, Portugal or Italy in any detail, since they are not suitable for the British grower. In general the native American vines are not ideal for British vineyards; they tend to be too rampant, produce an inferior wine and need a longer growing season than we can offer.

The hybrids, Euro-American crosses, are more interesting however, following devastation wrought in France by phylloxera, an aphid that killed all the European vines from the 1860s, vines which were at that time on their own roots. The French experts of the time strove to find some solutions to this terrible disaster.

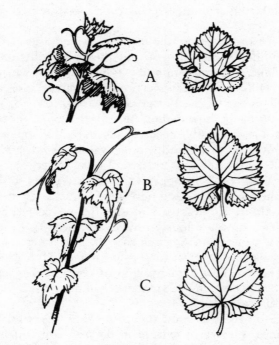

19 *Leaf types*
(A) The growing tip and leaf typical of the European Vitis vinifera vine. Note the open growing tip and classic, beautifully-cut symmetrical leaf with deep cuts between each of the five leaf lobes.
(B) The growing tip and leaf shape of the hybrid or European-American cross vine. The leaves are larger than those of vinifera, with no interlobal indentation. This vine is the Oberlin 595, showing the typical 'shepherd's crook' of the Riperia parentage.
(C) The American vine has a large plate-shaped leaf with even less accentuation of form than the hybrid leaf in general.

Their first reaction was to import and plant native American vines, known to be immune to phylloxera, but the wine from these vines was impossible to the French palate. So the next step was to try to cross the European vines with the American vines, to try to produce vines with inbuilt immunity to phylloxera and yet capable of being able to produce a high-quality wine.

Experts in different areas of France worked on this problem – there was Johannes Seyve working in the Loire region, Kuhlmann in Alsace, also Siebel and Conderc, all of whom bred thousands of crosses and each, in time, produced a handful of passable vines. Naturally the vines which were crossed with high-quality classic French vines stood a greater chance of producing an élite offspring than those crossed with the lower grade vines.

Although for producers in the lower classified areas of France these new vines fulfilled the need – in that they were phylloxera-resistant, mildew-resistant, lime-tolerant and produced honest wines – they were not the answer for the fine wine producing areas such as Bordeaux, Burgundy, Champagne, the Loire Valley and so on. So, yet again, the answer to this problem remained unsolved. It was not until it was realized that it was possible to graft the pure Vinifera scion onto the American rootstock that the dilemma was resolved, and at last each area was able to replant with the traditional varieties associated with that area. Gradually the European vinefields struggled to their feet once again, after the most severe and punishing blow ever suffered.

Ironically, although the salvation came from America, both the cause of the problem, the vine louse, phylloxera, and also the debilitating fungus mildew came from America as well. The Americans unwittingly had much to answer for. Near total ruin for *all* the European winefields, not just in France and Germany, and of course financial disaster for thousands of growers, many of whom could not exist in limbo until the answer was discovered.

A footnote on hybrid vines: they crop more heavily than the pure European vines, the wines mature faster and consequently 'live' less long in bottle, and lacking high-quality taste are, therefore, of an inferior denomination and subsequently not classified.

In France any vineyard planted wholly or in part with hybrid vines and seeking 'Appellation Controlée' status would automatically be refused. From 1992, when we in Britain can be said to have been producing wine seriously for ten or more years and, as such, become eligible to apply for such a status, we will have to abide by the same criteria if we wish to apply for a quality structure.

Many French hybrids are bred from classic French vines – for example the Chardonnay, Gamay, Pinot Noir and others – and naturally have inbuilt character advantages.

On the other hand, one or two German Viticultural Research Stations, who have been responsible for the magnificent range of Vinifera crosses available today (mostly German × German vines, though some French vines are used), are turning their interest to one or two of the very best French hybrids, and crossing them yet again with German vines to try again to produce a really fine quality wine vine and retain the élite phylloxera and mildew resistance inbuilt into the hybrid vines. The modern German vine research expert is not fanatically 'anti' the hybrid vine, realizing the massive advantages it provides and, providing they avoid using vines that produce 'Foxy' wines (these are hybrids with the American vine *Labrusca* in their parentage) and only use those with a classic French parent, they reason that fine vines will evolve from their work.

Before listing and describing the French and German vine varieties of proven or possible use to the British grower, a word or two on the new German crosses. The story begins in Thurgau, a canton in Switzerland, where a viticulturist by the name of Müller, or Mueller, began life. He subsequently went to Geisenheim Viticultural Research Station on the Rhine (Rhein in German) to work on vines. In 1882 he developed the now well-known vine, Müller Thurgau, claimed to be a cross between the Riesling and Sylvaner vines. This vine proved to be very successful, so much so that it is now the most popular wine vine in Germany, and also in Britain.

Doubt has been thrown on the claimed parentage. Much of the recent research at Geisenheim has been to try to breed the Müller Thurgau again to prove this Riesling × Sylvaner parentage. To achieve this aim they have cross pollinated Riesling with Sylvaner many thousand times. No Müller Thurgau have resulted, but this work has produced several other excellent Riesling Sylvaner crosses, namely Ehrenfelser, Multaner, Osteiner and Oraniensteiner. Therefore, the Müller Thurgau parentage has not been proven, and there is speculation that it is, in fact, a Riesling × Riesling offspring. Not that this matters to the winegrower or wine drinker; if Müller Thurgau grows well on a given site and produces good wine that sells well, then little else really matters.

Müller Thurgau was the earliest Vinifera crossbred, and the obvious success of this new vine led to both Geisenheim and Viticultural Research Stations in other areas of Germany experimenting further, crossing various German varieties one with another and also crossing certain French and Italian vines with German vines – no doubt to try to obtain vines with greater mildew resistance, good setting and cropping potential, capable of reaching high sugar and making fine attractive wines.

A veritable rash of new vines appeared in the 1920s and 1930s. A very few made the grade and are now accepted in the German vineyard and have become popular with their customers. But the German wine drinkers are notoriously unwilling to buy a wine from a new grape variety, and stolidly buy just the wines they know and love, and the grower finds it impossible to sell anything out of the ordinary. So we find that most new varieties are much ignored by the wine growers, other than Ortega, Kerner and Nobling; they prefer to grow the Müller Thurgau (22,641 hectares), Riesling (18,740 hectares), Sylvaner (15,879 hectares), with Rulander, Scheurebe, Morio Muskat, Elbling and Gutedal providing the most popular of the lesser varieties. (See pp. 114–15 for full list and hectares planted.)

Happily for us in Britain quite a fair percentage of these newer

German crosses suit the geographical and climatic conditions we offer. A good many ripen their grapes very early and, providing the vine is well bred, preferably with a Riesling parent or at least grandparent, the wines will show some finesse, an attractive fruity acidity and, therefore, plenty of backbone and good bottle life.

It has been of great interest to me to maintain an experimental section to my vineyard, where I have grown a wide collection of these new German crosses and also many of the older and often forgotten French varieties, as well as today's French vines from the Loire, Champagne and Alsatian wine regions. The collection encompasses over one hundred varieties of vines with possible potential for Britain.

Trials are conducted on growth rate, pollination success or failure in a poor summer, cropping yield, sugar and acidity, and, subsequently, whether the variety is capable of producing a fine, elegant, palatable and marketable wine. Mildew and botrytis resistance and attraction are noted, plus the vine's ability or otherwise to ripen its wood really well before winter – the latter one of the most vital criteria in a vine's behaviour. Records are taken at monthly intervals throughout the growing season, allied to temperature, rainfall and feeding, and the spraying programme.

The very best test for a vine is a bad year, which really sorts the sheep from the goats. Any vine that can survive cool wet weather during flowering, a cool damp summer and indifferent autumn weather, and *still* produce a good crop of ripe grapes, also ripen wood, and make an elegant wine, just must be a winner.

Whether a vine grower grows vines for pleasure or for profit, it is a complete waste of valuable time, effort and expense to care slavishly for useless vines that either refuse to set a crop in most years, or at best set a crop of inferior grapes that never achieve a good sugar (or must weight) and make indifferent wine.

To beat this problem there are proven fine vine varieties – we do not have to resort to hybrids or second- or third-rate Viniferas capable of producing mere 'vin du pays' or 'ordinaire' class wine.

The purpose of this book begins to evolve – after first giving a description of the many vine varieties that are grown in Northern Europe, there follows a short list of highly recommended vines. To underline this section of the book, one only has to look at a decade of British summers. In an average ten-year-cycle, we can expect perhaps one or at the most two outstandingly wonderful summers, five moderate to good summers and three totally abysmal summers.

It is vital for survival, if a commercial planting of vines is made, that a viable crop be harvested each and every year, even after bad summers, otherwise one is quickly heading for financial ruin. Much expense is showered on a vineyard each year, more in a poor year with increased spraying, and to be faced with sour unfit grapes at harvest, if any grapes at all, is ruinous. This is equally important to private growers.

Therefore, the answer is to plant early-ripening grapes, of which there are now a very fair selection to suit all sites, and to make a fine range of wines. The argument raised here will be that early-ripening grapes attract wasp damage. Look back to the ten-year weather cycle – one might have problems with wasps in two out of ten years, but one would pick ripe grapes even in poor summers. Surely this is more acceptable than harvesting ripe late-ripening grapes in just one or two years out of ten, and picking under-ripe grapes in seven or eight out of ten, requiring a scientific genius in the cellar who tries valiantly to create a silk purse from a sow's ear, either ending up with a thin acid cold wine, or a wine so swamped with sweet reserve (sussreserve) that the balance of excess sugar totally suppresses the low alcohol and fruity acidity in the wine – either way one cannot make a fine wine.

To plant early-ripening grapes, to pay great attention to either finding a perfect site, or otherwise doing all possible to create a site as near perfect as possible, allied to a system of supporting and training the vines for adequate yield per acre *and* effort and expense involved, are the guidelines for success in viticulture. The aim of this book is to explain how this may be achieved.

A further case for the early-ripening grapes is to consult the weather experts who tell us that the weather worsens and becomes more acute as we near the end of the century. Weather apparently revolves in 100-year cycles, becoming warmer towards the middle of each century and colder as we approach the turn of the century. They base this prediction on the fact that the polar ice cap is failing to recede each summer as it has in the past, and, if the present trend continues which with one or two exceptions does tend towards late cold springs, shorter summers with an early cold and wet autumn (1978 autumn excepted), then we will even have a struggle ripening early grapes in the open. The case strengthens.

One other pointer to the cooling of our climate is that the herring shoals have left the Scottish and Northern seas and come down south to warmer waters, areas they vacated some 40 years ago to go north when the weather was on the warmer swing in the 1930s and 1940s.

There follows a fairly full list of the vines grown in northern France and Germany, vines that either are, or could be, viable in Britain in the open vineyard, on walls, and the later varieties under glass. In addition various other local names for vines in different countries, a description of its growth habit, cropping potential, and the wine type and quality from each vine variety where known.

In the next chapter there is a short list of highly recommended vines.

Notes on the Classification of Vine Varieties

Whereas in France the Chasselas is used as the standard vine (other vines ripening either earlier, later or alongside the Chasselas) and in Germany the Riesling is their standard vine for comparison, I have adopted the Müller Thurgau as the British standard since more Müller Thurgau are grown than any other vine in Britain.

Therefore, a vine either ripens before, with or after Müller Thurgau. An indication of this ripening factor will be given, which will be useful in shortlisting the vines as suitable or otherwise for various sites.

A subject that will be more fully dealt with later in this book is the relevance of different training and pruning methods on the several distinct categories of vines. Most Vitis vinifera are ideally suited to cane pruning, either single or double Guyot, or to head or goblet pruning for certain vine types. The hybrid vines fall into two categories; the small bunch varieties responding best to a low trellis and to arched cane pruning, the large bunch varieties adapting best to wide spacing, being trained high and spur pruned, a system that also suits the native American vines in America.

Key
Training System	*Grape Ripening*	*Wood Ripening*
Cane pruning – C	Early – E	Good – W/G
Goblet – G	Midseason – M	Fair – W/F
Spur pruning – S	Late – L	Poor – W/P

For the Vinifera crosses and hybrid vines, the parentage is stated where known.

French White Vinifera Varieties

Aligote C   L

This grape is grown in the Burgundy and Champagne areas for making lesser quality wines than the great and noble Chardonnay, and just might be viable in Britain. No results yet. Vigorous and heavy cropping. Aligote, mixed half and half with Cassis, makes the quite delicious aperitif, KIR, a great reviver in cold weather.

Auxerrois C M W/G

Widely grown in Alsace where it is gaining ground as other vines, such as Chasselas and Pinot Noir, are being phased out and is used for making the lovely wine *Pinot*, together with Pinot Blanc grapes, the most popular wine for everyday drinking in the region. It is also gaining popularity in Luxembourg, where a beautifully balanced wine of classic style is made.

A vine of moderate vigour and cropping potential, favouring the more alkaline site, Auxerrois is attracting interest in Britain and several commercial plantings have been made, but to date few wines of this variety have been bottled and sold, so little can be said of its selling attraction in Britain. This vine has considerable potential for early alkaline sites.

Recommended by the EEC Commission for Britain.

Chardonnay C L W/G

One of the few great grapes in the world, the classic, noble and elegant wines from the Chardonnay include Champagne, Chablis and the great white Burgundies from the Côte d'Or. It will only ripen its grapes in a few favoured sites in England, thriving in an alkaline environment. The growth rate is initially slow in spring, but it does grow better later; it is a moderate cropper of glorious firm golden grapes which remain sound on the vine into late October. The leaves are a good olive green, shiny and well-rounded, a healthy vine.

The wine in poor seasons is but a shadow of its Continental cousin – but in a good year, wines with magnificent fruit, a fine racy acidity and good balance can be made.

Chasselas C L W/F

These are various clones of the Chasselas, but basically they all behave much the same. In general too late for the open vineyard in Britain, but fine on south-facing walls, the Chasselas is very widely grown in France as a roadside eating grape and, due to its lack of acidity, for making very ordinary wines. In Alsace it is being totally phased out to make space for grapes of higher quality. In habit it is vigorous with exaggerated leaf separations and lobes. Known as Gutedal in Alsace and in Germany, where it is also known as Moster, Junker, Sussling, Silberling, Frauentraube and Schönedel.

Chenin Blanc (Pineau de la Loire)

This vine produces the grapes responsible for many of the delicious, refreshing wines of the Loire valley in France, and has only recently been planted experimentally in Britain. We may find they ripen too late, but it is definitely worth the trial and effort. The vine is vigorous of habit and is a heavy cropper of large-shouldered bunches. The foliage is most attractive, the new growth being grey-green with pink edging. Worthy of trial in polytunnels.

Columbard C/S L

One of the three grapes used for the production of Cognac in the Charante region of France, a grape producing a high acid must, essential for producing brandy, or burnt wine. The other grapes are Folle Blanche and Ugni Blanc (St Emilion). Columbard is too late for growing in the open in Britain; the Cognac area is considered the northernmost limit for their specific vine varieties – but it would be interesting to try under a plastic tunnel along with several others of the more interesting borderline vines. The Columbard is a vigorous and a prolific cropper, and in hotter areas is suitable for white-wine production, being one of the few that retains sufficient acidity for a well-balanced dry wine. An acid wine is essential for distilling into brandy.

Folle Blanche C/S L

This classic grape is also grown in the Charante region for brandy production and is the basis of the finest Cognacs. The vine is vigorous and a moderate cropper, producing compact bunches which tend to attract mildew. The Folle Blanche produces a high acid and low sugar must, highly suitable for distilling, but not for wine in northern areas – though in the south of France, where it is known as Pique Poule, with the extra heat and longer summer, it produces sufficient sugar for a good wine. Again, it is too late for Britain other than under glass or a polythene tunnel.

Gewurztraminer C M W/G

Grown extensively in Alsace and also in Rheinphalz and Rheinhessen areas of Germany, this vine produces grapes which create a delicious, fruity, full-bodied wine with a delicious, spicy bouquet and taste, greatly loved by the tourists and the export trade. The vine is vigorous and fairly late in Britain in ripening its spindleberry-coloured grapes. The foliage is of a lovely matt grey-green colour, the leaves almost round with no lobe separation.

The vine requires a polytunnel in good soil to enable it to succeed. It should be trained in the double Guyot method, with each replacement cane highly arched rather than flat, to encourage the buds at the nearer end of the cane, close to the stem of the vine, to be fruitful.

Madelaine Angevine (English clone) C E W/G

Originally imported from Alzey by Barrington-Brock, this vine has gained a good reputation in south-west Britain due to early ripening, being a consistent cropper and making a distinguished white wine with a fine muscat nose. Fruit sets well even in poor weather, and yield is heavy with good sugar.

The vine has proved very useful to the German vine breeders as a parent vine, being the mother of Forta and Siegerrebe and maternal grandmother of Reichensteiner. The qualities described above are instilled into its offspring.

Madeleine Angevine is a vine of good vigour, reasonably healthy, throws and sets a good crop (often three bunches per lateral) and ripens in late September in the rare heatwave summer, and early to mid-October in a poor late summer. The vine ripens its wood admirably in autumn.

Madeleine Sylvaner C E W/G

Another old French cross, presumably between Madeleine Royale and Sylvaner. It has excellent vigour on its own roots, flowers early, sets well and carries a moderate crop of very early ripening grapes. Wood ripening excellent.

The wine from Madeleine Sylvaner can only be described as exquisitely delicate with a bouquet of spring flowers, a heavenly wine; grown in a soil in which it is happy this vine is a winner for less favourable sites. Watch for wasp damage when grapes ripen in mid to late September.

Muscadelle de Bordelais

A muscat variety, the third and least important grape used in making Sauternes, contributing a certain element of bouquet. The habit is vigorous and adapts to either cane or spur pruning.

Muscadet C   L   W/P

The vine that produces Muscadet wine, also known as Melon, a floppy, cabbage-leaved vine of low fungal resistance, and of limited interest to the English winegrower. Too late for Britain.

Muscat C   L   W/P

There are several varieties of Muscat, but the one variety that concerns us is the Alsatian Muscat. In Britain in a good year this vine ripens its grapes – large loose bunches of round yellow grapes, very coarse flavoured to eat. The vine is vigorous, producing a mass of bright yellow cane, and the wine – you either like it or you don't – only suited to good early-ripening sites.

Palomino and Pedro Ximenes C   L

The two grapes are grown in Hereth in southern Spain for sherry production. It is believed the latter vine is the Riesling of Germany.

Perle de Czaba S   E   W/G

A very old French grape vine which is best suited to be planted on a wall. It ripens early, is of controllable habit and produces a lovely white wine with a very charming and acceptable flavour. Very often these old Vinifera vines only crop on long six-bud spurs, the sixth bud being the first to be fruitful. This can also apply to Precoce de Malingre and the Gamays, Noir Hatif de Marseilles, etc.

Pinot Blanc C   L   W/F
(Known as Weissburgunder in Germany)

A vine of moderate vigour and cropping potential, and though often confused with the Chardonnay, the two are different vines. The vine is slower than some to respond to spring and maintains this tendency throughout the growing season – suddenly ripening rather than doing so gradually, and right at the end of the ripening period. The wine is a lesser wine than the Chardonnay and is grown in the eastern French wine areas, producing an aromatic fruity wine with a flinty backbone.

Pinot Gris C   M   W/G

Known as Rulander in Germany, the Pinot Gris is of moderate vigour, a fairly light cropper, bearing small branches of greyish-mauve grapes. Perhaps a tendency to lack a certain quality as a single-grape wine, I find it is best to produce a wine from Pinot Blanc, Pinot Gris and also the Auxerrois grape, which gives a very pleasant end product. Pinot wine fermented out to dryness makes a really delightful pure fruity wine.

Also known as Tokay, Tokay d'Alsace and Gran Clevner.

Precoce de Malingre S E W/G (or Van de Lahn)

An ancient French vine of somewhat shrubby habit which responds best to long six-bud spurs rather than cane pruning, when it will crop heavily. Extremely early ripening grapes, which make a very charming light non-muscat wine, pleasant and refreshing. Highly recommended for late cool sites and better sites.

Riesling (see p. 81)

Sauvignon Blanc C L W/G

This vine is grown in most regions of France, including the Loire Valley, which indicates that it just might be viable on good sites in Britain. It appears to be somewhat slow to budburst and growth is very moderate. The foliage is classically well cut and defined, grey-green in colour with pink edging to the sturdy leaves. The wine is sound and rich in extract, this being a sauternes grape.

Also known as Sauvignon Jaune, Sauvignon Fumé, Blanc Fumé and Quinechon in France, and in Austria and Germany as Muscat-Sylvaner.

Semillon

This grape makes the famous Sauternes wines with the Sauvignon Blanc grapes.

Sylvaner (see German section)

Traminer C L W/G

The Traminer was grown widely in Alsace until the Gewurztraminer, a clonal selection from the Traminer, was discovered and distributed by M. Oberlin of the Oberlin Research Institute in Colmar in Alsace late last century. The Gewurztraminer has totally ousted the older Traminer; it ripens to a glorious dull red colour and lives up to its name – *Gewurz* meaning spicy. Traminer is a day or two, even a week earlier than Gewurz throughout the growing season and has slightly smaller leaves. A light cropper and generally too late for Britain.

Ugni Blanc C   L

This is the third grape grown in the Charante region for cognac production, and along with the other cognac grapes would be too late ripening, other than under glass or plastic. Several British growers have bought acres of glasshousing and are planting these houses with both later ripening wine grapes, as well as dessert or eating grapes.

This grape is the Trebbiano in Italy and also known as the St Emilion in France.

French Red Vinifer Varieties

Cabernet Franc C   L   W/G

One of the great four grapes that are grown and blended for claret – red Bordeaux wines. Cabernet Franc is usually responsible for but a small percentage of the grapes for these most noble and glorious of red wines, Cabernet Sauvignon and Merlot providing the lion's share between them. Too late in Britain except with glasshouse or plastic tunnel protection. Both Cabernets are also grown in the Loire region.

Cabernet Sauvignon C   L   W/G

The grape providing the backbone, classic elegance, austerity and, in a really good year, almost endless bottle life to clarets. Most Medocs are created from approximately 40–50 per cent Cabernet Sauvignon, 50–40 per cent Merlot, with a smattering of Cabernet Franc, and a mere 1–2 per cent of Petit Verdot for bouquet – each chateau having its own private and secret recipe percentage of each grape which makes each claret an individual and different from its neighbour. Again too late for the open vineyard in Britain, but *very* rewarding in a plastic tunnel.

Gamay S   L   W/G

There are many different clones of Gamay used in France; the Gamay is widely grown and the vine develops different characteristics and adapts over the centuries. At the same time, man selects clones for propagation with qualities suited to his vineyard, and in this way slight differences appear within one variety. In Britain we should obviously grow Gamays from the northernmost winefield area in France, the Gamay having adapted to the more northerly latitude. Therefore, buy from Loire nurseries.

The Gamay is the lesser vine of the Burgundy region, where it is ideally suited to the granite soils of the Beaujolais region – on the limestone of the Côte d'Or it only makes an inferior wine. The Pinot Noir will only produce classic wines in the Burgundy area; on the Beaujolais soils wine from the Pinot Noir grapes is a mere shadow of the Côte d'Or wines.

The Gamay responds well to head or goblet pruning with long spurs with six buds. It may ripen too late in moderate and poor years on less favourable sites – but is worthy of a trial should you be interested in growing red wine on very hot sunny sites.

Merlot C L W/F

The Merlot is the second grape of the Bordeaux region, forming the body and softer characteristics of all great clarets. Seven Pomerol wines, notably Chateau Petrus, are created from Merlot alone.

Too late for Britain other than under glass or a plastic tunnel. For further details refer to notes on Cabernet Sauvignon.

Meunier C M W/G

The Meunier, or Pinot Meunier, is the third grape of the Champagne region – it is tough vine, buds late, and enjoys soils in which the Pinot Noir is not happy. It has a white down on its leaves, hence its name – it is called the 'dusty miller' in its English form, the Wrotham Pinot. The wine ages faster than a Pinot Noir wine, with a lesser bouquet, but adds certain necessary characteristics to Champagne as a whole, which is mainly composed of Pinot Noir and Chardonnay grapes.

Known as Müllrebe in Alsace and Germany. Good frost resistance.

Noir hatif de Marseilles E

An old French Vinifera, well recommended to British growers in the early 1960s, but soon swamped at that time by the hybrids Seibel 13053 and Pirovano 14 for red wine. Though probably somewhat lacking in vigour and of mere moderate or low yield, the quality of the grapes is excellent and well worth growing on a wall.

Pinot Noir C M W/G

The great and noble grape of Burgundy, and also the grape providing the backbone substance and elegance of Champagne. The Pinot Noir only produces this refined quality in specific areas and in certain soils – elsewhere the wine shows but a fleeting shadow of its true potential. It occupies 76 per cent of the Champagne region.

Being a grape that thrives in the northernmost winefields of France, it has obvious potential in Britain for white-wine production, if not red. In certain soils the effort will be fruitless: the vine is only happy in a calcareous environment – bear this in mind.

The vine will ripen its grapes in southern Britain, but it is not a vine of great vigour, nor a heavy cropper, so will only suit the grower who seeks a quality wine.

One or two growers in Britain have tried making a single-grape red wine from this grape, with little success so far. The results are thin, of poor extract, rather acidic wines. I do not think the breakthrough in making a good red English wine will be found in the Pinot Noir alone, though it may play a part in the final answer.

Petit Verdot C L

The Petit Verdot is grown in the Medoc area of Bordeaux, and as little as 1–2 per cent is planted in the vineyards of the great chateaux to give bouquet or fragrance to the great clarets. Though, once again, the wine is not suitable for outdoor culture in Britain, I have included notes on the great Bordeaux grapes with good reason.

Claret is a composition, a wine made from carefully judged proportions of three or four classic grape varieties; alone each would lack certain characteristics necessary to make a great wine, but genius in matching a deficiency with its antidote, found in another grape, each wine with certain proportions to suit the consistently maintained taste of that wine year after year, creates the greatest red wines in the world. Champagne is produced in a similar manner.

Why then do we stubbornly produce austere, single-grape wines, when a blend of two or three or even four grapes could well create a wine of rare excellence – certainly the trials on red wine production are going to lead us in this direction. Think on this suggestion carefully – more later.

White German Vinifera Varieties

The old natural varieties will be listed first and will be followed by the newer crossbred vines.

Riesling C L W/G

Though not alphabetically first, the Riesling, by quality alone, demands pride of place.

Today Müller Thurgau occupies a greater area in Western Germany than any other grape, but the Riesling is still king. Planted in the best sites in each area so that it may become as ripe as possible before harvest, the greatest area of Riesling is the *Rheingau* – an area that offers ideal soil and a perfect south-facing site. The other areas where the Riesling is predominant are the *Mittelrhein* and the *Mosel, Saar* and *Ruwer* areas.

Being a late-ripening grape, even in Germany, the Riesling only attains perfection in really good summers such as 1971, 1975 and 1976. In poor years skilful use of the must of an early-ripening sweet grape, such as Ortega, is used to push up the sugar content, otherwise sussreserve (the pressed and preserved unfermented juice of sweet grapes) is used to mellow the greater acidity of a poor year.

Culturally sound, the Riesling, or Weisser Riesling, is possessed of fair vigour, and carries a viable crop of grapes – grapes remarkable for their high acidity combined with a most delicate fragrant bouquet and a glorious racy elegance – a really noble classic wine.

The Riesling is one of the few white wines which will last many years in bottle following a great vintage, especially when made from grapes affected by the noble rot, a botrytis that affects the grape skins and evaporates the water, thus concentrating the sugars. In France it is known as *Pourriture Noble*, and as *Edelfaule* in Germany.

The grape is grown extensively in Western Germany, in Alsace, Luxembourg, and also on the Danube near Krems in Austria, where it is known as Rheinriesling.

The vine is considered too late for Britain, but is worth trying, if only for interest, if one can offer a perfect site. I would recommend the use of poly-tunnels. In Germany and Luxembourg they do not enjoy more than two or three great vintage years in a decade.

In descending order of hectares planted in Germany, the next most popular vine is the...

Silvaner (or Sylvaner) C L W/P

The Silvaner used to be the most widely-grown vine in Western Germany, but the popularity of the Müller Thurgau, due to its earlier ripening and, therefore, greater reliability, has meant that the Müller has now outstripped all other varieties and occupies 26 per cent of the winegrowing area of Western Germany.

The Silvaner is suited to deep loam or calcareous soils and a warm climate. It ripens later than Müller Thurgau and produces an abundant crop of grapes. The wine tends, on comparison with Riesling and Müller Thurgau, to be bland, soft and rather broad, with little bouquet and low acidity. The wine is, however, pleasant, harmonious and full of fruit, but is definitely not an elegant, high-quality wine. It ripens too late for use in Britain.

Rulander   C   M   W/G
See PINOT GRIS in the section on French grapes.

The Rulander is not widely grown in Western Germany, being mainly planted in the Palatinate and in Rheinhessen, and to a lesser degree in certain southern regions of Baden. It was introduced by and named after Johann Seger Ruland in 1711 and is a clone of the Pinot Noir. This vine has a considerable potential either alone or when blended with Auxerrois, Pinot Meunier, Pinot Noir and Chardonnay for warm early sites in Britain.

Elbling
Originally widely grown in Germany, in fact believed to date from Roman times, the Elbling has now virtually disappeared except on the Moselle above Trier on the Luxembourg border, and also on the bulge of the Moselle above Cochem, whre the soil is not suitable for the Riesling.

The Elbling is virtually a mass production wine, producing a vast crop of low-quality grapes, mostly used for blending due to their excessive acidity and low sugar even in average years. Recently it was totally phased out in Luxembourg, but has been allowed again, no doubt solely due to the yield.

It is of little or no interest to the English vineyard.

Gutedal   C   L   W/M
See CHASSELAS in the list of French vines.

The Gutedal is not much grown in Western Germany other than in the southern area where it is used mostly as a table grape.

Weissburgunder   C   M   W/F
See PINOT BLANC in the French vine list.

Gradually gaining ground in Western Germany; very successful on the Isle of Wight, lower character than Pinot Gris or Auxerrois.

Several other lesser and obscure varieties are grown in certain areas of

Western Germany, but in such small numbers that it renders them of no interest. They are purely of local interest and, as such, never likely to be available to us.

The New German Crossbred Vines

Before listing and describing these vines I feel a few notes may be of some value to help readers sort the sheep from the goats.

First, we must for ever be deeply grateful to the mass of German research into the crossbreeding programmes which have produced the initially bewildering mass of new vines. The benefit of certain of these new crosses is that, whilst retaining the advantages of one or both parents, some ripen earlier than either parent, and this makes them a very real prospect as far as the English vineyard is concerned.

Second, as the breeders and the nursery men selling these vines are inclined to praise all equally, there *must* be some scale by which we can assess which are likely to be really outstanding. Professor Becker of the Geisenheim Viticultural Research Station impressed on me that to make a fine wine, as opposed to a merely ordinary wine, a vine must have Riesling in its pedigree, either as a parent or a grandparent. Therefore, when looking up this vine or that, take especial notice of the vines from which a vine was bred and try to instil into your memory the parentage of these vines used more usually as parent vines, so that when you have the opportunity of tasting the wines from these new crosses, you will begin to be able to identify whether a vine is of Riesling, Sylvaner, Gewurztraminer or Pinot parentage. Any vine with Müller Thurgau as a parent will obviously have Riesling as a grandparent.

Such study also enables the grower to begin to shortlist the vines more likely to make the type of wine he will like, and a wine that will sell well.

Naturally, there is no sure way of discovering the true merits and drawbacks of any vines other than planting, growing and cropping them, and making single grape wines from them. This is obviously a research programme that takes a minimum of from four to five years, for, after all, the wine is the final and crucial test of a vine's true potential.

This trial work has been undertaken by a few growers in Britain. I have maintained an experimental vineyard since 1966 in Devon and currently have over 100 different varieties on trial, a separate entity and interest from my commercial vineyard. As a result of the research into growth, flowering and setting potential, yield, wood ripening and wine quality, I have managed to put together the following notes on the different cultivars, combined with data from German research.

In the next chapter the system will be explained, showing how the short list of élite recommended vines were chosen, which it is hoped will be a guide to anyone proposing to plant a vineyard and also helpful to a grower planning to expand an existing vineyard with a different vine, with a degree of confidence.

White German Vinifera – Crossbred Vines

(In parentage details, the maternal parent is listed first and the paternal parent second.)

Mueller (*Müller*) *Thurgau* C   M   W/P
(*Known as Rivaner in Luxembourg*)

Now the most widely-planted vine in Western Germany covering over 26 per cent of the total area dedicated to vines, due to its ability to adapt to most soils and situations and produce well-ripened grapes, the Müller Thurgau is also the most widely-planted vine in England, but, due to certain cultural difficulties, many are not so enthusiastic as they were about this vine.

Except on hungry limestone soils, the Müller Thurgau tends to produce too much wood at the expense of fruit, and unless constantly summer pruned and having the sub-laterals pinched out, one can find the canes meeting at three metres overhead, and little or no crop to show for this massive energy. Also Müller Thurgau shows little inclination to ripen its wood in the autumn, and entering winter with unripe wood, leaves the wood open to attack by frost, botrytis, phomopsis; following a poor cold summer-autumn-winter, one sometimes has virtually to cut right back to the crown of the vine in a vain attempt to find replacement wood. Flower set is very poor in a cold wet year, when coulure and millerandage decimate the drop (see p. 172).

The wine is very pleasant, with a muscatel flavour, with some style and a harmonious quality, particularly from limestone where the yield is good. However, the keeping power is short – about 2–3 years in the bottle.

Albalonga Rieslaner × Silvaner   C   M

Bred at Wurzberg, this vine can be too vigorous, a prolific cropper which ripens its grapes alongside Müller Thurgau. Prune to two long arched canes. A high sugar content, the wine being elegant and fruity with breeding, matures slowly and keeps well. Not grown in Britain to any degree. It is maybe too late in ripening to be useful here.

Aris 716 Oberlin (Riperia × Gamay) × Riesling Klon 91
C   L   W/G

A high-quality grape, low yield – produces masses of small bunches of small grapes and ripens late. Recently withdrawn for export to Britain.

Bacchus (Silvaner × Riesling) × Müller Thurgau

Introduced in 1961 at Geilweilerhof, Bacchus shows a habit similar to Müller Thurgau, but is more reliable in flowering and superior in quality. The flavour of the wine, with a hint of muscat, is most attractive. Worthy of serious trial in England.

Ehrenfelser Riesling × Silvaner

Bred in 1929 at Geisenheim, this fairly vigorous vine yields less than Müller Thurgau. The grapes attain a high sugar or must weight with good acidity, ripening a week earlier than Riesling, creating a mature fruity wine of Riesling type. It may be too late for Britain.

Faber Pinot Blanc × Müller Thurgau   C   M   W/F

Developed in 1929 at Alzey, this vine needs a good site and is tolerant of most soils, is hardy against frost and ripens earlier than Müller Thurgau. Faber carries a really heavy crop, attains good sugar with a balanced acidity – and the wine is fresh, fruity and vigorous. Wood ripening is only fair, poor in a cool wet year. Prone to millerandage.

Findling

Findling ripens two weeks earlier than its parent, Müller Thurgau, and also sets a better crop in the off-seasons, making this vine a very worthy subject for serious trial in England.

Forta 100 Madeleine Angevine × Sylvaner   C   M   W/F

Forta requires a good site and is very hardy against winter frost. Yields some 2–3 tons per acre, with sugar and acidity higher than Müller Thurgau and a flavour not unlike that of Pinot Gris (Rulander).

Freisamer Silvaner × Rulander   C   M

Bred in 1916 at the Viticultural Institute in Freiburg, Freisamer likes a good site and soil, is frost hardy and combines the high quality of the Rulander parent with the early-ripening and high-yielding potential of the Silvaner. The wines are well balanced and full bodied with an appealing bouquet. This vine has not been much planted in Britain.

Gloria Silvaner × Müller Thurgau

Developed at Geilweilerhof, the wine from the Gloria grape is neutral, full bodied, with only a faint bouquet, with a higher sugar and lower acidity than Silvaner – thus a vine of little interest to the fine-wine grower.

Gutenborner Müller Thurgau × Chasselas Napoleon   C   M

This grape has the character of the Müller Thurgau, being juicy and neutral, and was bred at Geisenheim. The wine from a Sussex vineyard is fresh and attractive. The low yield must be a cautionary factor.

Huxelrebe Gutedal × Courtillier Musque   C   E   W/P

Developed in 1927 at Alzey, Huxelrebe thrives in a warm, well-drained soil, a good site and freedom from frosts. The vine can be extra vigorous and is very fertile, throwing a massive crop of grapes, which must be lessened, or the vine will exhaust itself and fail to crop the next year. The huge bunches of grapes ripen some ten days before Müller Thurgau with a high sugar and acidity reading.

The flavour of the wine tends to be a little obtrusive to some, with a pungent muscat flavour, and due to poor wood ripening this vine is being phased out in both Germany and Britain.

Kanzler Müller Thurgau × Silvaner   C   M   W/P

Introduced in 1927 by George Scheu in Alzey, Kanzler likes a good site as the wood does not ripen easily. It is of moderate vigour and cropping potential. The wine is rich in extract, has a fine full fruity flavour with a delicate bouquet, but due to poor wood ripening this vine has no future in Britain.

Kerner Trollinger × Riesling   C   M   W/G

Bred at the Weinsburg (Wurtemberg) Institute in 1969, Kerner shows good frost resistance, adequate vigour, ability to crop in the third year and quite excellent wood ripening, which makes this vine one of the best of the new crosses for Britain. It carries an adequate crop of grapes that make an outstanding wine, well suited to the British palate in that it is not sweet and cloying, but fresh and clean with a haunting muscat nose, and is delicate to taste, rich in character and of great quality and elegance. Highly recommended.

Mariensteiner Silvaner × Rieslaner   C   L

Crossed in 1971 at the Wurzberg Institute, this vine is vigorous, hardy, needs a good site and ripens its wood early, but, in spite of German reports endowing this vine with good cropping potential and grapes of a good sugar-acidity balance, culturally it seems unhappy in Britain and so cannot be recommended.

Morio Muscat Silvaner × Pinot Blanc   C   L

Developed in 1961 by Peter Morio at Geilweilerhof, Morio Muscat requires a deep humid soil and a good site. It yields a heavy crop, ripening later than Scheurebe, which makes it too late for Britain. Should the grapes not be ripe at harvest, the acidity would be overpowering. When fully ripe, however, the wine has an overpowering full muscat bouquet and flavour. It is mostly used for blending, and would be valuable to introduce a little spiciness and depth of character into bland neutral white wines. The Germans use Morio Muscat sussreserve for this purpose.

Mullrebe German name for Pinot Meunier

Multaner Riesling × Silvaner

Bred at Geisenheim, the Multaner has proved to be less successful than Ehrenfelser, and so cannot be recommended.

Noblessa Madeleine Angevine × Silvaner   C   E

Introduced at Geilweilerhof, this vine shows only limited yield, but ripens its grapes early with a high must weight. It could be a good vine here.

Nobling Silvaner × Chasselas C L W/G

Developed in 1939 at Freiburg im Breisgau, this vine crops heavily, bearing massive dessert-sized bunches of grapes. Together with Kerner it is one of the few new crosses to have caught the imagination of the conservative German buyer who, in the past, only liked old tried and trusted names. However, due to its breeding, the wine shows a certain blandness and softness not attractive to the British public, so it will not be a winner here. It also ripens rather too late.

Nobling needs to be spaced 2m (6ft) apart as it produces strong, thick wood.

Optima (Silvaner × Riesling) × Müller Thurgau C E W/G

Introduced at Geilweilerhof in 1971, this vine shows limited yield with very early ripening of the grapes and is culturally sound. It attains a high sugar with a balanced acidity and the wine has a lovely fragrant bouquet. As a result of growth and ripening trials, I cannot recommend this vine as its ultra thin skinned grapes are highly susceptible to botrytis.

Oraniensteiner Riesling × Silvaner

Developed at Geisenheim, little is known about this vine culturally, but it attains a good balance of sugar and acidity.

Ortega Müller Thurgau × Riesling C E W/F

Bred at Wurzburg in 1971, the vine demonstrates adequate vigour and yield, but wood ripening can be a problem in a poor wet autumn. The grapes ripen very early, attain a high sugar combined with a very low acidity, making the grapes more suitable for blending with a high acid must than for a single grape wine. The wine has a fine bouquet and a long bottle life. It is very prone to millerandage.

In a poor year it is a very useful grape to add to a higher quality grape that might show a low sugar reading. This is usual practice in the fine-wine areas in Germany. The stalks *must* be removed before the grapes are pressed; being fleshy and soft they impart an unpleasant flavour to the wine.

Osiris Riesling × Rieslaner C E W/G

Osiris was bred at the Wurzberg Institute and demonstrates adequate cultural habit and ability, ripening wood well and yielding a good crop of grapes which ripen before Müller Thurgau. The wine is similar to

Riesling, has a fine bouquet with a fruity harmonious acidity. This vine was highly recommended to me by Dr Hans Ambrosi, Principal of all the State Wine Domaines in Germany, and would be well worth a trial here – a vine demonstrating such good acidity combined with early ripening and grapes capable of making such a distinguished elegant wine is a rare combination. Sadly no Osiris are available to us yet.

Osteiner Riesling × Silvaner   C   M

Bred at Geisenheim, Osteiner ripens early, gains a good must weight and high acidity, giving wine with Riesling similarities. It is not grown in Britain so nothing is known of its habit or performance here.

Perle Gewurztraminer × Müller Thurgau   C   E   W/G

Developed jointly by the Alzey and Wurzberg Institutes, Perle (Wurzberger Perle) is adaptable to most soils and sites, has greater resistance against winter frost than any of the other new crosses, and ripens its replacement wood well. Should the Ice Age conditions advance, then this will be the vine to grow! The wines are mild, light and flowery, and the grapes ripen to a dusty pink colour. This vine can, with confidence, be recommended for culture in Britain – though not a vigorous vine, it is a reliable moderate cropper, and thus is a viable vine here.

Rabaner Riesling Klon 88 × Riesling Klon 64   C   L   W/G

Developed at the Geisenheim Institute, Rabaner is mostly grown on the Mosel, is of moderate vigour, yield is limited and it ripens as late as Riesling which rules it out for Britain. Rabaner wine is more neutral and less fruity than Riesling – it is mild, light and green, with low acidity.

Regner Lugliencabianca × Gamay Frueh   C   M   W/G

Produced at Alzey in 1929, Regner is a Lugliencabianca (a table grape) × early Gamay crossing. The vines like a good site, good porous soil but not chalk, and apparently it is no more susceptible to downy mildew than Müller Thurgau, and powdery mildew is no problem. Harvest is a few days later than Müller Thurgau. The vine is one of the more promising of the new crosses; it sets fruit well in a poor spring and carries a really viable crop of fine grapes. As it is not of Riesling parentage, the wine is enjoyably different.

Reichensteiner Müller Thurgau × (Madeleine
Angevine × Calabresser Frohilch)   C   E   W/M

Bred at Geisenheim, the vine thrives on a good well-drained site. It likes
a fairly rich soil, has but a slight tendency to botrytis, is vulnerable to
stem rot, and the wood ripens late, like Müller Thurgau. Growth is
moderate to strong, flower set is good, even in a poor cool spring, and
the vine regularly carries a good crop of sound grapes. The wine is of
better quality grown in Britain – it can have a really glorious flowery
nose. The wine is slightly neutral, of Müller Thurgau style, and though
less definite in character, is of fair quality. Wood ripening can be poor.
Open bunches resist botrytis admirably.

Reichensteiner is one of the better of the new crosses grown in Britain
so far.

Rieslaner Silvaner × Riesling   C   M

Developed at Wurzberg in 1921 and grown solely in Franconia, it thrives
on less favourable soils and sites, ripens two weeks earlier than Riesling,
liking shell lime soil best. The wine is rich in alcohol, juicy, with a
Riesling-like acidity, though not quite of Riesling quality. The wine
matures slowly in bottle, reaching its best after four to six years, with
good keeping capacity for much longer. There are no British results to
quote, though from a description of the qualities of Rieslaner, a trial
would be well worth while.

Scheurebe Silvaner × Riesling   C   L   W/G
(*Also known as Sämling 88 or S88*)

Bred by George Scheu at Alzey in 1916, Scheurebe demands a good site
but is happy in most soils, and requires shelter from wind and frost.
The vine is a heavy cropper, but the grapes ripen late, although they
remain sound if left on the vine and will slowly assimilate sugar well
into winter.

The wine is of considerable quality, having a charming bouquet, an
elegant harmonious fruity flavour, more full bodied than Riesling with
a pleasant fresh acidity. Scheurebe could only be recommended for the
very best sites in Britain, as it ripens later than Müller Thurgau, which
is itself a borderline ripener. It would be interesting to grow Scheurebe
under glass or in a plastic tunnel. Earlier than Ehrenfelser.

Schönburger Pinot Noir × (Chasselas Rosé × Muscat
Hamburg) C M W/G
(*Also known as Rosa Muskat*)

Produced at Geisenheim, Schönburger adapts well to all soils and conditions, sets well at flowering in spite of awkward weather, and produces a full and fruity wine of excellent flavour reminiscent of a spicy Gewurztraminer. A quality wine, Schönburger is one of the best of the new crosses and produces a better wine in Britain than in Germany, as does Reichensteiner, due to the longer, slightly cooler, growing season. A good hot south-facing slope is essential for this grape.

Septimer Gewurztraminer × Müller Thurgau C E W/G

Bred at the Alzey Institute in 1927 by George Scheu, Septimer shows moderate vigour, seems adaptable as to soil and site, ripens its wood well, and ripens an early crop of quality grapes. The yield is adequate, the grapes having high sugar and low acidity. The wine is of attractive flavour with the Gewurztraminer bouquet and finish. Due to early ripening, this vine is well recommended to the British grower.

Siegerrebe Madeleine
Angevine × Gewurztraminer C E W/G

Developed at Alzey Institute in 1927 by Herr George Scheu, Siegerrebe will not tolerate calcareous soil or liming, is of moderate vigour, and can be temperamental during flowering if the weather is uncharitable, but if all goes well the yield is good. The grapes will ripen by mid September in heatwave years, but in an average, moderate or poor summer the grapes will be fully ripe by early to mid October. The grapes attain a high sugar and a low acidity. The wine has a glorious full bouquet, and a full spicy flavour not unlike a Gewurztraminer, and the wine asks to be finished with a degree or two of residual sugar for dessert wine production. May well need an infusion of high-acid grape juice at harvest, say 15 per cent to raise initial acidity to 8–10 tartaric.

Traminer C L W/G

This variety has mostly been phased out due to the greater attraction of its successor, the Gewurztraminer, or spicy Traminer. There is some speculation as to whether the Gewurztraminer is a special clone of the Traminer, or a separate crossing. The Gewurztraminer was discovered by Oberlin in Colmar in Alsace in the late 1800s and recommended by him as a better vine to all the Alsatian growers.

Würzer Gewurztraminer × Müller Thurgau   C   E   W/G
(*Also known as Wuerzer and Wartberger*)

Developed by George Scheu at Alzey in 1932, Würzer shows adequate vigour, prefers a neutral fertile and well aerated soil, and a good site. The vine is a heavy cropper and the grapes ripen early, well before Müller Thurgau – and the wood ripens well by autumn. The grapes attain a high must weight and the wine has a generous harmonious character akin to Gewurztraminer, but can have a grassy, herbaceous flavour from some soils.

German Red Vinifera Vines

Several of these vines are French vines with a German name – when this is the case the reader will be referred to the earlier section on French grapes.

Camina Portugieser × Spatburgunder (Blue Portuguese × Pinot Noir)

Bred at Geilweilerhof in the Rheinpfalz, Camina probably ripens too late for Britain, and produces too late for Britain, making a wine with a good balance of acidity.

Deckrot Rulander × Farbertraube   C   L   W/G

Introduced by the Freiburg im Breisgau Institute, Deckrot is used for blending, and is not a single grape wine. European vines with a strongly coloured grape juice have presumably descended from wild vines, yielding inferior wines alone and are known as Farbertraube – colouring grapes. Much work is being done with these in Germany now to try to produce a vine, or vines, that will make a good red wine. Some of these colouring vines have blood red juice, and providing they do not have a disagreeable flavour, they will be of interest to the grower. It is late ripening and suitable for training on walls.

Domina Portugieser × Spatburgunder

Also bred at Geilweilerhof, Domina is earlier ripening than Camina, and produces a pleasant full-bodied wine. Worthy of trial in Britain.

Dornfelder Helfensteiner × Heroldrebe

Bred at the Weinsberg Institute. Dornfelder ripens its grapes well in Britain, and produces an attractive lightweight red wine not unlike a Beaujolais Nouveau. Dornfelder holds much promise for red wine production in southern Britain.

Dunkelfelder Farbertraube IV/4(4) × Frohlich   C   E   W/G

Bred at Geisenheim, Dunkelfelder offers early bud burst, moderate vigour, ripens its wood well, but is susceptible to botrytis. The wine is, of course, deep coloured, with reasonable acidity. This is a very beautiful vine, with classically cut leaves which go through all hues of green to maroon, to deep red-purple in autumn. Produces masses of small bunches of currant sized grapes that ripen extremely early. Dark red juice.

Helfensteiner Fruhburguder × Trollinger

Bred at the Weinsburg Institute in 1960. Being a well-bred vine, Helfensteiner is bound to produce a good quality vine, but the colour will not be as intense as some.
   Mid-season ripening.

Heroldrebe Portugieser × Limberger

Introduced in 1960 at the Weinsberg Institute, the cultivation of Heroldrebe is confined to Württemburg. The yield is good with big bunches of large berries; rather a late ripener for Britain other than on walls.

Kolor Blauer Spatburgunder × Farbertraube

Introduced by the Freiberg Institute in 1938. Similar to the Spatburgunder (Pinot Noir) in habit and performance, with wine similar to Deckrot.

Mullrebe (*Also known as Schwarzriesling*)

A sport of the Blauer Spatburgunder (Pinot Noir), the Mullrebe (Pinot Meunier) makes wines of good colour, but the low acidity means the quality is not high.

Portugieser (Blue Portugese)   C   L   W/G

A heavy-yielding vine that makes wine of a coarse nature, suitable only for bulk production – carafe quality. The vine probably originated in lower Austria, and was introduced to Bad Durkheim in Germany in 1800. It is late ripening. Wood extremely brittle when winter pruned.

Rotberger Trollinger × Riesling   C   M   W/G

Rotberger was developed at Geisenheim in 1971, and demonstrates reasonable vigour, throws a very reasonable crop of grapes with large bunches and berries. It is obviously not a colouring grape by its breeding, but its intended as a single-wine grape. It is a grape of some quality. It would probably make a good white wine as there is no great colour intensity in the skins. Being fairly late ripening this vine needs a good site. Wine of Riesling style, blends well with Kerner, Scheurebe, Optima and Ehrenfelser.

Spatburgunder (Pinot Noir)   C   M   W/G

Fully covered in the French section, the Spatburgunder is only grown for red wine in one or two areas in Germany, principally in the Ahr valley, and also at Assmanhausen just north of Rudesheim at the western extreme of the Rheingau. Produced as a single grape wine, the colour is little more than rosé, and the bouquet and flavour an elusive fleeting shadow of the great Pinot Noir wines of Burgundy. Highly recommended for white wine production in Britain for blending with Auxerrois, Pinot Gris and Chardonnay.

Trollinger (Black Hamburg of England, Frankenthaler of France)

Trollinger is too low in acid, being essential a table grape, to make a balanced wine with any bottle life or improvement. It is solely grown in Württemburg, being the most widely grown variety in the area – 4591 acres. It is, however, a vigorous wine and best drunk when young.

Austrian Vines

Much valuable research has been conducted in Austria, both on vines and on viticulture in general, the most famous in this field being the late Dr Lenz Moser at Krems on the Danube. He also introduced and practised a form of high trellis with the fruiting area of the vine at face rather than knee level. Many, indeed most, of the vines growing successfully in Austria are far too late for Britain – Austria is, after all, many hundreds of miles further south than the south of England – but just one or two vines have proved themselves to be viable here.

Blauberger

Introduced into England in 1981, it promised to be as interesting as Zweigeltrebe.

Jubilaumsrebe Portugieser Blau × Blaufrankisch   C   L   W/G

A new Austrian variety which regularly produces very high sugars over a period of 12 years in one site. The vine has good vigour, grows strong cane which ripens well in autumn and produces grapes with the most elegant and attractive bouquet – an intensely rich smell and taste, which should make a classic white wine. It ripens in mid to late October on a good site, so is too late for other than the best sites.

Ramdas (White/hybrid)   C   L   W/G

This vine has a most unattractive habit, the cane having no strength or will to climb or hang on and the pale green large round leaves being like limp wet lettuce. Flowering is late, forming loose bunches of round green berries, which are seedless. Due to this vine being unwilling to climb, it would be suitable for G.D.C. trellis. The vine has no tendrils. It is a heavy cropper with excellent wood ripening. The wine is rather bland.

Zweigeltrebe (Black) Blaufrankisch × St Laurent   C   L   W/G

This vine has extreme vigour, great big dark-green glossy leaves, and flowers late, but appears to catch up during the latter end of the summer. A heavy cropper of large loose bunches of dark black grapes that make an acceptable white wine when blended with other white grapes, but will only ripen in southern counties. Some interest is being shown by English growers, and several acres have been planted. Wood extremely brittle at winter pruning. Single grape wine is thin, earthy and lean.

French Hybrid Vines – White Wine

Though many thousand of hybrids were bred in France in the last century, with time, obviously the lesser were rejected and those yielding better quality wines were retained. Today, hybrids are still grown in many of the areas of France that concentrate on making Vin du Pays and Vin Ordinaire, for local consumption – most of the lesser-known areas of the south of France in fact. The better hybrids are very popular in the eastern States of the USA. Those that have been or could be grown in Britain are listed, hybrids that ripen their grapes during our growing season. It must be emphasized, however, that should a commercial grower seek *seal of quality* status, the British equivalent of the French, German or Italian guarantee of origin and quality, then he will only be granted this seal for his wine if this wine is made from authorized Vinifera varieties, and passes the organoleptic and taste tests. This is designed to protect both the consumer and the reputation of the more responsible growers.

Ravat 6

A Chardonnay hybrid of moderate vigour, prone to oidium and a heavy cropper. The best of the white-wine hybrids for quality, making a fine wine of Burgundy style. Spur pruning is necessary.

Ravat 34

Another Chardonnay hybrid, earlier ripening, of moderate vigour and more winter hardy than Ravat 6. Spur pruning is necessary, but the wine has less bouquet than Ravat 6.

Ravat 51

More vigorous and hardy than either of the foregoing vines, but a lighter bearer. Cane pruning is necessary. It provides a clean crisp Chablis or Champagne-style wine.

Seibel 5279 (Aurora)   C   M   W/G

A very early, very vigorous, healthy vine, rather drooping growth which demands spur pruning. Bunches are long and loose, berries are small, grey-yellow and of an attractive spicy flavour. The wine is well balanced. This vine is becoming the standard variety for commercial wine production in the New York Finger Lakes area.

Seyval (Seyve-Villard 5276)   C   M   W/G

This vine is the second most popular vine in Britain, having been planted alongside Müller Thurgau during the development of viticulture in this country. Though a hybrid, Seyval seems particularly suited to our soil and climate, producing a clean fresh fruity light single-grape wine, pleasant enough, but without much length of flavour, but with a remarkably long bottle life when grown on chalk. It is particularly suited for blending, being a relatively neutral juice, and makes a lovely wine when combined with Müller Thurgau, or Siegerrebe, lessening to an extent the intensity of these two grapes.

Culturally, it can suffer from a poor set, from coulure (abortion of the floret before flowering), and tends to ripen rather later than is comfortable. It produces a low-sugar, high-acid must, and ripens its wood very well. Yield can vary from one to nine tons per acre according to the weather at flowering, and whether the summer is nonexistent or hot. Either cane or spur pruning is required. The vine is also very popular in the eastern wine-growing States in the USA.

French Hybrid Vines – Red Wine

Baco No. 1   Riperia × Folle Blanche   C   M   W/G

A vine of great vigour, so 2–3 metres between vines is recommended. It is practically immune from mildew and botrytis. A fairly heavy cropper, the grapes make a clean slightly spicy wine which, though not foxy, is not very attractive to the British palate. The bouquet is slightly reminiscent of claret. Not recommended.

Chambourcin (Johannes-Seyve – 26–265)

This grape was bred in the Loire area by Johannes-Seyve and is a prolific cropper of large black grapes that ripen too late in the open for an average British summer. The wine has no pronounced flavour, but has good depth and body. This vine responds best to spur pruning and is a good wall vine.

Foch (Kuhlmann 188–2) 1942 Pinot Noir × Gamay × Riperia   C   M   W/G

Bred by Kuhlmann in Alsace, Marechal Foch is the earliest ripening of the Foch/Millot/Joffre trio. Foch is a vigorous and healthy vine, being a small-berried hybrid it requires cane pruning, and it produces a

Burgundy-style wine without the finesse or elegance. Grapes ripen August/early September.

Joffre (Marechal Joffre) C E W/G

Joffre ripens between Foch and Millot, bearing a lighter crop of grapes which at very best make an ordinary wine. Not recommended.

Landot 244 (Landal)

This healthy vigorous vine also requires cane pruning, yield is moderate, the wine has great depth of colour and is very similar to a Beaujolais. Good quality.

Leon Millot (Kuhlmann 192–2) C E W/G

Millot is more vigorous than Foch, is later ripening and bears a heavier crop – the vines respond well to arched cane pruning. Excellent wine may be made by blending 25 per cent Millot with 75 per cent Triomphe d'Alsace, far better than either can achieve alone.

Oberlin 595 C E W/G

Bred in Alsace, this Vinifera Rupestis cross is a vigorous healthy vine, giving a modest to good crop of small tight black bunches. Very early ripening, with good wood ripening. Extremely useful as an indicator, showing when to apply the pre-blossom spray to all other vines as it comes into flower ten days before all other varieties.

Pirovano 14 C L W/G

A vine suited to growing against a wall where it is capable of producing masses of eating grapes. Very late ripening.

Ravat 262 (Pinot Noir hybrid)

This vine can have flower-set problems, ripens its grapes early to mid-season, and requires cane pruning. Makes a quality wine.

Seibel 13053 (Cascade) C M W/G

An early-ripening, hardly prolific vine – was grown quite a good deal in Britain as a red or rosé wine grape. The wine is initially rather harsh and obvious, and really needs a year in bulk before bottling. It has a readily identifiable individual taste – a hybrid taste not to the liking of a good many people. This was the grape most grown in Britain for red wine by amateur growers; it is also popular in the Finger Lakes area of the USA.

Triomphe d'Alsace (Kuhlmann 319–3)
Knipperle × Riperia × Rupestris　C　E　W/G

This vine ably demonstrates hybrid vigour and disease resistance, but *can* suffer badly with coulure and millerandage prior to and during flowering respectively if the weather is too cold and wet at this time. Should the weather be kind, however, the vine can bear a very heavy crop of intensely-flavoured black grapes. The wine has a strong flavour and needs keeping in bulk for two years followed by a year in bottle before one should begin to think about drinking it. It has a long bottle life, a lovely colour, and an acceptable flavour similar to a red Bordeaux. It is one of the best of the hybrids, together with Leon Millot. (Knipperle = Kleiner Raüschling = Gelber-Ortlieber.)

A List of Other White Vines

Ascot Citronelle

This vine is reluctant to crop out-of-doors and maybe needs a glass-house. Prune to six-bud long spurs.

Madeleine Royale

Again a shy cropper and not recommended for the open vineyard. Much used as a parent vine for early French crosses. Spur prune to six buds.

Muscat de Saumur　M　W/G

An early ripening golden Muscat grape, which has been pushed aside by the new German crosses, but due to the early ripening and the high quality of the grapes, this vine is worthy of fresh interest. Like most of the older French varieties, the yield is comparatively low, but a percentage of some high-quality must in a larger batch of more mediocre must is a good way of raising the quality overall. For areas other than southern counties a south wall is recommended. Six bud spurs.

Perle de Czaba E   W/G

Another old French white grape, very early ripening with more moderate vigour and a quality end product. As with Precoce de Malingre and Muscat de Saumur, Perle de Czaba is worthy of serious trial as a grape to boost quality. Many of these old Viniferas require *six bud pruning* as the first five buds on every lateral are blind, the *sixth* carries the embryo fruit bunches. This also applies to Gamay, and the usual method of training all vines alike on the Guyot system would explain why growers have tended to discard these old French Viniferas as poor or non-existent croppers.

Perlette

An old French white variety, vigorous in habit and producing a low acid wine. The grapes are seedless and plentiful. Useful as a quantity grape, it is early ripening.

American Vines Grown in England

Alden

A vine of good vigour, disease-free, but of inconsistent bearing in Britain. Grapes are white, and ripen in early October.

Brant

Though of Canadian origin, the Brant is widely grown in Britain as a wall vine. It grows most vigorously, ripens its wood well in autumn, produces a good crop of black grapes which make fair red wine if allowed to mature for a year or two. The added bonus is the glorious autumn foliage colours, which develop a rich scarlet and golden banding, and make this vine an ideal ornamental wall plant.

Brocton

This variety produces good sweet grapes.

Campbells Early

Produces large attractive bunches of grapes and appreciates a light soil.

Concord

This is the leading commercial vine in the New York State and eastern vineyards, being grown for wine and eating. This is a vine bred from Labrusca, so the wine has the unmistakable 'foxy' flavour. In Britain it is too late for the open vineyard, and needs the extra protection of a wall or fence to ripen the grapes. Its red autumn foliage is beautiful.

Emerald

This vine ripens consistently in the open vineyard in Britain, producing a vast crop of spherical green grapes that make a fair wine.

Himrod Seedless (Ontario × Thompson's Seedless) New York 1952

The attraction of this vine is that it produces seedless grapes of a good flavour. In Britain protection from a cloche or a wall is recommended.

Schuyler (Zinfandel × Ontario) New York 1942

This vine ripens a moderate crop of black grapes well by early November. They are pleasant to eat and make a very fair wine. It is of moderate vigour and has a good yield. A Zinfandel cross that can ripen in Britain must be interesting for trial work.

Slade Blue

This variety can be a shy cropper, but in certain areas crops well – obviously soil matters.

Russian Vines Grown in Britain

Amurensis Hybrids

The majority of black-graped Russian vines have been bred from the Pinot Noir, the classic black grape of Burgundy. They tend to crop freely and are better suited to wall culture because they are rather late for the open vineyard. *GAGARIN BLUE, KUIBISHEVSKI* and *TERESHKOVA* are the most usual to be found in Britain.

Renewed interest is being shown in these Russian vines due to their early ripening, and the fact that the bunches are very open and, therefore, less liable to mildew and botrytis attack.

Gagarin Blue

This vine tends to set enormous open bunches of small berries if it is cold and wet during flowering. Given good weather during flowering a marvellous set of large dark maroon rather soft berries are produced which ripen in early September. Of moderate vigour, Gagarin Blue has rounded ribbed blue green leaves, and is worthy of trial, but is prone to botrytis.

Kuibishevski

A vigorous vine with superb hard maroon cane which ripens well by autumn, throws and sets enormous bunches of dark red grapes that ripen well from mid-September to October. Excellent disease resistance, and quite the best Russian vine on trial.

Tereshkova

A vine of moderate vigour, with hybrid appearance, total disease resistance producing smallish tight black bunches. Tereshkova appears to have a latent virus which causes rapid deterioration.

5

Recommended Vine Varieties

When growing a large number of vines on an experimental basis, trials are conducted on all the vines along the lines listed below, in order that one can assess total potential and viability, and, as a result, decide whether or not each vine variety is suitable for the open vineyard in Britain.

1 A vine must demonstrate adequate, but not excessive, vigour.

2 A vine is preferred if it has dark, thick, glossy leaves; such leaves are far less attractive to mildew and botrytis than a downy, dull leaf. Also, vines are less likely to suffer from extreme heat and sun or cold if the leaves are thick, dark and glossy, and can continue to convert energy into sugar; a pale, thin leaf becomes limp and floppy and quickly ceases to function.

3 A vine must show ability to produce adequate pollen and to set the flowers quickly and well, more particularly in cool, damp conditions. A vine flower is reluctant to pollinate if the temperature at flowering is lower than 10°C (50°F). Some vines manage well in poor conditions, whereas others fail to set any grapes at all. When a vine does not ripen its replacement canes adequately, the vine has to be pruned back so hard that the grower finds there is insufficient wood to bear sufficient fruit in the following season.

4 A vine must produce a viable yield and be able to do so with reliable consistency. The fruit buds for the year to come are laid down in July of the current year, the success of this operation being very reliant on the weather and temperature during July. Some varieties do manage to crop with remarkable regularity regardless, whereas others totally

lack any ability to cope and fail to crop in a year following a poor July. Müller Thurgau and Seyval are particularly sensitive here.

5 The grapes must most obviously be of good quality; this is a direct reflection on the breeding or parentage of any particular vine. A grape must achieve a good sugar-acid balance and possess the qualities that provide the wine with sufficient bouquet and flavour and give a good extract from the pulp.

6 One of the most important attributes of any vine is that it will produce a fine, elegant and highly attractive wine – none of the aforegoing characteristics are of value if the wine is inferior.

7 The most important characteristic of a vine is its ability to ripen its replacement wood really well before the onset of the winter frosts. Without this ability the vine falls prey to the ravages of debilitating mildew and botrytis attack in winter and subsequent die-back.

White Grapes

Müller Thurgau

Due to the British acreage devoted to Müller Thurgau, the recommended list must begin with this vine. In the ninety-plus years since it was introduced, Müller Thurgau has gradually become the most popular vine in all Germany, ousting the previously dominant Sylvaner from first to third in the acreage charts. The Germans do not consider Müller Thurgau a vine of quality, but it is a good, reliable and generous cropper in Germany, where they enjoy half our annual rainfall, slightly hotter midsummer months and a two-and-a-half week earlier flowering and bud-burst, which allows the grapes longer to ripen on the vine before harvest. In Germany, due to these factors, Müller Thurgau does not tend to suffer from botrytis to such a degree as in Britain, for with the slightly longer and hotter growing season it ripens its wood better than in Britain and, is therefore less prey to die-back and fungal attack. It produces good, honest, fruity wines with a slightly sweet finish so loved by the Germans, an able successor to the Sylvaner.

Müller Thurgau is also grown on a small scale in Alsace and in Luxembourg, and, due to its evident popularity on the Continent, it was the obvious choice for widescale planting in Britain in the 1960s.

Having grown vines seriously since 1966, it does seem to me that the late sixties and early seventies enjoyed earlier springs and later autumns than we have had more recently. Maybe I am influenced by the memory of the superb years of 1969, 1970 and 1971, but there is a definite trend towards cold, wet, late non-springs and early, cold, wet autumns for the past five or six years, the one exception being the three-month long 'Indian summer' autumn of 1984. But certain vines, notably Müller Thurgau, do need an adequate length of growing season and a reasonable autumn to ripen their replacement wood – and this they have not had since 1983 and 1984.

This raises a big question-mark over this particular variety. Without sufficent ripe replacement wood, the vine is at a severe disadvantage when it faces the frosts of winter and the year to come. Some growers are tempted to leave long canes of unripe white wood, which are prey to autumn, winter and spring infection with botrytis, and, in consequence, carry a mediocre crop – many fruiting laterals being barren if no sound fruit buds were laid down in the July of the previous year. The situation does not improve. The only answer is to be hard, and prune back to ripe, sound wood, even if it means a calculated drop in crop for a year, which will happen anyway if masses of unripe wood is left after pruning. The Müller Thurgau crops best when cane-pruned and Guyot-trained.

There is no doubt that grown on a really good calcareous site and when a good year follows a good year, Müller Thurgau will crop magnificently and produce a really fine wine.

As luck would have it, Müller Thurgau is no longer the only choice; with the few pure viniferas and the many new vinifera crosses to choose from, it is possible closely to match a quality vine with any given viable site and soil type. Owing to the cultural faults and inconsistent cropping habit, it is no longer possible to recommend Müller Thurgau for the English vineyard.

Seyval

The second vine to be listed must be the Seyve-Villard 5–276, now named Seyval. Originally recommended with Müller Thurgau for planting in Britain by Ray Barrington-Brock, the Seyval has been grown alongside Müller and occupies nearly as many acres.

Culturally, the Seyval has fewer problems. It is a vine of moderately vigorous habit, ripens its wood superbly, but suffers a very severe disability in that it cannot manage to set fruit if the weather is cool and wet at flowering. With a good set, Seyval can be a very heavy cropper producing from 5–9 tons an acre.

As a single-grape wine, Seyval is not possessed of the fruit and balance of the Müller; it tends to have a lovely fresh flinty acidity but falls a little short in body and strength. The Seyval consistently attains a much lower sugar and higher acidity by harvest than the Müller, a disadvantage as it is a later ripener than Müller.

As a blend, the two wines create an excellent amalgam, the soft, almost muscat Müller nose and fruit stretching admirably with the fresh flowery Seyval to form a most harmonious wine of considerable elegance.

Seyval is, however, a hybrid wine, a cross between a vinifera and an American vine, and as such would not be allowed in a vineyard of 'appellation contrôllé' status in France. And it follows that if, in due course, we in Britain are granted a scale of qualities for our wines similar to those in operation in France and Germany, a vineyard planted with hybrid vines would not be eligible.

Growers already committed to Seyval regard this vine as their bread and butter, due to the more consistent and heavier cropping behaviour it displays compared with Müller. This is an important economic point in its favour. Being a hybrid, the Seyval also displays a greater resistance to fungus attacks than the pure vinifera, which counts as yet another advantage. The Seyval produces to the best of its ability on limestone soils to which it is ideally suited.

In 1974 the EEC Commission on viticulture saw fit to issue a list of vines they considered suitable for wine production in Britain. This list is as follows:

Recommended Vines

Auxerrois, Müller Thurgau and Wrotham Pinot

Authorized Vines

Bacchus, Chardonnay, Ehrenfelser, Faber, Huxelrebe, Kanzler, Kerner, Madeleine Angevine, Madeleine Royale, Madeleine Sylvaner, Mariensteiner, Ortega, Perle, Pinot Noir, Pinot Gris, Seyval and Siegerrebe.

This list was based on a selection of vines already being grown in Britain and submitted to the commission for their approval. Obviously, many more vines were in existence here at that time and being grown on trial – all were included on the application, but the above represents those the Commission saw fit to nominate at that time.

Keeping this list in mind, there follows a list of vines that have proved themselves to be of particular merit, to be really viable for wine growing in Britain. These vines are listed in alphabetical and not preferential order.

Auxerrois

Culturally easy, in that it does not display extreme vigour, Auxerrois has lovely dark glossy leaves which are not mildew attractive. In the limited experience gained so far, in that Auxerrois has not been grown in Britain for sufficient years for the vines to reach an advanced maturity, it would appear to be an adequate rather than a heavy cropper, but the obvious quality and appeal of the wine makes this vine worthy of inclusion.

As a wine, the White Pinot is not well known in Britain. In Alsace it is the wine that all the Alsatians drink themselves for everyday consumption, reserving Riesling for the special occasion. It is a wine that easily accompanies most food without domination and has instant appeal with its clean, fresh nose, elegant flavour and lovely long finish. Wine against wine, the Auxerrois has more body and style than the Pinot Blanc (or Weissbergunder), but the two blend admirably being similar, if different.

Auxerrois is also attracting much interest in Luxembourg. It is highly praised by Professor Huberty of the Reimich Viticultural Institute, where they make an excellent Auxerrois wine. Professor Huberty is the member of the European Commission which put Auxerrois on the list of British vines.

The grapes are loose within the bunch, so mildew is less likely, and Auxerrois is not too particular if the land is not well-drained. The grapes ripen alongside Müller Thurgau, in the second or third week in October in a moderate to good year. It is a vine to be recommended for an early hot site.

Faber

This Pinot Blanc-Müller Thurgau crossing is a very handsome dark-leaved vine of good vigour; it sets fruit well in a good year and bears a magnificent crop of grapes which ripen just before Müller Thurgau. The wood ripening is poor in a cool wet year, millerandage prone, but it is more hardy against winter frost than Müller Thurgau. Taking all these factors into consideration, Faber is a possible vine for winegrowing in Britain. Faber wine is really first class, in the top league of the best five or six single-grape wines. Botrytis prone.

Huxelrebe

Huxelrebe shows great vigour, a heavy, indeed almost massive cropping capacity which, unless *severely* restricted, will result in no crop for a year or two. The potential of this vine is, therefore, obvious. Culturally no problem, ripening no problem. Some find that Huxelrebe tastes a little pungent when young – but given some bottle age the wine develops an attractive colour and a full fruity flavour, a smooth mellow wine.

Kerner

Kerner is one of the best of the new crosses and is a vine with very considerable potential in Britain due to the fact that it sets fruit well in a poor year, and crops well in the year following a poor year. Kerner shows moderate vigour, the leaves remaining green after other vines have developed autumn colouring, thus continuing to function and enabling the grapes to continue to gain sugar.

Kerner is not not a heavy cropper, but produces superb grapes, a quality inherited from its Riesling × Trollinger parentage. The grapes return a high acidity which balances the good sugar content and the resultant wine, with its glorious delicate, flowery nose, can be quite outstanding when tasted against any other wine from any of the new crosses. It is a really fine quality wine, of Riesling style.

Kerner ripens its grapes compararatively early, midway between the earliest Siegerrebe and Madeleine Angevine, and Müller Thurgau. Wood ripening is early and really excellent. Highly recommended, and one of the best five or six vines for the English vineyard.

Kernling (selected superior clone of Kerner)

Kernling demonstrates the excellent wood ripening and classic wine quality of Kerner but ripens two weeks earlier which must indicate that this vine has massive potential for Britain.

Madeleine Angevine

Is widely used as a parent vine in Germany for breeding new varieties of vine, Reichensteiner, Forta 100, Siegerrebe and Noblessa for example, Madeleine Angevine has proved itself in Britain to be a really reliable outdoor wine grape.

It demonstrates adequate vigour, and has no flowering or setting problems, even in a cool, wet flowering period, ripens a large crop of grapes early and well, even in a poor, cool sunless summer. Madeleine Angevine makes an attractive fruity wine with a delicate flowery nose, reminiscent perhaps of an Alsatian Pinot or Tokay; a wine with good length.

Madeleine Angevine will bear from 3–4 tons of grapes per acre, and wood ripening is excellent. This vine is really highly recommended for all sites, particularly for those less favourable sites where an early-ripening reliable grape is of paramount importance.

Madeleine Angevine must is inclined to be low in acidity; consider, therefore, interplanting this variety with a grape chosen for its high acid at harvest, and also for its suitability for blending to the major grape at a previously ascertained percentage. The two grapes may then be harvested at the same time, providing both ripen together. There is an added advantage of there being two different pollens available which results in bigger berries and bunches. There is no necessity to have a second variety because the Oberlin clone, the strain of Madeleine Angevine grown in England, is totally self fertile, in spite of earlier concern on this. The alternative is to grow a separate plot of a secondary grape if the ripening times are different, for example Reichensteiner, Seyval, Auxerrois or Pinot Noir – all are fairly high in acid. One of the best five or six vines for England. If wasps are a problem, either harvest early, or fit nets of very fine mesh to keep the wasps from the grapes. Harvest for correct acid rather than high sugar here.

Optima

Due to results from recent trials, Optima has shown itself of adequate vigour and capable of bearing a fair crop of very early ripening grapes of good size and of a pearl colour. The grapes reach a fairly high sugar quite early. The (Silvaner × Rielsing) × Müller Thurgau parentage gives the wine a generous and attractive quality, of Riesling style, and the residual acidity gives the wine a well-balanced, harmonious flavour. This vine is recommended, making wine of quite superb quality. Being very thin-skinned, Optima is very botrytis prone; a cautionary factor.

Ortega

This vine was quickly realized to have some potential for the British vineyard being an early ripening grape and an adequate cropper, thanks to its Müller Thurgau × Siegerrebe breeding. This grape is to be found occupying one-tenth of all the fine Riesling vineyards in the Rheingau region and the Riesling vineyards of the Mosel Valley, where, in the moderate and poor seasons when the Riesling grapes do not achieve total ripeness, up to 15 per cent of the very sweet Ortega grapes may be added to the Riesling wines.

Alone Ortega makes a rather soft, bland wine with a fine bouquet requiring long bottle maturing. The wood ripening is only fair, the berry set is variable, good in some years, poor in others which indicates that this vine variety is not consistent.

Regner

This cross between the Italian table grape Luglienca Bianca and the Gamay is the best white grape to date of all those grown on trial at Wye College in Kent. The vine shows moderate vigour, very fair cropping potential and early ripening of the grapes. The bouquet and flavour of this wine will obviously be very different to the usual German crosses due to the breeding of the vine. Regner apparently produces an attractive and marketable wine, and is certainly a vine worthy of trial.

Reichensteiner

This vine, a Müller Thurgau × (Madeleine Angevine × Calabreser-Frohlich), is one of the better of the new vines to be planted in Britain.

Aesthetically, it has the most beautifully cut foliage and an attractive habit, shows good vigour, apparently suffers no loss in production of flower in the year following a poor season, sets well in a cool damp flowering period and also ripens a good crop in moderate and poor summer-autumn growing seasons. These grapes must be harvested early.

In the Rheingau, the wine develops little individual character when in direct comparison with the rich velvety elegance of Riesling and similar wines, and is considered of little potential as a single-grape wine. In Britain, however, in our cooler island climate, Reichensteiner evolves with more style, a most attractive elusive nose, a light, refined and delicate wine, but perhaps achieves its best potential when blended with a dominant grape.

Reichensteiner's main fault is very poor wood ripening after a poor summer; bunches are however open and remain botrytis free, yield 2–3 tons per acre. A very highly recommended vine.

Schönburger

Until recently the Schönburger was thought to be too late ripening for Britain, but experience has proved it to ripen alongside Müller Thurgau. In Germany the Schönburger does not show any outstanding qualities other than the most attractive nose, but little else. Again, qualities not able to develop in Germany evolve in our cooler slower summer. The Schönburger displays all the qualities of Gewurztraminer wine, the evocative scented nose, fine elegant flavour and the spicy prickly long finish – a really fine wine.

Schönburger is not a vine for less than a very good site, warm, well-sheltered and south-facing, and in the southern counties only. This vine produces a good crop each and every year, even in a poor year, and, *following* a poor year, it still bears 2–3 tons per acre. Wood ripening is very good. Highly recommended, and definitely in the top league.

Septimer

Included in this list due to early ripening potential, Septimer, a Gewurztraminer-Müller Thurgau cross, presents no cultural problem. The wine is soft and appealing and, although it attains a high sugar it is at the expense of a low acidity, which suggests that it might well blend with a neutral high acid must. It is worthy of further trials.

Siegerrebe

The Madeleine Angevine × Gewurztraminer offspring, Siegerrebe, displays good vigour, lovely dark thick leaves, and ripens its grapes probably earlier than any other vine. The Seigerrebe will not grow in an alkaline soil. Wood ripening is good in a good year, not good in a cold year.

In certain soils this vine displays difficulty in setting a crop, particularly if the weather is inclement at this time. Attempts to ward off setting problems may be achieved by using a zinc, *Zineb*, spray prior to flowering, and by dressing the ground around the vines with sulphate of potash in March.

Those who disregard this vine due to its extreme early ripening should bear in mind that it may ripen too early in a mere one or two years in ten and may then, in a heatwave, attract unwanted attention from wasps. However, in the other eight years of a decade we might enjoy two or three good summers, the remainder being mediocre to poor. In such years Müller Thurgau and Seyval suffer from a depressingly low yield and vastly under-developed oechsle or sugar content, and a high acidity; indeed sometimes no crop. The Siegerrebe, and other early-ripening vines, will ripen their crop in moderate and even poor years, and do so by mid to late September. Therefore, for consistent cropping and viability of the venture, surely the earlier ripening grape vines are the key to the success of winegrowing in Britain.

Würzer

This Gewurztraminer × Müller Thurgau vine combines early ripening with a quality end product, adequate vigour, a high yield and good wood ripening. Though a Gewurztraminer offspring, the grapes do not broadcast their existence with a strong and glorious aroma like the Siegerrebe, and are less attractive to wasps in a good autumn. Culturally sound with good wood ripening, Würzer is definitely one of the better of the new vines from Germany though the wine when young tastes somewhat grassy, herbaceous and green.

Black Grapes

There are those who stoutly claim that it is impossible to grow good red wine in Britain. They have been right to date, but a few of us are trying and trying again to create a red wine with sufficient body, and colour, combined with an attractive nose and some elegance, to create a marketable product.

To date most efforts have been with single-grape wines, with Pinot Noir, Wrotham Pinot, or with Seibel 13053. Each of these grapes produces a single vine with yawning deficiencies. The Pinot Noir, away from its native heath, is seldom if ever even a mediocre wine; it is thin, pale and lacking in intensity of bouquet and depth of flavour. Wrotham Pinot, an ancient offspring of the Pinot Noir, suffers from the same inadequacies, its only merit being that it ripens earlier and thus gains more natural sugar. The Seibel, a hybrid, produces a rather thin, acid wine, with a high beetrooty colour, and takes time to mellow from a rather coarse earthy flavour.

These grapes, and the one or two other varieties grown in Britain for making red wines, are clearly not the answer. We do not have a climate, the heat and length of summer, for these single grapes to achieve a balanced end product.

Our aim must be to make a quality wine, otherwise the project must be totally abandoned. To recap, we do not have the particular soil, the Jurassic limestone of the Côte de Nuits or the Tertiary limestone of the Champagne area, nor the climate to make a success with the Pinot Noir grape. Therefore, we look to Bordeaux for inspiration.

Claret, the red wine of the Bordeaux area, the Medoc region in particular, is created from a blend of up to four grape varieties. The Cabernet Sauvignon provides the backbone, much of the acid, body and the sometimes limitless bottle life of claret of a great year. The Merlot grapes provide the soft mellow roundness of the wine, and the 2–3 per cent of Petit Verdot gives claret its glorious classic bouquet. All the great Châteaux have their own recipe of percentages of each grape, for many a closely guarded secret. Cabernet Franc and Malbec are also grown.

Maybe there is a lesson here for the British winegrower, not in the vine varieties, which require a longer, hotter summer and would not ripen in the open here, but in the principle of finding several grape varieties each with certain qualities, which, combined, would make a well-balanced attractive and palatable wine.

We need to find a grape which will give a good-quality high yield as the basis of the wine; also required is a grape to offer style, backbone and long life to the wine; a grape to give the wine a rich deep colour; and somewhere along the line to find a grape to give the wine an attractive nose. Some hybrids are bred from classic red grapes, such as

Pinot Noir and Gamay and have much of the style of their vinifera parent combined with early ripening and little hybrid taint. In Germany today the best of these hybrids are being used to try and create good red wine grapes, so let us not totally dismiss them.

Triomphe d'Alsace and Leon Millot

Much work has been done by the author on red wine production looking at all the varieties available to us. Research trials have proved that Triomphe d'Alsace and Leon Millot are the only two varieties so far that are capable of producing a wine that smells and looks like a red wine, also tastes like a red wine, a wine of a glorious deep garnet colour, a complex mellow wine with a harmonious balance of acidity, tannins and masses of fruit, a real red wine. This end was not lightly achieved, however.

Good wine was not obtained until the vines had matured and been established some seven or eight years; no doubt the excellent Devon soil has made a great contribution, plus a superb, hot, south facing well drained site. Therefore vine maturity is of paramount importance; one can assume that the vine roots have penetrated the soil to a great depth, forced to so do in the hot, drought ridden years of 1982, 1983 and 1984, tapping reserves far below the surface.

The second lesson to be learned was that red wine of the style and character we were searching for required at least eighteen to twenty four months in bulk to encourage a slow and gradual maturing period, and then benefitted from a further six months in bottle.

Cash flow, always a problem when one has wine quality and wine maturity as an overriding aim, demands that one cannot keep the wine until it has attained full and total potential, but fortunately we do have some valued patrons who buy wine to lay down until it has reached its full potential. To drink big wines too young is infanticide; to have the reserves to be able to drink a bottle of each vintage a year until it reaches its zenith is a rewarding experience.

Great years such as 1982, 1983 and 1984 enabled us to harvest these grapes with an oechsle of 92–97, giving a wine that needed no Tate and Lyle and a natural alcohol content in excess of 12 per cent by volume. This must be fairly unusual for red wine in such a northern latitude.

German colour grapes

Deckrot – Rulander × Farbertraube (Freiburg)
Dunkelfelder – Farbertraube × Frolich (Geisenheim)
Kolor – Spatburgunder × Farbertraube (Freiburg)
The Farbertraube is a 'colouring grape' descended from wild vines, yielding inferior wines with very intense coloured juice and only used for crossing.

There are also many new strains, as yet not off the stocks or available to us, but with luck they will be released for general sale before too long – if they prove successful.

There follows a list of other red grape vines, without this colouring or staining ability, that are or have been grown for wine production in Britain, with varying degrees of success or otherwise.

Pinot Noir (Spatburgunder in Germany)

The noble classic grape of Champagne and of Burgundy (the Côte de Nuits) where it grows in soils that suit this vine so well. Could be considered as a 20 per cent part of a red vine planting, to up the bouquet, backbone and quality of the end product. Lime often in acid and neutral soils.

Rotberger (Trollinger × Rielsing)

This German cross has quite considerable potential due to its Riesling parent – it is a vine of good vigour and sets and bears a heavy crop of grey-black grapes, big berries and big bunches. It ripened in Devon in 1984, but the vine needs a good warm site to succeed. May make a better white than red wine.

Dornfelder

Dornfelder trials in England indicate that it readily ripens grapes really well even in an extremely difficult season such as 1986. Dornfelder produces a light red coloured lightweight wine of potential and acceptable flavour, similar to a Beaujolais Nouveau; thus surely this vine must be worthy of considerable interest to the English grower.

Western Germany: most widely grown vine varieties in hectares

Bacchus	460	Blau Burgunder	2,968
Weissburgunder	775	Limberger	399
Elbling	1,243	Mullrebe	878

Gewurztraminer	447		Blau Portugieser	4,478
Gutedal	1,198		Trollinger	1,884
Kerner	1,274		Others	582
Morio Muskat	2,560			
Müller Thurgau	22,641		Total hectares	
Riesling	18,740		black varieties	11,178
Rulander	3,067			
Scheurebe	2,092			
Silvaner	15,879			
Traminer	360			
Others	2,297			

Total hectares
white varieties   73,791

Total hectares devoted to winegrowing in W. Germany = 84,966

Tomorrow's English Vineyards

There is a whole new and exciting breed of vines being released from the German research stations today, vines that have almost total inbuilt disease resistance, vines bred from the classics such as Riesling, and yet in spite of being modern hybrids (produced from crosses between the classic European vinifera vines and native American and Russian vines), the wines from these vines in top flight blind wine tastings are totally indistinguishable from wines from their noble parent.

Yesterday's Vineyards

In Britain, yesterday's vineyards were almost entirely planted with Müller Thurgau and Seyval, just a few warily ventured into a third variety. Today's vineyards, which were initiated in the mid 1970s following the M.T. and Seyval disaster years of 1972, 1973 and 1974, are planted with Reichensteiner, Madeleine Angevine, Kerner, Huxelrebe, Bacchus and Ortega and like cultivars, which are all very well, but require constant vigilance against oidium, peronospera and botrytis. They are thus very expensive to maintain in terms of labour, time and effort, and of course costly chemicals.

The New Race of Vines

These new vines have been bred over a decade or more, and have undergone several years of research trials during which many were rejected. The wines from these vines have been made and assessed for several seasons before they have had their wraps off and been aired in many strict blind wine tastings where they have won their spurs by being rated as highly as pure elegant Rieslings and others, with no trace of hybrid flavour.

Spraying

These vines need just one fungal spray application a year: the pre-harvest fungal application is all that is recommended. For those growers about to plant a vineyard, or others contemplating expansion, these new vines should surely feature largely in the area to be developed once they have had a three year trial period in this country and proved themselves capable of ripening their grapes in our growing season. The first imports were made in 1988, so by 1990–1 we should have some positive answers.

EEC

Although at present the EEC decrees that no hybrids are allowed to be planted in AC and VDQS vineyards or similar, if these new vines are to be as valuable to the German wine economy as I suspect, they will become so as sons take over from fathers. Having seen these vines in the research station vineyards, old prejudices will fall, and the strength of the German wine lobby will be aimed at relaxing these rules regarding the planting of these super elite hybrids in German vineyards. Added to this is the health lobby – a growing and increasingly powerful percentage of consumers. Then surely vines that need spraying just once a year if at all must be tomorrow's vines on all fronts.

Varieties

Most of these vines are still identified by numbers and thus have no names; just two so far are named, Orion and Phönix. Apply to Derek Pritchard, Dunkery Vineyards, Ordesa, Wootton Courtenay, Minehead, Somerset for all details of varieties, names, supply and prices. He will also give you an update of the suitability of these new vines.

6

Rootstocks

All vines were grown on their own roots from the dawn of viticulture until the mid- to late-nineteenth century. Imported from the United States of America in the nineteenth century was an insect that was to change winegrowing dramatically — an aphid, that devastated every vine from France right through Europe to the Near East.

This aphid was the Phylloxera. It has such a successful life-cycle and is so resistant to all known methods of control that it is still today virtually impossible to eradicate. When it was discovered, all manner of methods were tried to kill this aphid, which, in its underground stage, was eating through the roots of the vines. After many many years, during which time all Europe was gradually inundated by phylloxera, thousands of growers were ruined, and wine production virtually ground to a halt, it was realized that though phylloxera was endemic in the United States of America, the native American vines existed in full production in spite of the ever-present phylloxera.

Therefore experiments were inaugurated whereby the European vines were budded or grafted onto the American rootstocks. These plants were immune to the ravages of phylloxera as the vigorous roots merely sprouted again and again when chewed by phylloxera, and yet the wine remained true to the vine variety of the scion, grafted onto the top of the American stock.

The answer had been discovered to this horrific problem. And gradually France and Germany began to replant their vast winegrowing areas. At the same time much time and effort was devoted to attempts actually to cross-pollinate European with American vines, the resulting wines being known to us as hybrids – *produceurs directs* on the Continent.

The aim was to breed vines with inbuilt phylloxera resistance with the ability to produce wines as fine as the wine from the European parent vine. The former was achieved, but the latter fell short, most of the offspring being vastly inferior to the European parent, but each breeder

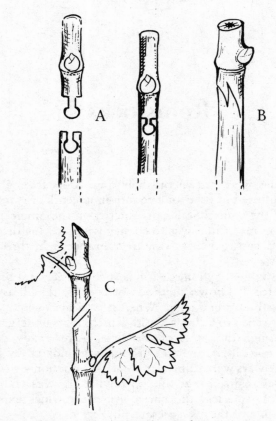

20 Bench grafting is carried out in March, April, using gentle heat to form a callous to cement the two together. This is brought about by placing the budded material in deep boxes of damp sawdust in a warm, humid atmosphere. The joint is bound with raffia. The top left examples (A) show the omega graft, a joint that is both cut and joined using the omega grafting machine. (B) shows the whip and tongue hand cut graft. (C) Green grafting is done in the vineyard during flowering, and is used for working an unwanted variety over to a better vine. Both stock and scion are cut at the same angle, placed together, both being of the same diameter. Bind together with elastic tape or even wool, then tie a vine leaf closely around the joint to prevent drying out.

managed to produce a handful of reasonably successful vines which show more vigour than the European vinifera vines, and the best show a degree of the European style and character in the wine.

List of Rootstocks

Name	Number	Breeding	Resistance to Calcium	Resistance to Phylloxera and other attributes
	41B	Chasselas × Berlandieri	up to 30–40%	Vigorous stock for poor soils. Good affinity with most Vinifera, giving good set and good crops. Not fully Phylloxera resistant. Not recommended.
	SO4	Berlandieri × Riperia	up to 18–20%	Very resistant to Phylloxera, suitable for clay and loam. Medium vigour, encourages early ripening. Well recommended.
Kober	5BB	Berlandieri × Riperia	up to 20–22%	Very resistant to Phylloxera, suitable for clay and loam, but tends to be *too vigorous* on all but the poorest chalk soils.
Kober	125AA	Berlandieri × Riperia		Suitable for most soil conditions and becoming very popular for use in Britain.

Name	Number	Breeding	Resistance to Calcium	Resistance to Phylloxera and other attributes
				Encourages a good flower set. Recommended.
Teleki	5c	Berlandieri × Riperia	up to 40%	Suitable for clay and loam and will tolerate a high chalk level in the soil. Moderate vigour.
Teleki	8B	Berlandieri × Riperia		Suitable for rich clay and loams.
Couderc	3309	Riperia × Rupestris	up to 10–25%	Suitable for open fertile and permeable soils which dry out in summer. Very early ripening.
	420A	Riperia × Berlandieri	up to 20–22%	Retards maturity, suitable only for very early ripening vines, e.g. Siegerrebe. A male plant.

Most rootstocks are produced from just three of the many native American vines, namely *Vitis Riperia*, (known as the riverbank vine), *Vitis Rupestris* (the rock or mountain vine), and *Vitis Berlandieri*, the Texan vine. By crossing these vines with each other, rootstocks with different tolerances and virtues have evolved.

Vitis Riperia is vigorous and has large leaves, encourages early ripening due to its inbuilt short growing season – this is an important feature for vines grown at the northernmost limit of the vinegrowing zone. It also has excellent inbuilt resistance to phylloxera and to cold wet soils. *Vitis Rupestris* also shows good phylloxera resistance, and tolerance of drought, heat and wet – and also encourages early ripening. *Rupestris* is very vigorous and has small leaves. *Vitis Berlandieri* shows similar phylloxera resistance, is able to withstand hot dry conditions, and to thrive on strong limy soils. Contrary to both *Vitis Riperia* and *Vitis Rupestris*, stocks with strong *Berlandieri* influence tend to prolong maturing late into the growing season, which would tend to advance ripening beyond the British growing season into winter. This would therefore, only be of use with vines that tend to ripen too early, Siegerrebe for example.

A fairly wide range of rootstocks are used on the Continent, allowing vines to be grown on a great number of soil types, including highly calcareous soils, solid clay and rank wet soils. It is important that the stock has an affinity with *Vitis Vinifera*, that it has the ability to set and carry a good crop of grapes, has a high fertility, and has a tolerance of wet or cold soils, and the ability to withstand drought.

A short list of the rootstocks more readily available to the British winegrower is found on pages 119–120.

Conclusions

5BB can be too vigorous for all other than very poor or very alkaline soils; on a good soil it tends to produce far too much cane and leaf at the expense of fruit. On an alkaline hungry soil, or with vines of naturally low vigour it is a good choice. 420A is far too late in ripening for other than the very earliest ripening grapes. For a very alkaline soil 41B may well be the only stock to cope with the conditions, coping as it will with up to 30–40 per cent of chalk in the soil. 5C will also tolerate up to 40 per cent chalk in the soil, and will do so without the excessive vigour of 5BB.

125AA and SO4 are the two more widely used rootstocks, and suit conditions here well. The Kober 125AA is the more vigorous, and is thus better for hungrier and alkaline soils, whereas the SO4 seems to suit most soils and situations, and demonstrates a moderately acceptable vigour; perhaps the best rootstock to date.

Putting Rootstocks into Perspective – Grafted or Own-rooted Vines

Those fortunate enough to have drunk pre-phylloxera wine, wines from vines on their own roots, state that these wines were greatly superior to wines from grafted vines. To support this theory, winegrowers in certain areas of France are seeking to replant areas with vines on their own roots in areas that are phylloxera-free. Others condemn these theories, but wine is after all only rainwater, which is taken up via the vines' sap system through the roots, via the trunk or stem and the branches to the rods, leaves, and finally to the bunches of grapes which assimilate sweetness. This transference and gradual buildup of sugar and other nutrients in the grapes is known as photosynthesis, the action being wrought by the leaves with the aid of sunshine.

The sap suffers a check at the site of the graft, due to the xylem, or sap channels, having been severed and re-joined at the time when they were grafted. Few are directly re-aligned. There is subsequently an unavoidable check and drop in sap flow. Grafted vines might well, therefore, be slightly later in reaching bud burst and run slightly late throughout the whole season in comparison with ungrafted vines of the same variety. This could well be the reason behind grafted vines giving slightly lower must weights at harvest, and very often a lower yield than the same variety in an ungrafted state. The sap might also pick up some minute degree of undesirable flavour from having been transported for a short distance within the inferior American wood – purists might well support this opinion.

Certain vines that are in greatest demand in Britain, due to their having proved themselves highly adaptable to our climate and length of growing season, their ability to set flower well and to bear a viable crop in a poor year, are only available on their own roots. They are not available as imported grafted vines, as they are not grown on a vineyard scale on the Continent today. Therefore, if an English or Welsh grower wants to plant these vine varieties, he has no option other than to plant rooted cuttings.

Phylloxera in England

Since the outbreak of phylloxera in Somerset in 1985 and 1986, and subsequent discovery in a Suffolk vineyard in 1986, the use of grafted vines has gained far greater importance for future plantings. The risk of phylloxera spreading in England must be recognized. Whether these outbreaks are the only outbreaks, and the problem and risk will subside, or whether these infestations are but the tip of the iceberg preceeding a massive outbreak, we just do not know. Whatever, it may be a wise precaution to ban entry to one's vineyard to those who own, work, or have recently visited known infected vineyards, in an attempt to restrict the spread of phylloxera, for the beast can be carried in clothes or in mud under a car.

To Sum Up

I have given the pros and cons of planting non-grafted or grafted vines a good airing, and it is now up to the individual to make up his or her own mind. If one is planting vines for home use only, where there is no vast capital expenditure and subsequent financial risk, the problem does not arise, but if one is planting commercially, there is obviously a risk, however slight or obscure it may seem.

Many commercial growers have sections of ungrafted vines, because they want to grow certain vines that are only available on their own roots. Some established growers tend to increase their acreage with non-grafted vines as they are less expensive. There is always the chance that a grower will again import phylloxera in a batch of vines from the Continent; this is less likely with vines from a reputable source and clean bill of health, but in order to eliminate this risk, it is an excellent idea to soak the vines in a sterilizing bath on arrival. A four-per-cent solution of chinosol will kill all unwanted insect life including phylloxera. Unrooted cuttings can be bathed in a four-per-cent solution of chinosol which will kill all overwintering insect eggs.

Phylloxera is a notifiable pest. There is no compensation for an infested vineyard for the law at the present time demands that the vines are grubbed and destroyed. It may be in the interest of growers to approach their insurance companies with a view to insuring against the unlikely event of this devastating pest attacking their vineyards. It would perhaps be a good idea for a group of growers to approach their insurance broker with a view to taking out a joint policy.

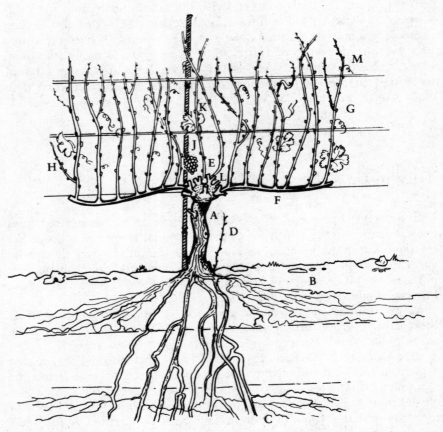

21 Parts of a vine   **A** Stem   **B** Surface roots   **C** Deep feeding roots   **D** A water shoot   **E** Head or crown   **F** 2-year wood   **G** Fruiting laterals   **H** Sub-laterals   **J** Grapes   **K** Replacement canes or rods   **L** Spurs   **M** Tendrils

7

Vine Planting

Whether one vine, ten vines or ten thousand vines are being planted, good site analysis and preparation repays the grower handsomely.

Soil Analysis

The first move is to have the soil analysed to discover whether the site is deficient in any important element, to determine the acidity or pH of the soil, and to take advice on how best to rectify any deficiency, or diminish any excesses. Contact your local ADAS advisers, via the Government offices in your county town, who will assist in this matter, as it is important to settle any problems at this stage, and to be aware of any adjustment that might be needed in the long term so this can be checked annually and dealt with as the necessity arises.

In general, an alkaline environment, soil with a pH of 6.5 or more, is preferred by vines. If the reading is lower than this figure, then the site will have to be limed, and the reading checked annually to see if the pH needs a boost. Magnesium limestone is preferable to straightforward lime, as it breaks down more slowly, and the magnesium content prevents this important second element becoming deficient.

Nitrogen is less necessary to the well-being of vines than potassium and phosphate. Nitrogen encourages growth, and is therefore only necessary should the vines show a marked lack of vigour, or if the vines are planted in soil of really low fertility. It is advisable, however, to supply nitrogen in the first and second year to push the vines into establishing a good root system, followed by sufficient cane in the second year to bear fruit in the third year. It is important that vines should begin cropping in the third year.

It is best to supply nitrogen in the form of organic manure, either well-rotted farmyard manure or well-rotted horse manure. In this way the soil structure is enriched and improved by the humus. Manure also contains other valuable elements essential to plant well-being. Some advice on when and how to apply the manure will follow shortly.

Potash is vital to the vine. Potash encourages flower production, the setting of the flowers, is essential for fruit production, and vital for assisting the cane ripening in autumn. Potash deficiency is denoted by a pale leaf colour and by browning and drying of the leaf perimeter.

Magnesium deficiency is identified by a yellowing of the leaf area *within* the veining, which tends to remain green.

Boron normally occurs in soils of low pH of 3.5–4.5, but can also be found in neutral and alkaline soils.

Early and distinctive sign of Boron deficiency is the development of a mottled chlorosis from the leaf margins, and as the deficiency becomes more acute the chlorotic areas spread and become necrotic. In more severe cases, the young leaves may be deformed, small and brittle. In due course, the growing tips of the shoots die and sublaterals form. Vines with Boron deficiency suffer shoot restriction, and display short, thick internodes. The symptoms as described are more likely after flowering (see p. 171 for identification).

Boron deficiency also causes a considerable reduction in fruit set, or poor pollination, giving bunches with berries of varying sizes, some normal and others small and seedless and failing to develop. This is known as Millerandage or 'Hen and Chickens'.

Boron should be applied twice; as a foliar spray prior to flowering at the three-leaf stage, and immediately following flowering. Do not under any circumstances apply a stronger dosage than that recommended, or Boron toxicity can occur.

Boron or Borax can be acquired in the soluble form known as Solubor from Borax Consolidated Limited, Borax House, Carlisle Place, London, S. W. 1. Application rate is 2–3 lbs per acre, or 1½–2 oz per 5 gallons of water. The west-country agent is Edwin Tucker of Crediton and Ashburton.

Boron as Solubor is compatible with the following:
  Fungicides: Benomyl, Copper, Bordeaux mixture, Dinocap, Maneb, Sulphur, Mildothane, Thiram, Zineb
and is *not fully compatible with:*
  Manganese Sulphate, Zinc Sulphate and Simazine,
and finally Solubor is *not compatible with:*
  Zinc arsenate, Calcium arsenate, also oil and oil-based materials.

How to interpret ADAS Soil Reports

pH

pH is a measure of soil acidity. The soil should be maintained at a pH that suits the vines, which is within the range of 6.0–7.0. The one exception is the vine Siegerrebe, which is happiest in an acid soil.

The lime recommendation gives the amount in tons per acre (tonnes/hectare) of ground limestone or chalk required to raise the top 15 cm of soil to the above pH. Over liming should be avoided as it can lead to trace element deficiencies. (To convert tonnes/hectare to cwt/acre multiply by 8.)

The amounts of available or existing phosphorus, potassium and magnesium are given as milligrams per litre of soil (mg/l). Each result is also expressed as an index. These range from 0 (deficient) to 9 (excess); most agricultural soils have indices between 1 and 3.

Index	Phosphorus Mg/l	Potassium Mg/l	Magnesium Mg/l
0	0–9	0–60	0–25
1	10–15	61–120	26–50
2	16–25	121–240	51–100
3	26–45	241–400	101–175
4	46–70	401–600	176–250
5	71–100	601–900	251–350
6	101–140	901–1500	351–600
7	141–200	1501–2400	601–1000
8	201–280	2401–3600	1001–1500
9	over 280	over 3600	over 1500

An index reading of 3 is sufficient, denoting a well-balanced soil needing little or no adjustment.

Site Preparation

Good site preparation repays the grower handsomely. First study the weed population. If there is a heavy infestation of pernicious perennial weeds such as docks, thistles, nettles, bindweed, couch grass, and buttercups, these must be killed off well before planting, otherwise trying to tackle the weeks once the young vines are in position is an almost impossible task. Buttercups indicate an acid soil.

Do not be misled by the appearance of a weedfree grass field, for once the field is ploughed weed seeds that have lain dormant for 10, 20, 30 years or more, will germinate on being turned and exposed to sun, light and rain. Within weeks one can have a sea of knee-high docks and waist-high thistles which will totally swamp and stifle the newly-planted vines.

It is preferable to prepare the site six months prior to planting, by burning off all the herbage with Roundup, then having the area deep ploughed. This applies equally for a proposed spring or autumn planting programme.

In due course weeds will appear. When the leaves are fairly well-established, kill the weeds with an application of Monsanto's Roundup – used at the recommended dose. See instructions for tractor spraying. In a 3-gallon knapsack sprayer use 9 ounces of Roundup to 3 gallons of water. Roundup kills these weeds stone dead, maybe a second application will be needed, but once dead they stay dead. About a month before planting, have the site ploughed for a second time, followed a fortnight later by rotovating first one way, and then in the opposite direction. This will leave the ground in a fine tilth for planting.

Grafted vines always arrive in early spring, and the site must, therefore, be ploughed in the autumn. This enables the winter frosts to work on the soil, reducing it to a friable workable condition, ideal for planting. Should the weather be impossible for planting when the vines arrive, or if the ground preparation is unfinished, unpack the vines and bury them in a trench dug into the soil deep enough to accommodate the roots and almost all the stems. This heeling-in keeps them perfect until conditions are right for planting.

Should any soil deficiencies have been discovered, then if the conditions are suitable, the artificial fertilizer or corrective chemical should be applied before the preplanting rotovation, so that it is incorporated into the soil before planting.

The same applies to organic manure, either well-rotted farmyard, well-rotted horse manure, or compost. All are of great value, providing soil-improving humus, nitrogen and other elements in a natural form. Far better than anything out of a bag. On a free-draining light soil, apply the manure just prior to the pre-planting rotovation, but on a heavy soil in a low rainfall area, apply the manure after weed killing and before the initial ploughing.

When liming soil, always apply the line at the *opposite* season to the manure, so if one is applied in autumn, apply the other in spring, and vice versa.

Should the site be damp, seek expert advice about having land drains laid to have excess water removed. Vines do not like waterlogged soil, so it is essential that poor drainage is dealt with prior to planting. In reality poorly drained soil is unsuitable for viticulture.

Vine Spacing

The next task is to decide on the spacing of the rows in the vineyard. To a degree this is decided for the grower, either by the scale of the enterprise, whether it is an amateur or professional planting, whether it is to be one of many enterprises on a farm, or whether the vineyard is to be the sole enterprise.

Should the grower already have tractors and cultivation and spraying machinery, he will not feel inclined to purchase special vineyard equipment. Therefore, his vines will be planted wide enough to allow him to use this machinery. The disadvantage here is that when vine rows are situated wider than 2 metres (6 ft) apart, the vineyard loses its microclimate; no heat is retained once the rows are widely separated. This is particularly desirable during the last two months of the ripening period, in September and October, when the temperatures are declining and the grapes need every possible advantage to aid ripening.

The ideal distance for the vine rows would be 1.30–1.50 metres (4–5 ft) apart. This gives adequate room for the vine dresser to attend to winter and summer pruning, spraying with knapsack and lance, or mini-tractor and turbo sprayer, and harvesting the grapes, while still maintaining the microclimate.

Thus the ideal method is to train the vines along traditional lines, such as one sees in all the main winegrowing areas in France, Germany and Luxembourg. The advantages of so doing are undeniable, crop consistency is more predictable, both at a minimum level in a poor year and at a fully acceptable ratio in a moderate or good season.

The planting distance of vines one from another within the rows is dictated by the fertility of the soil, and the degree of vigour of the vine variety. Thus on a very poor rank chalk soil with little or no energy contribution, the vines will need planting a mere $\frac{2}{3}$ m apart (2 ft), whereas in a soil of moderate vigour, the vines should be planted 1.30 m (4 ft)

apart, and in a strong fertile generous soil the planting distance recommended is 1.60 m (5 ft). Strong rampant American hybrids need a full
2 m (6 ft) spacing.

A secondary factor to the soil quality is, therefore, the growth habit
of the vines to be planted. Vines of low vigour should be planted really
close together; by planting a greater number of such vines in a given
area the yield of that area will be maintained on a par with a more
generous wider-spaced vine variety. Each vine can, therefore, carry and
ripen a lighter crop than a more vigorous fruitful vine, but due to there
being more vines in a given area, a viable yield is maintained. For vines
of low vigour on a poor soil a vigorous rootstock, Teleki 5BB in
particular, is to be recommended for this situation (see the chapter on
rootstocks).

Vines of moderate vigour should be planted approximately 1.30 m
(4 ft) from one another; again this is a flexible distance and the final
choice will depend on the degree of soil fertility. Excessively vigorous
vines need more room if they are not to overcrowd one another and
need a distance of up to 2 m (6 ft) between each other. In this way the
greater energy can be better harnessed for higher fruit yield without
overcrowding.

Wide planting and High Trellis

There is a section of growers who follow the example of the famous
Austrian, Dr Lenz Moser, who devised a higher trellis than that of the
northern European vineyards and spaced his rows some 3 m (9–10 ft)
apart. Using really vigorous vines, purpose bred, which ripen considerably later than the vines we grow in Britain, it was discovered that
this system allowed a far greater area to be tended per man, thus cutting
production costs. This was achieved by total mechanization and the
system has proved to be fully viable, given the suitable location, climate
and vine variety. The vines are trained with a permanent arm either side
of the stem and pruned to six-bud spurs in winter.

These principles were taken a step further in the United States of
America at the Geneva vine station, where a high double wire was
supported by 2 m tall T posts, and the vines were trained alternately to
each wire. The system involves no summer pruning, growth is left to
hang downwards at will, forming a green double curtain. The system
is expensive as far as land use is concerned, and was evolved especially
for the extra vigorous vine varieties grown in the hot humid eastern
States of America, and for mechanical harvesting. This system has been
tried quite extensively in New Zealand, but many growers are reverting

to a lower trellis. The climate there encourages massive annual growth and yield, conditions that favour the native American vines such as Concord and Niagara, and also the more vigorous European-American hybrid vines.

This system of training cannot really be recommended for every British site in general, for the reasons set out in a later paragraph, but if a grower is determined to go ahead on the GDC system, then perhaps a few references to site, varieties and procedure might be helpful.

As far as sites are concerned the GDC trellis might be preferable if the grower was only able to plant in a known frost pocket, or on a cold frosty river valley floor, to try to keep the bearing area of the vines up above the cold air, or in a vigorous cold heavy clay soil, to take up some of the vigour that vines in such a soil would demonstrate. Secondly, a farmer who already owns a fleet of full-size agricultural equipment – tractors, rotovator, sprayer etc., and would thus only contemplate a vineyard if he could use his existing tractors and implements.

One would also suggest a higher trellis for those with bad backs, for weekend growers, who work elsewhere all week, and perhaps for growers of more advanced years. Above all the grower would have to have plenty of land for a commercial venture, realizing that the GDC yields $1-1\frac{1}{2}$ tons per acre compared to the 2–5 tons an acre on the traditional closer lower system.

An eminent west-country GDC grower who maintains an immaculate and well-run vineyard, very fairly summed up the pros and cons of the high trellis system thus...

Points Against the Geneva Double Curtain System

1 GDC System is really best suited to vigorous hybrid vines, as the vast majority of vinifera varieties take so long to drag themselves up to furnish the high-wire system.
2 Most vinifera vine varieties take eight years to reach the full cropping potential that vines trained lower achieve in a mere three to four years. Most grafted vines begin to decline from the 15th year, needing to be replaced in their 20th to 25th year, so a far shorter period of full cropping is enjoyed.
3 Vines trained high are far more susceptible to wind and gale damage.
4 Grapes are far more prone to devastating bird damage, situated as they are on the top surface of the vines in full view of the bird population.
5 Wood ripening is not so good particularly with vinifera varieties, much die-back is suffered and unripe wood falls prey to winter botrytis.
6 Less popular with harvesters.

Points in Favour of the Geneva Double Curtain System

1 Cheaper initially; only 450 vines per acre (*c*. £450 at 1989 prices, as opposed to 2000 vines for the Guyot system costing in 1989 *c*. £2000), but I suspect the soaring prices of enormous end posts and high tensile wire cancels out most of the cost advantage today.
2 Quick and easy ground maintenance; herbicides can be used under the vines without risk of spraying vine-leaf area, and the wide avenues between rows can be grassed and mown quickly with a tractor mower.
3 Less work; no summer pruning, tucking or tying – low labour input.
4 No bending, undeniably a great plus factor.

And so there you have it, the choice is yours. Bear in mind however, that none of the northern vinegrowing areas in Europe use the GDC; the further north the vineyard the lower and closer the vines, in an endeavour to trap and conserve the heat collected by one's best friend, the earth. Vines are trained low and close in the Loire valley, in Champagne, in Alsace, in Burgundy and in Chablis, in Bordeaux, even in the hot and arid Rhône valley, also in Luxembourg and in Germany. The only areas where a high trellis is found are certain areas of Cognac, where for making Brandy the demand is for acid grapes, and also in the Saône river valley to the east of the Burgundian Côte d'Or, where the lower price of their wines compared to those from neighbouring Burgundy demands a reduction in labour costs; also this area is prone to spring frosts.

Realize that GDC yield drops to a mere $\frac{1}{2}$ ton an acre in poor seasons. In the one or two heatwave summers in each decade the yield can be as high as 10 tons an acre. Such yields tend to debilitate vines by lowering cane and spur ripening and the vine suffers the following year from having overcropped. The GDC grower therefore needs more land to make a living, and is always extending his or her vineyard in an effort to gain a regular yield of sufficient quantity.

But it must be agreed, there *are* certain very real advantages, and that for certain growers this may be the only answer for their particular site, for their available time, or their physical abilities. The low labour commitment is very attractive.

A vineyard can be converted from one system to the other in just two years, once the vines are established and mature, so if any grower feels he or she has made the wrong decision, or their life style changes and they suddenly have more or less time, or their health alters for better or for worse, the situation is not irreversible. The GDC system is there as an alternative and as such should be considered.

Further evidence on planting distances is given in the Ontario Ministry of Agriculture and Food publication, *The Grape in Ontario*. It is explained that vigorous varieties such as Concord, Niagara, and Catawba should be planted at wider spacing distances than less vigorous vines, Delaware and Foch for example; spacing should be adjusted to variety and soil type. The main competition in a vineyard on standard trellis is between adjacent vines in the row, competition between vines in adjacent rows being minimal until the rows are *very* close together. In New York, very high yields of Concord were obtained when rows were 1.30 m (4 ft) apart with the vines 3 m (10 ft) apart in the row. This they say is not a practical distance until suitable equipment is developed to work in such rows. It illustrates, however, that yield increases are possible by increasing vine population and yet not excessively increasing competition along the row.

Rows 2.7 m (8 ft) apart with vines 3 m (10 ft) apart in the row give 121 more vines per acre than vines planted 3.3 m (11 ft) apart. This will give a substantially greater yield per acre. Tests in Ontario indicate that the *yield per vine* will be almost as high with the closer as with the wider rows. Equipment must be adapted to this closer planting. Row spacings of less than 2.7 m (8 ft) will give further yield per acre increases.

These trial results obtained from an area devoted to the culture of the excessively vigorous native American vines and the marginally less vigorous Euro-American hybrids are highly significant – obviously in an area where all growers are fully equipped with large-scale cultivating and spraying equipment it would not be economic to alter row widths until that equipment fell into disrepair. If and when this should occur it would be for them sound economic sense to plant another row of vines between each existing row, and buy a narrower tractor and implements to suit the closer rows. In three years the yield would be doubled.

In England we are fortunate in that narrow horticultural tractors and implements are imported from Germany and from Japan; at the top end of the market the Ferrari and the Kubota are really first class.

To look back to pre-Phylloxera days in Champagne, the vines were then grown *en foule-provignage*, that is to say on their own roots, and every year when the annual rods were cut back to the head of the vine, one long rod was retained, laid in a trench from the parent vine to a vacant position, and the furthest tip of this cane was left sticking up out of the soil and tied to a stake or a bamboo. This layer (*provignage*), grows far more quickly than a young independent vine, being nourished by the parent vine and quickly developing its own roots along the rod.

A layer was taken from all vines annually, so that given time there were 16,000–20,000 vines per acre, compared with the 4000 vines per acre of today, where the vines are grown trained neatly to a post and wire trellis *en ligne*.

The density of vines when the earlier methods were employed kept the vineyard warmer and, in windy conditions, much calmer, and, benefiting from reflected heat from the ground, the vines flowered earlier and the grapes ripened sooner than on the trellised vines of today. The vines lived longer on their own roots, some 70 years or more, as opposed to the 25 to 30 years of the modern Champagne vine.

Therefore, one has several choices of planting systems: the traditional Guyot, simple or double, head pruning, cordon and spur pruning, the Mosel system for very steep sites, and the two high trellis systems – the Lenz Moser and the Geneva double curtain method.

To use this choice sensibly to suit the site and the vines is the intelligent approach to the problem; sum up all the factors before finally making up your mind. The costing on all these methods is not wildly different today when one puts the repairs to the high systems against the initially slightly higher cost of the traditional low Guyot trellis.

Vine Trellis

If the finances can stand it, to set out the trellis prior to planting is preferable in that it saves putting in the posts and wire later when the vines are in position and, therefore, vulnerable to damage. For the larger vineyard, a tractor and auger are the quickest and most efficient method of siting the end posts.

Prior to posting, mark out the vineyard with lengths of nylon cord, each marked with a knot or with a piece of string of another colour tied on to denote the stations for the posts (or the vines) down the rows. The individual sites can then be marked with bamboos as one moves the string on to the next line.

The end posts of each row need to be really substantial – some 2.70 m (8 ft) in length and 10 cms (4 ins) in diameter. The hardwoods, oak and chestnut, are the best for longevity, with tanalized larch as a second choice. Some growers use reinforced concrete, others angle iron – and remember, all end posts need adequate bracing. This can be achieved by placing a bracing post on the inside of each end post, held by placing a brick under the soil onto which the lower end of the bracing post is placed. The other alternative is to bury a large stone or to auger an anchor disk on the outer side of the trellis on a chain – see diagram.

End posts should be driven in 1 m (3 ft) below ground. If the site should be impossible for a tractor to gain access, then the holes can be made with an iron bar and rammed home with a beetle. Should the ground be very rocky, then a hole will have to be made with an iron bar, pick and long-handled spade, the post set in, and the soil shovelled in, soil and stone in separate layers and rammed, layer on layer. When a post hole is taken out by a tractor auger, the soil will also have to be

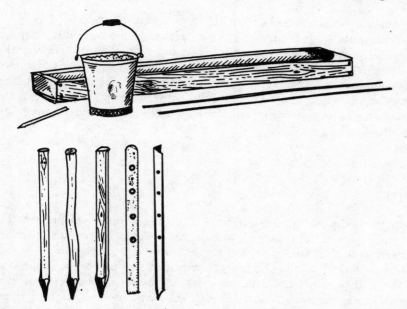

22 Making your own trellis support posts out of concrete. Make a wooden mould out of boarding, incorporate 2 strengthening rods in the casting, and before the concrete sets punch holes through the casting at carefully measured points where trellis wire will pass through the posts.

Materials which can be used at trellis posts: de-barked round tanalized larch, round chestnut, split oak, re-inforced concrete and angle iron. End posts 2.6 m (8 ft), intermediate posts 2 m (6 ft).

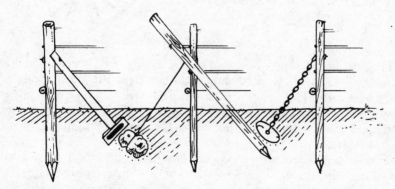

23 Three methods of bracing end posts: the first with an inner wood strut braced against a brick or stone; the second anchored with a stone on the outside from a slanting brace post, as used universally in Alsace; the third using an anchor chain fixed to an auger-driven disk (see also p. 142).

rammed home, stone and soil in alternate layers.

When putting up the trellis prior to planting, the intermediate posts can also be sited with the tractor auger; these posts should ideally also be 2 m (6 ft) in length, and, if wood, should be 7 cms (3 ins) in diameter. Again angle iron can be used. Intermediate posts should be set no further than five vines apart in a Guyot trellis, otherwise the trellis will suffer damage in gales when the vines are in full leaf in mid-summer and autumn.

Wiring

Once the posts are in position, the supporting wires are strung up. The height of the bottom wire is to a degree decided by the site, the vine varieties and the state of play of the grower's lumbar region.

On an early hot site, the bottom wire can be fixed higher than on a cooler higher site. Early vine varieties can be strung higher than borderline ripeners which need all the assistance going to encourage ripening. Again, if you are not as young as you might be, then set your bottom wire at a level which you can reach and will continue to be able to reach, otherwise the vineyard will be a nightmare in years to come.

24 Section through a post hole showing wedge-shaped stones fitted between the outside edge of the hole and post, and rammed tight. The bottom layer of stones is the most important: if well done, this layer prevents any movement of the post. This is the method the Romans used.

To give a guide here, the wire can be as low as 37 cms (15 ins) or as high as 60–75 cms (2 ft–2½ ft) should the site be really good and bending one's *bête noir*. The bottom wire should be of 12-gauge wire for rows of up to 25 vines; if longer you will need 10-gauge to stand the strain. The upper double wires for shorter rows can be of 14-gauge, for longer rows 12-gauge.

Double wires are recommended practice today as a labour-saving device for the upper wires, so that the growing fruiting laterals can simply be tucked between the double wires rather than taking added time to tie each one to each wire. Some growers use just two double wires, others have as many as four. A further suggestion is to fix a series of hooks to each end and to each intermediate post, and raise the double wire as the fruiting rods grow by slipping them up to the next row of hooks on each post. To maintain a degree of tension on each wire, a short length of chain is fitted to one end of each wire and can be tightened or loosened from their hooks on the end post at will. There are also simple angled wire-tightening devices available from Germany, or more expensive rachets than can be fitted to one end post of each row.

Remember to slacken off the wire each winter, as wire contracts during very cold weather and can pull out, or at least loosen, the end posts at this time.

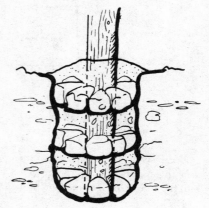

25 Here the alternate layers of stone and earth are shown, all of which must be rammed tightly. Slope the top layer of earth up to the post to shoot off rain water and prevent the post hole becoming waterlogged.

It is worth trying alternatives to wire; Fyffe-Monro market an excellent monofit plastic equivalent which is pleasant and easy to handle, is tough and resilient, and if cut by mistake knots up again permanently.

Spreading the Expenditure

The alternative is to put up the trellis at the end of the first or second year, during the winter months after pruning. In this way the expenditure on the vineyard can be staggered. The first year involves the purchase of the vines, bamboo supports for each vine and rabbit protection. This takes the use of 1-cm mesh wire netting around the perimeter of the site, burying the netting under the soil, down and than outwards, to prevent the little wretches burrowing underneath.

There is an alternative to putting down a perimeter anti-rabbit fence. This is to use clear polythene 500 gauge vine cylinders made by Dunelm of about 18 in ($\frac{1}{2}$ m) high, one slipped over each vine and its supporting bamboo. This, of course, allows rabbits access into the vineyard, but prevents them from eating and killing the vines. These cylinders can be bought ready made, or made using sheets of clear 500 g polythene and a staple gun. The clear polythene allows the grower to watch the progress of the vine inside, which responds well to its mini glasshouse and grows away strongly. Weeds can be seen and removed.

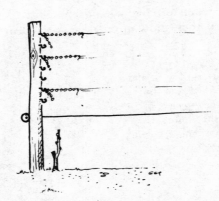

26 Extensively used in Germany; the upper double wires can be raised as the vine growth develops by raising the chains holding the wires to higher hooks screwed into the end posts. Intermediate posts have hooks at corresponding levels.

Planting

Vines can be planted at any time during the dormant season, from leaf fall in early November through to late April or early May. Given a mild winter, autumn-planted vines start away earlier in spring having established a good root hold during winter, but should the winter be very wet and cold, vines can die at this stage if waterlogged.

Grafted vines are only imported in March and April, and should be planted immediately. Vines on their own roots can be planted throughout the season. Cut all the vine roots back to no more than 7–8 cm (3 in) in length prior to planting. The newly-cut root ends will quickly sprout new roots.

Whether grafted or on their own roots, vines should be planted deep enough, so that a mere 7–8 cms (about 3 ins) is above soil level. This ensures that they do not dry out in a dry windy spring, and keeps the graft just above soil level so that the scion does not form roots and thus force itself away from the rootstock. Although not necessary in the average British mild winter, the Continental practice is to ridge the soil

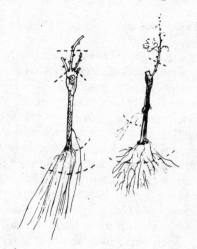

27 How to prune a grafted vine (left) and
a rooted cutting *before planting*. With a
grafted vine select the strongest and
straightest of the scion shoots, and cut it
back to leave just 2 or 3 buds. Remove all
other shoots. Cut back the shoot on the
rooted cutting (right) to leave just 2 buds
also. Prune the roots back to leave just
8 cm (3 in) in both cases.

from the avenues between the rows over the grafts in autumn to protect
them from the ravages of frost. This soil is then pushed back into the
avenues in spring.

The degree of preparation of the planting hole will be determined by
whether one is merely planting a few vines, or planting a larger area, or
planting on a commercial scale. For the very best results when planting
vines in a garden, or on a wall, follow the directions given on p. 249
showing the digging of the hole, the drainage layer in the bottom with
the forkful of manure or compost on top, and some fine soil for the
next layer, into which the vine roots are spread out evenly. Fill in with
the rest of the top soil, tread well, and finally put the coarser sub-soil
on the top, again firming very well with the foot. This method ensures
that the vine has a great start in life; good drainage to eliminate wet
feet – nothing makes a vine fold up and die quicker than a waterlogged
soil – plenty of nourishment when the roots most need encouragement.
With such treatment a vine will grow away well in the first and second
year and be sure of being fit to fruit in the third year.

On a vineyard scale, when one is tackling hundreds or thousands of
vines, such preparation would be too costly and time consuming. Here
the grower relies on having ploughed the ground six months prior to
planting; in the interim the wind, rain and frost will have broken it
down and it will have become more friable; also the soil will, ideally,
have been corrected for any deficiencies, limed and/or manured if necessary, and will thus be in an excellent condition following the final
rotovation, during which all the improving and nourishing elements
will have been thoroughly mixed into the soil.

The Vines

Always soak vines in buckets of water up to their tops for some hours before planting to ensure that they are damp at this time. Trim the roots of the vines back to just 8 cms (3 ins) long, and trim the top growth back to leave just two or three buds. Take out a hole of a good spade's depth, plant the vine into the bottom of the hole with the roots fanned out well, push the earth back around the vine again, tread well and pull more earth around, leaving a mere 8 cms (3 ins) of the vine above ground. When planting a great number of vines, it does help to have a gang of people, both for the marking out and for the planting operation, one or two to dig the holes, one to set the vines in the holes correctly, another to follow with a spade to align the vines with each other as he fills in the earth and firms them in really well with his foot.

Each vine *must* be supplied with a bamboo or similar support of some 1.30–1.60 m (4–5 ft) in length. This is used as an anchor to which the vine is tied as it grows and to prevent the sappy, vulnerable young growth from snapping off in a gale, and keeps the stem or leg of the vine straight. For the tying-in of the vines to their supports, paper or plastic-covered plant ties are useful; the comparatively new Japanese plant tier is excellent, it staples a strip of plastic tape around the plant and bamboo, a tie which lasts more than a year and needs but a single trigger action. This tool is quicker than twisting plant ties or tying twine.

Polythene Mulch

A practice whereby a grower may save a great deal of time and expense is by laying a strip of black polythene along the rows where the vines are to be planted. This mulch has two advantages; it keeps the area between the vines in the rows totally weed free, and also conserves moisture during the summer months. Some lay the plastic mulch before planting, using a dispenser that is trailed behind a tractor and tucks both outer edges into the soil as it progresses. The vines then have to be planted through the film. Others lay it after planting, which means the vines can be more expertly planted beforehand and a small cross made in the polytheme film above each vine with a knife and the vines are then eased through the holes. With the latter method the black polythene then has to be let into the soil with a spade blade to prevent it being caught up and blown by the wind.

Young vines grow away very strongly under this plastic mulch, with no weed competition and no stress from drought. The polythene will

28 Planting the vines in strips of black polythene totally eliminates weed growth between the vines, and it traps moisture during the growing season and thus prevents vines dying in drought conditions. Vines make three times the growth in the first year, and thus will give a really good yield in the third year. This system is highly recommended.

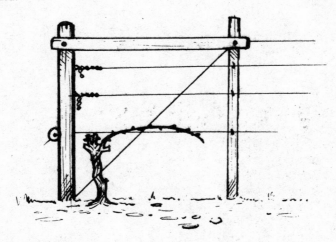

29 A fourth method of bracing end posts; using a second post and a cross bar at the top, then running a strong wire from the *top* of the inner post to the *base* of the end post removes the stress from the top of the end post and creates an excellent support.

last for three years before breaking down and the vines will have developed far better than unprotected vines during this time.

The area of earth between the rows of polythene can be kept clean with rotovator, hoe or herbicide, without risk of damaging or spraying the vines while they are young, tender and vulnerable, and without damaging the roots with machinery.

In the Nahe valley in Germany, I saw a newly-planted vineyard with acres of young vines set in rows of black polythene. One highly successful vineyard in Gloucestershire adopted this plastic mulch for the first three years and the progress of the vines was most impressive. The first crop, taken in the third year, had an excellent must weight and very acceptable yield – all due to the great start the vines enjoyed.

8
Training and Pruning

The traditional Guyot simple and double (single and double Guyot methods) will be discussed first, following the newly-planted young vines through to their first harvest. This section will be followed by a brief dissertation on other viable training methods in practice in English vineyards.

Why do we train vines? Why not let the vines simply take their own course unheeded? This may sound an attractive thought, but unfortunately a vine, left to its own devices, would expend all its annual growth energy on extending shoots in every direction. Few if any bunches would form and, if they did, the grapes would be minuscule. Man has learned to prune and train all his fruit trees and bushes to channel this vigour into fruit production, and the vine is no exception.

In the first year newly-planted vines do not demand much attention, other than to be supplied with a support to which they must be tied, and to which they can cling by virtue of their tendrils. Bamboos of 1.50–2.0 m (5–6 ft) in length are the most usual support; alternatively the galvanized metal vine supports imported from Germany by Lamberhurst vineyard, though more expensive, will last for many years.

The newly-planted vines may have been pruned ready for planting by the supplier, but if this is not the case, if there are several shoots at the top of the vine, choose the strongest and cut it back to leave just two buds, and remove the others. This can be done prior to planting, or after planting. If you happen to plant during a very hard winter, pull some earth up over the graft until May to protect it from frost.

Following budburst, which will occur sometime in May, the actual time being dependent on the year and on the geographical latitude and height above sea level, the two buds will develop into shoots. In this first year only one rod is required, so when the two small shoots develop, look at them both carefully and rub off the weaker thinner shoot completely. All energy will henceforth be directed into the production of one good cane or rod, which should be tied at intervals to the support to prevent winds and gales snapping it off at the base.

It is important that the vineyard be kept clear of weeds so that the vines have no competition for available nutrients, air and light. In the first three years the young vines are obviously highly vulnerable to herbicides or weedkillers, and so it is therefore recommended that the grower tries to keep the vineyard floor clean by hoeing or rotovating and, should pernicious weeds apppear, to spot-weed them with a knapsack sprayer, with a hood fitted to the lance to prevent spray drift.

It is now that the benefits will be reaped of having prepared the site properly some six months before planting. If you have made a real effort to eradicate all weeds before planting it will make an untold difference upon the effort of keeping the vineyard weed free after planting and during the two non-productive years. Matters will be even better if the black polythene mulch is in place – the vineyard will be a joy rather than a constant task master.

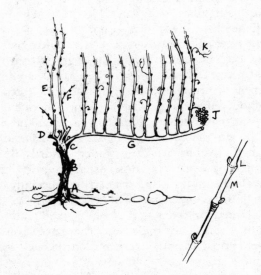

30 *Single Guyot vine* **A** Point of graft **B** Stem or leg of the vine **C** Head of the vine **D** Replacement spur **E** Replacement rods **F** Sub-laterals **G** Two year old rod **H** Fruiting Rods **J** Grapes **K** Tendrils **L** Node **M** Internode

First Winter Pruning

Pruning can be tackled at any time between the beginning of January, when the vines are deeply dormant, through to late April. Pruned as late as April, when the sap is rising within the vines, they will bleed. This does not matter, and the vine will come to no harm. Severe frosts often occur during January, and vines must *not* be pruned *during* frost, or the vine will suffer die-back from the pruning wound. In cases of extremely low temperatures, such as those experienced from January 1986 to February 1987, damage can occur to the vines. Below −12°C roots can burst below ground, and below −25°C the buds on the vine are killed. It is advisable, therefore, in a very hard winter, when there are severe frosts every day, not to prune until this period is past. In Britain the temperature does not drop to such devastatingly low levels as on the Continent, where vast areas of vineyards may be killed by frost. This happened in the winter of 1978/79 in Germany, where the temperature did drop below —25°C; vines planted in low-valley sites were the worst affected, those on the hillsides tended to escape.

To return to the year-old vines, these must be pruned down to leave just two or three buds. This may sound very hard, but the first two years of a vine's existence must be devoted to forming a strong and extensive root system, and this must be well established before the vine is asked to carry a crop. There are two good reasons to back up this advice. Firstly, those that try to crop their vines in the second year find that the vines suffer for having been overtaxed, by undercropping for *several* years. A vine will always look after its own interests in this way, by balancing a glut year with a lean year afterwards. Therefore, it behoves the grower to postpone cropping until the third year, and to regulate cropping each year thereafter by careful pruning, both in his own interest and in the interest of the vine.

The second reason for not cropping until the third year is that the wine from vines younger than three-years-old is thin, watery and tasteless, no more than a brief promise of wine from the same vines when older. In Germany wine from very young vines is known as Yungferwein, or virgin wine, and it would not be economically worth-when older. In Germany wine from very young vines is known as Yungferwein, or virgin wine, and it would not be economically worth-while, as well as a waste of time and effort, to produce a very third-rate wine that would more than likely not be saleable, let alone enjoyable. Even wine from three-year-old vines does not hold a candle to wine from five-year-old vines. However, vines rarely make wood suitable for cropping in the second year – so the temptation does not often arise.

The Second Year

The second year is devoted to producing two strong rods from each vine, pencil thick rods of 1.30 m (4 ft) or more in length. This is achieved by feeding the vines in the spring. If the rod or cane development was poor in the first year, by keeping wood competition down and by tying the canes into the bamboo or support system as they grow, and feeding the vines in March, vigour should be adequate in the second year.

For encouraging growth, should this be necessary, some form of low nitrogen fertilizer is recommended. A dressing of well-rotted manure of any type is the best form of encouragement, failing this a 5–10–20 bagged fertilizer is adequate, applied at the rate of two hundredweight per acre. The 5–10–20 numbers refer to the composition of the fertilizer, which is always given in the following order, N (nitrogen), P (phosphate), and K (potassium).

Spraying

During the first and second seasons, a skeleton spraying is recommended to ensure that the young vines are kept mildew and botrytis free. Spraying such young vines is not a lengthy task, either in time or effort, and the gallonage is minimal. A knapsack sprayer with lance is all that is needed. A spray every two to three weeks should be sufficient, shifting the applications to follow periods of heavy rain, as and when they occur. Pay particular attention to covering the underside of the leaves rather than the top, for it is on the underneath of the leaf that the mildew and botrytis spores gain hold two weeks before they are visible to the eye. It is the failure to act on this simple information that causes so many vineyards to be attacked by these fungal diseases. All too often the upper surfaces of the leaves are sprayed most admirably where it shows, but this is no deterrent to fungal disease.

The sprays to use and the appropriate dilution rates are given in the chapter on spraying; suffice to say here that sulphur and zinc are an excellent combination to use for the regular spray programme, used as wettable micronized sulphur and Murphy's Zineb. Spray against botrytis by adding ROVRAL to the sulphur and Zineb for July and August sprays. ROVRAL is far more efficient than the earlier botrytis sprays on the market, in particular Benlate, to which botrytis develops immunity.

Replace any vines that have died as soon as possible. It is a good idea to order five per cent more vines than are needed; pot these extra vines, and care for them in a cold frame or protected area. Therefore, when a

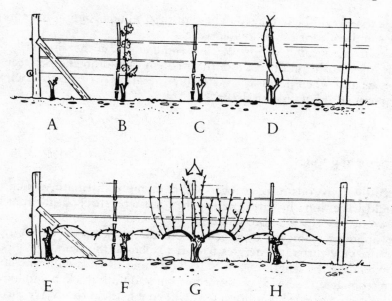

31 *Early training* **A** A newly planted vine **B** Growth at the end of first year **C** In January pruned down to 3 buds **D** Growth at end of second year **E** January pruning: Tie best cane down onto bottom wire (single Guyot training). **F** In fourth year use double Guyot, tie and cane down on either side of stem. **G** Double Guyot trained vine at end of the growing season. **H** At January pruning time cut away all but the two canes arrowed in diagram G, and tie these two down onto bottom wire.

vine fails to take, or dies at a later date, the containerized vine can be substituted at any time of the year without checking its progress, and full planting is maintained.

Laterals

During the growing season the vine will throw side shoots, or laterals, from the leaf axils. These take energy that would otherwise be better engaged in producing and ripening the long straight rods. Therefore, if the time can be found to go through the vines once or twice a month, pinching out the laterals after one leaf, the vine as a whole will benefit considerably. This practice is recommended each and every year, for the laterals do absolutely nothing for the ripening processes of the grapes or the vine wood, in fact, they divert energy that should be better used. By leaving just one leaf, there is no risk that the dormant bud in the leaf axil will be damaged. These dormant buds contain the embryo canes and fruit for the following year.

Try to maintain a weed-free environment within the vineyard, by a light top rotovation once a month or so, and hand hoeing between the vines as and when necessary. As well as aerating the soil, this helps to keep annual weed growth down.

Stopping the Vines

Once the two rods have reached 4–5 ft or more in length, which they should have done by late August, they must be stopped in order that the wood can ripen before winter.

Stopping is achieved by pinching out the growing tip of the canes, and the vine turns its energies towards ripening the wood as opposed to extending the length of the rods. The canes or rods will, one hopes, turn from green to a rich chestnut brown, and both thicken and harden, and obtain a ripened condition that will enable them to survive through the hardest winter and suffer no die-back or frost damage, and as such withstand the ravages of mildew or botrytis, which can wreck unripe overwintering wood, and thus jeopardize the next year's crop.

The Third Year

At long last the effort and work of the past two years seems worthwhile, and the long-awaited first crop of grapes and wine are within reach.

At the *very* latest, the trellis must be erected at the beginning of the third year so that the vines have a support system to which they can now be tied. It is recommended that the trellis goes in before planting if possible, or at the latest at the end of the first year.

Before discussing the training and care of the third-year vines, a word about weak and poorly-developed vines. Do not allow any vines that grow rods of less than 4–5 ft in length of pencil-thick-nut brown well-ripened cane, to crop in the third year. These vines must be cut down again, to leave a stub with three buds, to have a further year to develop before being allowed to bear fruit. Not all vines develop uniformly, and those that are weak must be given another year to make a better root system, and perhaps begin to bear in the fourth or even the fifth year.

In Champagne the young vines are not permitted by the growers to carry a crop of grapes until the fourth year. This is partly due to the low vigour output of the chalk soil, and to the nature of the vines. Most noble classic vine varieties are plants of but moderate vigour, and many will not develop sufficient frame and stature to begin to crop until a year later than the more vigorous and precocious German crosses.

The wine from three- and four-year-old vines is noticeably inferior in extract and body to wine from five-year-old vines, by which time the vine is approaching maturity. With grafted vines, maximum yield and performance lasts until the vine is 15 years old, and thence begins to wane. Productivity drops below a viable level by the time the vine reaches 20, 25 or 30 years of age, this state being dependent upon a combination of many factors, the principal being whether or not the vine has been overcropped, the soil type, the vine variety and the geographical location. The viable life of the ungrafted vines can be from 50 to 100 years, the span again dependent upon similar factors. This perhaps puts the recommended wait for the first crop until the third year into clearer perspective.

Pruning

At the beginning of the third year the grower is faced with the majority of his vines each with two rods or canes of 4–5 ft in length. With an eye to the drawings on pp. 147–155, it is recommended that the vines are asked to crop on only one of these two rods in the first fruiting year, and, if the plan is to adopt the double Guyot system, then this is introduced in the fourth year. This ensures that the vines are not overfaced, and are not allowed to carry a heavy crop in their first bearing year.

Therefore look at each vine carefully, and in general choose the stronger firmer rod to bend down onto the bottom wire of the trellis, cutting the second rod away, leaving just two or three buds on the spur that remains. The exception to this rule is when the lesser rod is badly placed to form the spur, for the buds on this spur are destined to become the fruiting rods of the following year, and should they be too high, too low or really ill-placed for such a purpose, then the rod better equipped to fulfil this purpose must be allowed to do so, and the other cane used to carry the crop of the current year. The good winegrower is sensitive to this problem, and always prunes for the future more than for the present. This principle pays in the long run as one achieves a vineyard of well-shaped vines with upright stems or legs, and a correctly placed head from which future wood is formed. When pruning, always look at the vine on either side of the vine about to be pruned; should a neighbour be over strong or weak, or indeed should the vine to be pruned be unbalanced, prune each vine to complement its neighbour on either side. If a vine is weak, prune it hard to leave fewer fruiting buds, if *very* weak cut it back to leave just a three-bud stub so that it may begin again. The absence of rod on the wire from a weak vine may mean that you can leave a bud or so extra on the rod from each neighbour, should one or both be vigorous. This helps to maintain production in the vineyard. Do not overcrowd a weak vine, however, for if denied light, sun and air, it will never grow well.

To re-cap, for the first cropping year, we have single Guyot-trained vines, each fruiting cane cut after the seventh or eighth upward facing bud, with fewer left on less strong vines. Cut the lesser rod down to leave a three-bud spur, the rods from this spur will form the two fruiting rods and spur for the following year.

Bud-Burst

In mid-late April, the buds will begin to change appearance from their hard nut-brown triangular form, first by throwing off their hard outer shell, and showing their pink or orange velvety undercoat. As the temperatures rise, the shoots burst out from their protective covering, and from then on develop at such a pace that one can almost hear and see them grow.

A keen eye is now required, firstly to ascertain which shoots are fertile and carrying embryo fruit and which are not, and to decide on which shoots have to be removed, also removing those facing towards the ground. Aim to leave six to eight shoots in this, the first cropping year, and rub off all unwanted shoots at the point where they join the main rod. You have at one move left only shoots which will be easy to train, and also have determined that the vine shall only bear from six to fourteen bunches, depending on whether each fruiting lateral provides one or two bunches. Should a third bunch form, remove the weakest of the three.

Temper the number of bunches left on each vine to the vigour and framework of the particular vine. It is important not to overcrop a young vine, because, since it is only recently established, to overcrop will severely undermine the strength of the vine for a long time to come.

The first spray must be applied as soon as the leaves reach fifty-pence size, a mixture of Zineb and sulphur. See the relevant chapter on spraying and follow a strict spray programme.

As soon as the fruiting laterals reach the height of the first double wire, tuck them between the two wires, and the support will prevent them from being snapped off in a gale. Continue to tuck the fruiting laterals between the wires – to an extent they help themselves by virtue of their tendrils which cling firmly to the wires.

Laterals

Laterals, or side shoots, will grow from the leaf axils of all the rod growth on the vine. These side shoots contribute nothing to the sugar assimilation within the grapes, merely taking valuable energy and food resources from the vine. So these should be removed, nipped off between finger and thumb, leaving just the basal leaf intact so that the dormant bud, which also lies in each leaf axil, is not damaged. This lateral removal is a constant chore during the height of the growing season, but is a valuable contribution towards better-quality grape production if it can be done.

Once the fruiting rods reach above the top wire, they must be stopped by having their growing tips nipped out. This further diverts the energy of the vine into grape production. The leaves of the vine, or indeed of any plant, use the energy absorbed from the sun to convert water and carbon dioxide from the air into sugar by photosynthesis; this sugar is assimilated by the grapes. By removing the material from the vine which is taking valuable nutrients that might otherwise be better employed, material which itself offers nothing in return, the grower is well on the way to harvesting riper grapes. Little and often is the answer with summer pruning – topping and lateral removal – as the vine suffers no shock and thus no set back.

As summer moves into autumn, and the bottom leaves begin to yellow and brown, these leaves cease to function, and, if the weather is fine, can be removed to allow sun and air onto the grapes, which again encourages ripening. This leaf removal is practised in Bordeaux as a matter of course, the extra air flow around the fruit greatly helps to prevent the risk of botrytis. If the weather is cold and wet, leave the leaves on as they keep the grapes dry and warm by deflecting the rain.

The harvesting of the grapes will be dealt with in another chapter.

The Fourth Year

The vines receive little attention from harvest until the winter-spring pruning. The pruning operation at the beginning of the fourth year presents the grower with a different task than that of previous pruning operations, in that for the first time there is fruiting wood to remove.

Before starting to prune a vine, stand back and look at it carefully. Ascertain whether it has several suitable young canes growing away from the spur or head of the vine. It it has, there are no problems, if not one has to choose the nearest suitable fruiting lateral. Look at the vine's two immediate neighbours, which may be weak or strong, to determine the length of the canes to tie down. Then cut away the horizontal two-year-old wood and fruiting laterals, leaving three or four young rods on or near the head of the vine from which to choose the new fruiting wood and spur.

One has to decide whether one is going to train the vines with single or double Guyot. The majority of vines crop satisfactorily with either system. A few varieties tend, however, to crop more heavily on the fruiting laterals furthest from the stem of the vine, whereas others crop more heavily on fruiting laterals nearer the stem. Naturally for the former one would recommend single Guyot, and for the latter, double Guyot would give a better yield.

Old French vines, such as Gamay, Precoce de Malingre and Perle de Czaba, only crop if head or cordon pruned with long spurs of six buds, the sixth bud being the first to carry fruit embryos.

The majority of the vines grown in British vineyards are trained by the double Guyot system. To achieve this, the grower firstly checks that the spur has provided him with two or three good replacement rods. First, he chooses the rod best placed to provide a spur, from which the fruiting rods of the following year will grow, and cuts this down to three buds. The other two are laid one each way on to the bottom wire, after the removal of the old horizontal wood and all the fruiting laterals. It is not always as easy as this – sometimes one has to use the fruiting lateral nearest to the head of the vine as a new replacement rod, if the spur failed to produce enough good pencil-thick well-ripened rods. Trim off all the laterals.

Always remember to think ahead and, realizing that the future is more important than the present, make sure that the spur is well placed to provide for the future. The spur should be so placed as to improve the shape of the vine, should be neither too high nor too low, and it should not face downwards or outwards. In this way, the vine leg or stem will develop and mature into an attractive upright stance, allowing freedom of sap flow. Should the stem or leg bend over, tie it to the bamboo to help it maintain an upright form.

Even if one has to choose a less than perfect replacement cane, the consolation is that this situation will be improved the following year. And, remember, if the vine has grown weakly, cut it back severely, either to a mere three-bud stub like a newly-planted vine, or back to single Guyot with a spur, with one short horizontal rod tied to the bottom wire. Also, do remember to look well at the neighbouring vine on either side, and balance each vine with its neighbours, compensating somewhat if a vine is weak by allowing the neighbour to carry an extra bud or two. Do not overdo this, and overshadow the weak vine, which must have plenty of air and light to be able to grow and to attempt to catch up.

Clear up and burn all the prunings; none should be left in the vineyard for they will rot and thus harbour botrytis, and can later attract other harmful wood rot fungus which can spread to living vines.

Fourth Year Maintenance

Maintenance in the fourth year is the same as in the third year, the main difference being that there are now double the fruiting rods forming. Reduce the total to some 12–14 at the most, rubbing off those that point downwards, and by selecting those that are bearing fruit, and removing the blind shoots. Avoid overcrowding by spacing the rods some 7 cms (3.5 ins) apart.

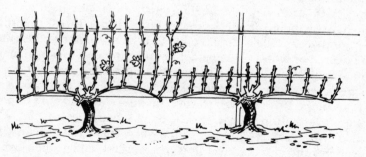

32 Most of the ancient French vines fail to fruit when double or single Guyot trained: Precoce de Malingre, Perle de Czaba, Muscat de Saumur, Noir Latif de Marseilles and the Gamays, for example. The vines are unfruitful on the first five buds, the sixth bud is the first to be fertile. So prune the fruiting laterals down to leave 8 buds, and the vine should show normal productivity thereafter. This system will reintroduce these old vines once again into the list of possibles for England. Rub off the middle buds after budburst, and leave the first and sixth to develop.

Cluster Thinning

The French experts place great importance on cluster thinning. Apparently we should remove the third and weakest cluster from each fruiting lateral *before* flowering. By so doing the actual yield is increased as the two remaining clusters set better, and attain a greater weight than three clusters, which remain small. It is vital to remove the third cluster, should it form, *before* flowering – if it is removed during or after flowering, all the benefits are lost. This practice applies to the whole range of vines, French viniferas, vinifera crosses, hybrids and American vines. The more far-reaching disadvantage of leaving three clusters on the vine is the debilitating effect it has on the performance of the vine in the following year. The Germans do not follow this practice. To them a vine must produce three bunches on each fruiting lateral to be worthy of existence and a place in the vineyard. So yet again we come up against the two totally different philosophies. The English grower must decide on which side of the fence his principles lie, with the classic French outlook whereby quality is all important, or to flog the vines as hard as possible, the aim being a high yield, and replace the vines in 15–20 years.

The fruit buds for the following year are laid down during July and August of the current year and, therefore, the weather at this critical time determines the potential of the vines and the vineyard for the year to come. In a poor cool year, the vines in Britain may well be flowering well into July, certainly they will be in the more northerly less favourable counties. Therefore, the vine may be exposed to the stresses of flowering and bud formation at one and the same time, and if the vine faces flowering without having been de-clustered, this is but an added stress.

Many vines will only flower and set a good crop in a year that follows a really good year. This is directly due to the weather at bud formation and the degree of wood ripening achieved in the previous summer and autumn. Should we, therefore, experience three poor years on the run, these vines are going to yield miserably for four years. This was brought home to us in the 1970s in no uncertain manner – all the more important to pay great attention to the choice of vine varieties to plant, for a handful of vine varieties manage to flower, set well and bear a really good crop in spite of a cold wet flowering period, due to their excellent wood-ripening properties. And if the long term forecast of the weather experts continues to be true, these élite vines are the only vines for the future of winegrowing in Britain.

Remember to pinch out the laterals if it is possible to do so, and to stop the vines when they are through the top wires of the trellis. This check to the upward growth, which usually occurs after the twelfth leaf of the fruiting lateral, usually coincides with the onset of flowering and

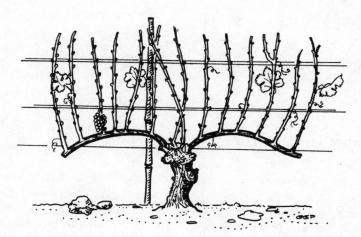

33 *Vitis Vinifera Vines* A mature double Guyot vine before pruning. Note the two replacement canes arising from the crown of the vine. There have been 14 fruiting canes left on the vine (12–14 are maximum recommended).

34 The same vine after pruning, double Guyot trained. Note the spur at the head of the vine to provide two replacement canes for the following year. There have been a total of 14 buds left on the top of the two replacement canes.

does much to divert the energy of the vine into the grape development rather than continuing to grow ever skywards. 12–14 leaves are sufficient to provender the swelling grapes satisfactorily.

The Fifth Year

In the fifth year 12–14 fruiting canes may be retained on all well-grown mature vines. Reduce weaker vines to 12 or less fruiting laterals.

To Sum Up

With vines, the grower must be sensitive at all times that he is working for the following year as well as the current year. He should not allow his vines to overcrop, he will try to keep the laterals pinched out, stop his vines in late June–early July – by taking out the growing tips, he will keep his vines free of mildew and botrytis by strict adherence to a good spray programme, and try to keep weed competition down by regular cultivation and limited use of herbicides. Above all when pruning he will prune and train the vines with the future in mind, leaving the spur in the best position to improve the shape of the vine, if necessary taking replacement canes from lesser positions, as these will be removed after a year and are but a temporary fixture. In this way the vines will improve year by year and the grower will reap a consistent regular harvest.

Too many growers prune for a massive crop leaving far too many buds and, if the year yields a bumper crop, then the next year will reflect this glut by a light harvest. Should, however, the year be poor, then he will have masses of unripe grapes to process and the wood, in failing to ripen, will not crop well the following year.

These principles sum up the winegrowers' creed and they apply equally to their methods of vine training, which may be worthy of consideration should your site not be conventional. This leads us to look at the factors that might lead us to train our vines by alternative systems.

The Mosel System

Should the site be very, very steep, and perhaps undulating with several facets and planes, making it entirely unsuitable for a post and wire trellis, then the Mosel style of training may be the answer. On the precipitous slaty sides of the Mosel Valley in Western Germany, the Mosel style of training is really a variation on the Guyot theme, in that two replacement canes are grown each year, which replace the two of the previous year at the winter pruning session. No wires are used, each vine being supported individually by its own 2-m (6-ft) stake. The stem or leg of the vine is grown to a height of one metre and, instead of training the replacement rods out sideways onto wires, they are bent in a complete arc downwards and lashed back onto the stem of the vine. This may be more easily understood by looking at the drawings on page 61.

Apparently this method shows no drop in production in comparison with the more traditional low trellis Guyot system. This method of support is no more expensive than the Guyot trellis due to the high cost of galvanized or high tensile wire today. Posts can be obtained fairly cheaply in country districts if one has the time and can obtain prices from a number of firms and sawmills. One plus-factor is that the grower can freely walk in both directions when tending the vines.

Goblet Pruning

A method of training suited to the Gamay vine is head or Goblet pruning. This system of training is practised in the Loire and Beaujolais areas, sometimes with a single low wire as support, more often with no wire at all. The vine is formed as a fairly short-stemmed, low-free-standing bush, spur-pruned back to the head or crown each winter. To train a vine for the head method, in the first summer and winter train as for the Guyot system. In the second year allow the new growth to extend to 0.33 m (1 ft), then stop this rod by pinching out the growing tip. This action will force the buds below this point into growth. Rub off all but the two top buds. These two remaining buds will develop and grow; if they do so strongly, stop each after 2 leaves and allow them to form lateral growth which should be allowed to grow on unchecked. It is a wise move to provide each young vine with a supporting bamboo to which the young growth can be tied to prevent wind damage, and to assist one to form a straight stem to the vine.

The winter pruning consists of cutting each shoot back to leave six buds each on mature, well-ripened cane – should the cane be very unripe, cut back to one bud below the unripe wood. The purpose of six-bud spurs with the old French cultivars is because the sixth is the first bud to be fertile, to carry fruit-producing buds. The old French cultivars being Gamay, Perle de Czaba, Precoce de Saumur and Precoce de Malingre. Other varities only need two-to-three bud spurs.

As the vine ages, the grower can gradually leave more and more fruiting spurs to the head of the vine, until a maximum of 12 are reached. He should thenceforward aim to leave 12 at each pruning for maximum quality production. These in turn will produce 12 fruiting canes.

In spring, when the buds burst and shoots appear, keep only the strongest and most fertile shoot on each spur.

When summer growth is at its greatest, the rods can be gathered together and tied, so that each supports the other. The shape that a vine so tied resembles is a goblet, hence the name of the training system. As with Guyot training, nip the tops out of each fruiting rod after the twelfth leaf. This concentrates the effort of the vine into grape production.

The Lenz Moser Training System

The Lenz Moser system can be simply explained as a cordon trained on a wire 1.25 m (4 ft) high. The vines are planted about 1.25 m (4 ft) apart, in rows spaced 3.5 m (10 ft) apart. Fruiting canes are taken from spurs, which are dog-trotted along the old rods, one pointing upwards, the next to the left, the third to the right, the fourth faces up again, and so on. The short fruiting canes are cut to leave six to ten buds to provide a replacement for the following year.

This system was evolved in the 1930s and 1940s by the world-famous Dr Lenz Moser of Rohrendorf, near Krems on the Danube in Austria. The inspiration behind this principle was to mechanize fully all work in the vineyard with full-scale equipment, which greatly expanded the area that could be cared for by one individual from one or two hectares to nearly four hectares. The initial capital cost per hectare was lowered, all this with no loss in yield per hectare. With the geographical location, climate and suitable vine varieties, his revolutionary ideas have been fully realized and have spread to other countries with similar latitude and climate.

The advantages are many: the wide rows can be green-manured in the autumn, which takes up the excess moisture in winter, and this is then ploughed back in the spring. Manual work is reduced to a minimum, and harvesting and pruning are conducted at face rather than knee level, which greatly reduces fatigue and encourages output.

In the hot, low-lying areas, this system serves to maintain a cooler shaded area in which the vines can function more effectively. They are also held above the spring frosts. Similar principles are adopted in Italy and in Portugal where vines are trained high and wide to form a canopy of shade over the grapes, as shelter is needed from the fierce daytime sun in order that the grapes can maintain their development despite the heat, in a cooler, shaded environment.

Vines that adapt well to the high trellis in Austria are the Gruner Veltliner, the most popular white grape, followed by Müller Thurgau. Others grown to a far lesser degree are the Welschriesling, Rhineriesling,

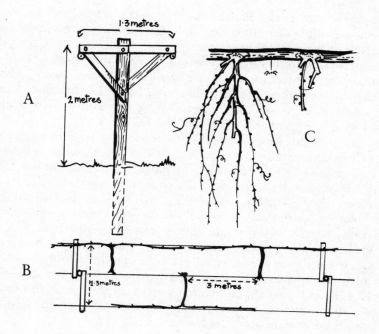

35 The Geneva Double Curtain system of vine training involves a high trellis system, end posts (railway sleepers or telegraph poles) well braced, and intermediated some 3 m (9 ft) long, 1 m (3 ft) below ground. Method of supporting the wires is shown in drawing A. The method of spacing the vines is shown in drawing B, which shows the vines on the trellis (as seen from above). Vines are 3 m (9 ft) apart and off-set from one another, so each vine furnishes an alternate side of the trellis. Drawing C shows a fruiting shoot before and after pruning. Note the replacement cane, grown to provide the fruiting shoot for the year to come; this has taken its place to the right of diagram C after the removal of the old fruiting wood. Note new spur.

Traminer and Muscat Ottonel. For red wine the Blue Portugeiser, Pinot Noir and the new Zweigeltrebe are grown, with increasing success. These vines are specially selected for their vigour and suitability to the high system.

In Britain's cooler, equable, maritime climate, the conditions are reversed and these principles do not apply to the same degree.

The Geneva Double Curtain System

Although the vine performance and grape yield from vines grown on the Geneva Double Curtain system have been discussed, no details have been given of the method of training.

The ideals behind this stem are but an extension of those of the Lenz Moser system, in that the vines are trained high, with wide, grassed alleyways between the vines. The difference lies in the fact that, instead of the single wire cordon, the Geneva Double Curtain has two, running parallel with one another.

The end posts for this system have to be massive, either ex-telegraph poles or wooden ex-railway sleepers. The wire also has to be very strong indeed. Some use high tensile wire, but have to bear in mind the danger of this snapping under stress, with the susequent whiplash effect.

A glance at the drawing illustrating this system will demonstrate better than words the way in which the vines are trained up and onto the parallel wires. Basically one vine is trained up onto one wire, the next vine to the other wire, and so on. On reaching the wire, via a bamboo, the rods are then trained out horizontally onto the wires and these rods are then spur-pruned each winter. It has been discovered through trial and error that different varieties require different numbers of buds left on each spur – some vines are fruitful from the first bud, whereas others require up to six buds.

In general growers have been leaving just one or two buds, but it has been found that for many varieties this is not enough. Many vines are fertile from the third bud (Reichensteiner is a case in point here); others, particularly the old French varieties, are only fertile from the sixth bud. So overall it would appear to be wise to leave more buds, and after bud-burst to look to each spur and rub off the infertile shoots, leaving those that are fruitful and showing two embryo bunches.

Many vine varieties, of those that are suitable for English wine production, do not have the inbuilt vigour to make them suitable for such a high trellis. Either they never really manage to drag themselves up to the level of the wire, or, if they do manage, do so reluctantly and with poor thin rods. It is, therefore, practical to use only the really vigorous varieties for any high trellis system.

The cultural, ripening and yield comparisons have already been aired as have the advantages of a higher system of vine training. A new grower has carefully to weigh up all the factors as presented, and adopt the system best suited to his particular site and degree of commitment, his age and his available time.

Other methods of training and pruning vines have been illustrated in this book for the interest value, but are not systems that will better the methods that have been adopted in this country. Readers may be

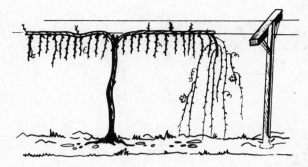

36 A Geneva Double Curtain vine following pruning, leaving long spurs of six buds, ideally facing down. The unpruned wood on the extreme right end of the vine shows the old fruiting wood hanging down, illustrating the curtain effect of the inverted cordon. With vines clothing both parallel wires, the term 'double curtain' may easily be visualized.

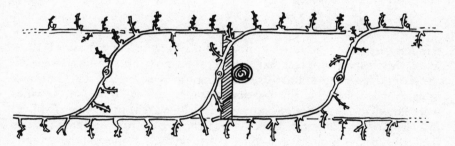

37 Following severe gale damage in several GDC vineyards, several growers have trained one arm of each vine on one wire and the second arm on the opposite wire to try to prevent whole arms being ripped off vines during storms. Strong cord connects the two parallel wires.

interested to see the Casenave cordon system (Fig. 40) which is perhaps useful when wood ripening is poor and spur pruning has to be considered.

Final Conclusions

A few reminders on pruning: firstly, never prune during a hard frost. The wood of a vine is very brittle when frosted and is apt to split at the pruning wound and will suffer die-back.

Secondly, if the replacement cane is bent down to the wire when frosted, it is more likely to snap. During really severe frost, when the

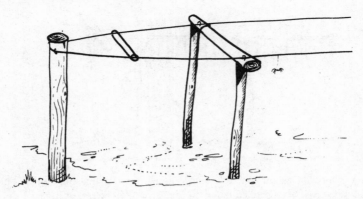

38 An alternative method of supporting GDS vines. The trellis is supported on gantries as shown which offer greater gale resistance, and eliminate accidents to grower's head from the T bars. Use either telegraph poles or railway sleepers as end posts, and put in a gantry every 8–10 metres.

temperatures drop as low as they did during the New Year of 1979, when the temperature reached − 10°C, the vine roots can burst beneath the ground. At − 25°C and lower, temperatures experienced in Germany in certain areas during this particular winter, all the buds on the vines were killed and the vines did not revive. Whole areas of vines were killed in Germany in the flatter areas with little or no frost drainage. When the vine is under such stress it must be left severely alone and the pruning postponed until after the frosts, when the grower can assess damage and take necessary action.

On the Continent, where they regularly suffer from far harder winter frosts than in Britain, they run down each vine row in autumn with a ridge plough and turn the earth sideways to cover the grafts of all the vines. This, of course, protects the graft union from frost to an extent. In spring the earth is then turned back into the furrow, into which the grower has first thrown the manure, so that it is covered by the fresh earth.

Always look out when pruning for the vine that has made poor growth. This applies equally to mature, old vines as it does to young vines before they have borne fruit. With a mature vine, if it shows poor wood development, prune it back very hard to single Guyot, just leaving a short replacement cane with a renewal spur. If the lack of growth has been really severe, then cut the vine back leaving just the spur with three buds and leave no replacement cane. In this case, the vine will have a complete rest from fruiting for a year and will, one hopes, produce two good rods and start fruiting again in the following year. When a vine suffers from such severe lack of energy, suspect vine weevil, or water-

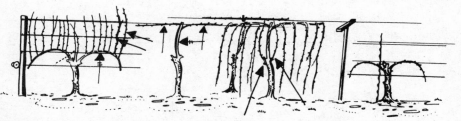

39 Showing how one adapts a Guyot trained vine to a GDC system during January pruning by tying up the better endowed fruiting cane and keeping the two furthest laterals as arms. Revert to Guyot by allowing two to three canes to grow from halfway up the leg.

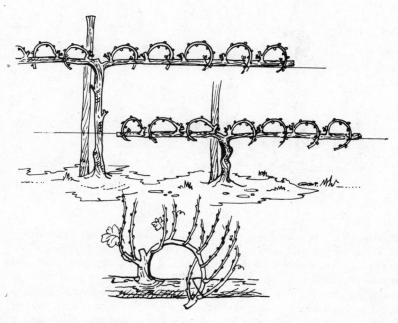

40 The Casenave cordon is but a further development on long spur training. Here 6–8 buds are retained, and are bent down in an arc and tied to the permanent arm. This arching tends to force all eight shoots into fruiting. Remember to leave a 2-bud spur at the base of each lateral to form the lateral and spur for the following year. Try the 6-bud spur and Casenave cordon with unfruitful Müller Thurgau. The bottom drawing shows a detail of both the fruiting cane and replacement spur.

logged subsoil due to poor or blocked land drains, or excessive winter rains. A vine does not like wet feet.

In the eastern states of the USA, the prunings of the vines are weighed and the total weight of the prunings from each vine is directly related

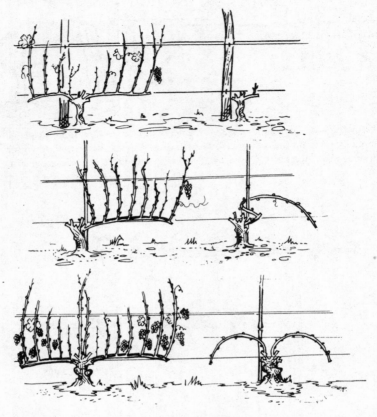

41 *Problems*   The first drawing shows a vine that has failed to throw any good replacement rods from the crown. There was no spur to provide these, and all the sap vigour has gone to the laterals at the further ends of the fruiting canes. The remedy is to remove all the old wood, leaving just a short length with a 2 or 3 bud spur. Feed well, and the vine should produce two good rods in the next growing season. The second drawing illustrates a method of inducing a vine that is reluctant to throw replacement wood from the crown. Bend the new fruiting rod around the support bamboo sharply: a mass of strong fruitful rods will be produced in this area, and the arched rod encourages an even fruiting. The third drawing shows a vine with a tendency to produce grapes only on the further fruiting laterals. This habit can be reversed by sharply bending the rods when tying in after pruning. This should encourage the rods nearer the crown to fruit equally well. Müller Thurgau can often show this tendency.

to the length of the rods and the number of buds left on each vine. The pruner learns gradually how many buds to retain on each vine. To go to such exact lengths is impractical for the stoic British grower, although this principle is sound and the British grower should be sensitive to this.

Closeup of nick with stone to keep it open

42 *Layering*   Should a vine die, or have to be removed, a long rod can be run underground, as shown, from an adjacent vine, to re-emerge in the correct position as a replacement. Allow 2 buds above ground, and cut away any extra, tying in firmly to the bamboo. This new vine will grow away with immense vigour. The umbilical can be completely removed a year later, when the new vine will have rooted strongly. For best results, cut a nick on the submerged rod near to where it emerges, and put a little rooting powder on the cut surfaces, and jam them open with a small pebble.

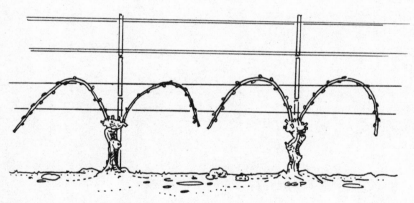

43 Method of training the lighter-cropping small-clustered trailing hybrid vines, e.g. Baco 1, Leon Millot, M. Foch, Oberlin 595 and Triomphe d'Alsace, etc. Space vines 1.60–2 m (5–6 ft) apart in the rows, and strongly arch the twin replacement canes over a training wire to encourage uniform cropping. Also recommended for Madeleine Angevine and others if they prove to be too vigorous for flatter Guyot training; also for Gewürztraminer, for without considerable arching, shoots nearer the stem are unproductive with this vine.

Several vine varieties are more brittle than others and it is all too easy to snap the replacement cane as it is being bent down, Seyval being the worst offender. It is advisable, therefore, to prune Seyval and any other brittle varieties during the dormant season and return in April to tie them down to the wire, for the sap will be on the move and the canes are far more pliable. With brittle vines, do not cut the cane destined for the spur until the replacement rod (or rods) is tied down, so that if the latter should snap, you have the other rod to tie down in its place.

Finally, in some seasons, one is compelled to prune later, perhaps because of severe weather in January and February, or maybe due to the sheer size of the vineyard. The cut wounds may well pour with sap – this does not matter and will not harm the vine, the wounds will seal in time. On the Continent they tend to prune later, suffering as they do from more severe winters with lower temperatures, and are forced to prune in March and April. St Vincent's Day, 22 February, is traditionally the day on which the Champenois begin pruning their vines.

9

Maintaining Fertility

The vinegrower should keep a keen eye on the well-being of his vines. On a fertile well-balanced soil there is less likely to be any marked deficiency developing than on a poor thin hungry soil. The vine is a voracious feeder, and to a degree looks after this for itself by considerable annual root extension to satisfy its demand for nourishment. The main root extends downwards through layer after layer of subsoil, the wine gaining added nuances and depth of character as the vine taps deeper sources of nutrient. Vine roots can extend 10 m (30 ft) or more, the greater pursuit after nourishment occurring in the poorer soils where the hungry vine seeks to maintain an even fertility.

The vine demonstrates its well-being or otherwise by the degree of vigour particular to the variety, the leaf colour, and the yield and quality of the grapes.

There are certain vineyards in England where no manure or fertilizer have ever been applied, over as many as 15 years. The soil and subsoil are obviously perfect for wine growing in such cases. Such sites are rare, and in the majority of vineyards a topping up of the nutrient levels is required periodically.

The behaviour of the vine and the leaf colour are the indicators of general health. The vine should demonstrate tremendous growth from budburst to flowering, and each fruiting lateral on mature vines should throw at least two, or even three flower trusses to show that all is well. The fruit buds of any year are laid down in the July of the previous year, and therefore, the weather at that time is critical to the yield of the following year. Hot dry weather is essential for laying down good fruit buds, and cold wet weather hinders the process.

New young leaf colour is always a light fresh green, the colour of young beech leaves, but as summer advances a healthy vine displays a good deep green colour, naturally with varietal variations. Some vine varieties display a grey green colour, others such as Gamay are a more olive green. Should the overall impression of the leaf colour tend towards yellow, then there is a definite deficiency, the type of deficiency dependent upon the particular soil, whether acid or alkaline, impermeable clay or whatever. A cold wet spring can cause vine leaves to remain yellow, a condition that will alter the minute the weather warms up, so do not worry unless this pale colour lasts into summer, in which case it could be nitrogen deficiency.

Manure

Manure raises the humus content of the soil, and is an especially valuable addition to clay and sandy soils. The humus improves the friability and drainage of the soil, and thus enables the nutrients to be more readily available to the roots.

On hungry soils a light dressing of well-rotted manure may well be needed every two or three years, less often on fertile soils. The vine does not need a high nitrogen diet, or it will grow masses of sappy cane, and little or no fruit. Use no artificial nitrogen, unless the vines show a total lack of energy – in which case only use the artificial if manure or compost is unobtainable. Manure also contains other nutrients including trace elements.

Liming

The great majority of vines are happiest in an alkaline environment the one exception being Siegerrebe. Should the vineyard soil be acid, then the lime can be added and rotovated into the soil before planting. Thereafter the soil can be dressed annually, biennially, or at longer intervals so that the pH or acid balance of the soil can be maintained. It is advisable to add lime at the opposite season to manure, so if the vineyard is dressed with one in the autumn, dress with the other in the spring.

The ideal pH to aim for is in the region of 6.5–7.0. One can either use magnesium limestone or straightforward hydrated lime. The former has the advantage of added magnesium. Do not give established vines a dollop of lime right onto the stem of the vine, but dress the whole area around the vines, so that the lime will percolate through the soil to the delicate peripheral feeding roots, and be quickly absorbed. Test the pH of the soil regularly each year so that a lime deficiency can quickly be corrected. Lime is essentially a soil sweetener, a soil adjuster; by raising the pH or calcareous content of the soil, the plants that prefer an alkaline environment will function at the best of their ability. A very chalky or limestone soil, or indeed over-liming, can lock up the magnesium, the most important trace element. This can also happen with an overdose of potash or phosphorus.

Magnesium

Should the leaf display a yellowing of the area between the veins, which remain green, then a magnesium deficiency is indicated, a condition that is very common with vines in a highly calcareous soil, or a soil that has recently been heavily limed. This condition is easily rectified by the application of one ounce of Epsom salts to each gallon of water per yard, which will produce a quick return to normal. Alternatively magnesium sulphate (Epsom salts) can be applied in its crystalline form directly to the soil by hand, or mixed in with the regular mildew and botrytis preventative spraying, 2 oz per 3-gallon knapsack sprayer load.

Potash

The needs of the vine once it begins to crop need to be carefully watched. To produce flowers and fruit a plant needs a good supply of potash; a dressing of 2–3 cwt of sulphate of potash per acre in late February will take care of this problem. Potash is also a necessary aid to sound hard wood ripening in autumn, and the spring dressing will cover this need too.

In the days before bagged chemical fertilizers, farmers used assiduously to collect all wood ash from the fire-places, and from burnt hedge-trimmings, and put it in an Ash House, a small purpose-built building in the yard usually close to the back door of the farmhouse. In the spring the wood ash was used to dress the fields, probably in rotation, for wood ash is rich in potash and in lime, and also the charcoal is excellent for sweetening the soil.

Today, when we are returning to burning wood rather than oil in our homes, we should make use of this valuable by-product. Collect the wood ash in strong plastic sacks, and use it as a spring dressing in the vineyard, noting the area or rows treated, so that a different area can be dressed each year. The value of wood ash and charcoal is much greater than the bagged substitute.

In areas of the country where Dutch Elm disease is rife, the trees should be felled, and the larger wood cut up for firewood, and the lesser wood burned, and the resulting ash re-cycled. Wood ash is also of great value in the vegetable garden, particularly to asparagus, broad, French and runner beans.

Do not dress Siegerrebe vines with wood ash due to the lime content.

Comfrey

Comfrey is another valuable source of potash, and also of nitrogen. Comfrey is a robust energetic plant that is found along river and stream banks, and it can be cut down to within 5 cms of the ground in late April or early May, again at the end of June, the end of August and lastly in October. Planted to windward of the vines, and planted several rows deep, Comfrey forms an excellent windbreak, especially if in alternate rows the plants are placed to cover the gaps in the row in front and behind. Feed the Comfrey with deep-litter chicken manure, and you will have unlimited green manure of tremendous nutritional value with which to mulch the vine rows. With the ever soaring cost of artificial fertilizer it will pay growers of all crops to think more about supplying their own manure and compost. As the Comfrey rots it releases as much potash as a dressing of sulphate of potash, and also a low ratio of nitrogen.

Phosphate

Phosphate is necessary for respiration, photosynthesis, and converting starch into sugar. Phosphate, applied in the form of super phosphate, can be added to the spring dressing if the grower elects to nourish his vineyard with chemical fertilizer. If compound fertilizer is to be used, choose one that has no nitrogen, is high in potash and moderate in phosphate content. The letters on the fertilizer bags denote the levels of the different elements inside – N is for Nitrogen, P is for Phosphate and K is for Potash. Alternatively the elements can be purchased separately, and mixed by the grower to the proportions he wants for his particular vineyard. Look for 0–10–20 or 0–15–25.

Zinc and Boron

Zinc and boron are again essential requirements for a vigorous flowering and successful pollination. Zinc is easily applied in the form of the routine anti-mildew spray Zineb. Apply two or three times before flowering, and also with sulphur for all subsequent sprays.

Boron

Boron as Solubor *is compatible with the following:*
  Fungicides.
  Benomyl, Copper Bordeaux, Dinocap, Maneb, Sulphur, Mildothane, Thiram and Zineb;
and *is not fully compatible with*
  manganese sulphate, zinc sulphate and Simazine;
and finally Solubor *is not compatible with*
  zinc arsenate, calcium arsenate, also oil and oil based materials.
  Boron normally occurs in soils of low pH of 3.5–4.5, but can also be found in neutral and alkaline soils. Usually deficient in the south west.
  Early and distinctive signs of boron deficiency is the development of a mottled chlorosis from the leaf margins, as the deficiency becomes more acute the cholorotic areas spread and become necrotic. In more severe cases the young leaves may be deformed, small and brittle. In due course the growing tips of the shoots die and sub-laterals form. Vines with boron deficiency suffer shoot restriction and display short, thick internodes. The symptoms as described are more likely to occur after flowering.
  Boron deficiency also causes a considerable reduction in fruit set, or poor pollination, giving bunches with berries of varying sizes, some normal and others small and seedless and failing to develop. This is known as millerandage or 'Hen and Chickens'. Many west-country soils are boron deficient. Signs of boron deficiency in other plants, which may prove useful as an indicator, are canker and die-back in apples and die-back in ornamental cherry trees.
  Boron should be applied once, as a foliar spray prior to flowering at the three-leaf stage. Do not under any circumstances apply at a stronger dosage than recommended, or boron toxicity can occur. Put 5 cc (1 heaped teaspoon) of boron into each 3 gallons of fungicide applied prior to flowering.
  Boron or borax can be acquired in a soluble form known as Solubor from Borax Consolidated Ltd, Borax House, Carlisle Place, London SW1. Application rate is 2–3 lb per acre, or $1\frac{1}{2}$-2 oz per 5 gallons of

water. The west-country agent is Edwin Tucker of Crediton and Ashburton.

Coulure and Millerandage

Coulure and millerandage are all too common in British vineyards. Coulure involves the abortion of the fruit embryo prior to flowering, and millerandage, (hen and chickens), is symptomatic of very poor pollination or fruit set, and results in a few of the berries in each bunch setting and swelling normally, the remainder staying the size of pinheads.

Coulure makes is presence known by a sudden browning off and shrivelling of the embryo flower shoot, and can be caused by potash, zinc or boron deficiency, sometimes by lack of lime in an acid soil. The symptoms are similar to an attack of botrytis, in which case the browned dry and shrivelled flower shoots drop to the ground. The preventative treatment is to spray with Zineb at least twice before flowering, and adding 5 cc (1 oz) of boron to every three gallons of spray, and to prevent botrytis from aborting the flower sprays, apply either Elvaron or Bravo before flowering.

Recipe for Spray, applied 10 days before flowering

Add to each 3 gallons of water:	Add to 300 litres of water:
2 oz Sulphur	40 oz sulphur
1 oz Zineb	20 oz Zineb
1 oz Elvaron or Bravo	20 oz Elvaron or Bravo
1 oz magnesium sulphate	20 oz magnesium sulphate
$\frac{1}{2}$ oz copper	10 oz copper
1 oz Solubor.	20 oz Solubor

Millerandage occurs a little later, actually during flowering. By applying the spray cocktail, the vines are brought into optimum nutritional order and thus 'hen and chickens' is less likely to occur. In cold wet weather the caps are unable to jump off the flowers, being damp – they need buoyant conditions. Therefore, the pollen is not released and cannot become airborne, and fertilization cannot take place. Pollination is most successful with a minimum temperature of 18°C (67°F). The caps can and do remain on, and in time botrytis will settle under the caps. In consequence only a few berries in each bunch are pollinated and the vines produce a negligible and useless crop, with few larger than pinheads. Some vines are more susceptible to both these basic functional failures; they are more sensitive to low temperatures, and flowering fails to take place at such times. Müller Thurgau is particularly susceptible, and needs fine dry weather for a decent set. Other vines are less sensitive, Madeleine Angevine, Huxelrebe, Optima, Regner, Kerner, Scheurebe and Reichensteiner for example.

The flowering may take 10 to 21 days, according to temperature and humidity, and can occur in late June, but in most vineyards in Britain begins in the first or second week in July. When weather conditions are perfect, warm, windy and dry, with a shower or so at night to set the

44 Various signs of boron deficiency. The first diagram shows the short, squat internodes, the second the gaps that form in the pith of the vine shoots. The third shows the short internodes at the growing tip which distorts and fails to extend. The fourth shows boron deficiency in a leaf: the leaves are always small, they lack definition and lose chlorophyll in the areas between the veins. The berry shows russeting on the skin when ripe, significant of boron deficiency. This will also happen on apple skins.

blossom, flowering is completed quickly. When it is cold and really wet, flowering struggles on for weeks, and the pollination is poor.

A further hazard can occur when cold wet weather coincides with flowering. During such adverse conditions, the caps often fail to be ejected from the flowers (they need favourable conditions to do so) and when they adhere to the flowers, more often than not botrytis will appear between the caps and the flowers. This forms a source of infection, which can form the breeding ground for a fast outbreak. The value of the anti-botrytis spray prior to as well as following flowering is, therefore, stressed most emphatically. If the vine enters the flowering period fully protected then infection is unlikely to gain a hold and to prevent botrytis from aborting the flower trusses.

Other Forms of Fertilizer for Vines

Alternative organic nitrogenous fertilizers such as hoof and horn, bone meal and fish meal are excellent in that the nutrients are released slowly and evenly over a considerable length of time. Such fertilizers are particularly valuable during the first two years, or at a time when fertility appears to be dropping. They are particularly valuable for indoor glasshouse vines where a slow release of energy is an excellent plan. Indoor vines respond well to a spring application of fresh ox blood or of re-constituted dried blood.

Hoof, horn and bone meal are unfortunately very expensive, but would be a sound investment used as a dressing under newly-planted vines, a handful to each hole.

Spent hops are reputedly an excellent source of nitrogen, again a natural product. Maybe an arrangement with a local brewery whereby a bottle or two of wine might be bartered for the week's spent hops would be an excellent arrangement. Spent hops are reputedly an invaluable addition to potting compost for vines.

The Problem of Extreme Vigour in the Vine

Certain vines exhibit such extreme vigour that they do so at the expense of fruiting. Obviously to plant vines in rich, fertile, energy-laden soil will encourage rampant vigour; such soils should, therefore, be avoided. Another cause can be from nitrogenous fertilizers being spread on land directly above one's vineyard and washing into the vines via natural subterranean drainage.

There follow a few methods of controlling this unwanted vigour which should be adopted at the discretion of the grower according to the degree of the problem demonstrated by the vines. Müller Thurgau is a vine that more often than not shows such tendencies.

1 The grower is advised to omit using any nitrogenous fertilizers; the vine will soon enough make any deficiency apparent should this occur.

2 Lay fresh straw on the ground in every other row. The straw then proceeds to take up nitrogen from the soil in order to break itself down. By laying the straw in every other row you are actually treating all the vine rows. The following year, treat the rows which were untreated the previous year.

3 In August, sow either rape or mustard, preferably the latter, in the rows which were not strawed in the current season. This takes up energy and moisture during the winter, and is then rotovated into the ground in the spring where it again uses up energy and bacteria from the soil as it breaks down and rots.

4 Leave more fruiting buds on the vine by training the canes in a high arch over a wire placed some 30 cm (1 ft) above the bottom wire, and then tie the tip down onto the bottom wire during winter pruning.

5 As a desperate last resort we are advised to cincture or ring bark the fruiting rod that we tie down to the bottom wire in between the third and fourth fruiting cane. A little double-knived tool is available from Germany which enables this task to be done quickly and efficiently.

6 Pinch out the growing tips of the growing fruiting canes after the twelfth to fourteenth leaf exactly one week *prior* to flowering. This increases yield, set and berry size.

7 Top the vines at 1.35 (4 ft) and keep the hedge to this height; the two last points will apparently increase yield by 10 per cent.

This helpful advice was given to a party of East Anglian growers by an expert on vine clonal research from Trier on the Mosel in Germany who visited a Norfolk vineyard late in 1979.

Due to the massive growth surge at this most vigorous time of year, the rootstock renowned for rampant growth, 5BB, will cause mature vines to shed their flower trusses before or during flowering, the florets being unable to cope with this condition.

Seyval and Calcium

The vine Seyval most dramatically drains the soil of calcium which would indicate that a pH test where this vine is planted is an annual necessity. The outcome will more than likely be that vineyards which include this vine will have an annual rather than three-yearly dressing of lime in soils low in lime. The Seyval vine will not prosper in the absence of adequate alkalinity, so this is obviously advice on which one should act. Pinot Noir also crops most dramatically following a dressing of lime, likewise Chardonnay.

Crown Gall

Vines are tolerant of frost in the dormant season down to −18°C, but splitting or even bursting of the bark and trunk can occur when the temperature drops down to −20°C, such as occurred in the January/February frosts in 1979. In Germany the temperature dropped to −25°C and vast areas of vines were lost. This splitting can allow the Crown Gall organisms to enter (*Agrobacterium tumefaciens*), identified by a spongy off-white mass emanating from the damaged area at ground level. This condition is far more likely in a grassed down vineyard, particularly where lush clover is present. Once affected, the vines usually lose all vigour and slowly die.

Towards Achieving Consistent Cropping

When we are fortunate enough to have enjoyed good weather during a given May and June, and these warm buoyant conditions extend through the time during which the vines are in flower and setting their fruit, no problems occur with vine flower production, flowering or pollination. When one poor fruit set and subsequent low yield crop up once in a while, the grower may still feel little cause for alarm. It is only when we experience three or four abysmal crops in sequence that we really panic and begin a frantic search for reasons for yet another partial or even total failure. The years 1977, 1978, 1980 and 1981 presented just this very problem; four years in which the majority of English vineyards produced far lower than average crops, some not even good enough to cover annual costs. Also 1985, 1986, 1987 and 1988.

Before looking into reasons and perhaps remedies for this disturbing trend, we must first put the situation into perspective. We must realize that the vineyards of northern France and Germany also suffered in 1980 in a similar way to ourselves.

The problems of 1980 affected all the winefields of northern Europe. A hot dry early spring brought forth a record number of embryo florets on the vines, a vast crop was predicted. The weather broke in mid-June, giving way to really cold temperatures and almost non-stop rain.

The florets either shrivelled, browned and dropped off with coulure prior to flowering; those florets that survived managed only to fertilize a small proportion of the berries in each bunch, the condition known as millerandage. Therefore the harvest was small and late in Burgundy, Champagne, Alsace, and also in northern Germany. So we in England are by no means alone with our difficulties, and are having to learn to accept that there are unfortunately more poor than good years.

On the Continent hail can and does cause total crop failure, and also the tremendously hard frosts experienced in such winters as 1977 and 1978 were twice as hard in Germany as those that struck Britain, and vast areas of vines were killed outright.

Appreciating that we have shared in years that have also been difficult on the Continent should not however be just cause for complacency. We must ever be looking for ways and means to encourage our vineyards to be more productive in the lean years, and achieve a regularly more consistent yield, and to this end a serious look into how the Continental grower nourishes, sprays and cares for his vines could well be rewarding. Little has been published on the science of feeding of vines in England other than general guidance, which varies widely from pouring on tons of FYM, or tons of artificial fertilizer from a bag, to those that advocate never feeding at all, resulting in no one being any the wiser. Little has been written on the preparation of the vines for flowering, pollination and their needs at this time; much can be done by the grower to assist his vines through this most crucial and critical period.

We should treat every year as if it is going to be a difficult year from budburst through to fruit set, and treat a good year as a real bonus – in this way we will never be caught out should the weather deteriorate during flowering. The vines will more likely manage to meet the demands of their resources and stamina in the best possible physical condition with some reserves to fall back on if needed. Once a good fruit set has been achieved, the grower can for the first time in a given wine growing season relax a little.

A final point must be made before discussing various ways and means by which it is possible to improve vine performance. If your vines are flowering, setting and cropping perfectly adequately, then do nothing to change your methods, you have obviously hit on the correct nutrition and management for your particular site – every vineyard presents differing problems and needs different treatment and care.

It is up to the individual grower to try to pin-point any failing in his own vineyard, and perhaps to put a little thought and effort into removing as many opportunities for failure as possible. There follow a few points on attempting to improve vine stamina and performance; it is hoped that each grower may be able to glean some snippet here and there that might improve their viticultural success rate.

The Lifespan of Vines

It might be helpful to point out that the useful life of a grafted vine is between 20 and 30 years, although many begin to decline from the 15th year. Therefore vineyards planted in the 1960s could well be now showing signs of lessening yield. Vines on their own roots can live and yield 50–100 years or more.

Rootstocks

The different applications and characteristics of a fair range of the more usual rootstocks onto which vines imported into England are grafted are covered in some depth in the appropriate chapter. Suffice to say in the context of this chapter that certain rootstocks have been proved to be unsuitable in the equable, mild, humid climate and fertile, even rich soils of England. Should the rootstock 5BB be planted on any other than on a very poor alkaline soil, this rootstock induces an unmanageable rampant vigour into the vines after several years, usually at the expense of fruit production. Therefore this rootstock should be avoided. 5BB tends to shed flowers and grapes. It also autumns early, thus failing to ripen later ripening grapes.

Nutrition

We learn of the tremendous importance of the vine of potash, an element which encourages the production and setting of the flowers of the vine, also the production and ripening of the fruit and, of *paramount* importance, encourages splendid wood ripening. Even if soil tests show sufficient potash present in the vineyard soil, an annual early-spring dressing is still recommended of sulphate of Potash.

Research with apples has shown that trees grown in a soil showing nitrogen deficiency suffer with a high percentage of degeneration of the embryo-sacs of the flowers before they reach the egg-cell stage. Apparently nitrogen increases female fertility. Advice on the timing of fertilizer application varies, but in general an early-spring dressing seems to be the most valuable. It can either be organic, which also benefits the soil structure, or a bagged chemical fertilizer with a nil N rating, moderate P and high K formula, 0–10–20 for example.

Zinc also has a vital part to play in the formation of good flower trusses and encourages a good set; this is best applied in the form of Zineb or the more expensive Dithane as a constitutent of the regular spraying programme alongside sulphur. Magnesium and boron deficiencies must also be watched for keenly. These chemicals can either be incorporated in the spray since magnesium sulphate and Solubor dissolve easily, or alternatively they can be applied to the soil direct, along with the fertilizer in early spring – apparently fertilizer especially formulated for sugar beet has boron included. Boron is only needed in minuscule amounts, an overdose is far more harmful than a deficiency.

Pollination

We have not studied the actual flowering and fertilization process with vines in any great depth in England to date. Therefore to study the results of the splendid scientific work done on apples and pears in this field may well give us some invaluable guidelines for a better understanding, and perhaps help improve the fruit set and yield with our vines.

The vine flower is most obviously designed for wind pollination by virtue of its shape, whereas the apple flower being situated within a wide saucer of petals is designed for insect pollination. Therefore a site that offers a really good fresh air-flow is a must – avoid small sheltered hedged paddocks. A vine flower is totally unprotected, having no petals, therefore under favourable conditions flower set will be quickly achieved given a good air-flow; a balance must be allowed, however, between air flow and row spacing so that in poor weather conditions during pollination some shelter is provided to improve the climate and warmth within the vineyard by the proximity of each row to its neighbours. A good air-flow helps to avoid mildew and botrytis by eliminating still, stagnant air.

Apparently the micro-climate, an improved climate created by the plants themselves within the vineyard, is lost once the vine rows are wider than 2 m (6 ft) apart, so here we have the first guideline.

Windbreaks

It is accepted that exposure and wind are the worst enemies of a vineyard. Therefore should natural shelter be insufficient, then a quick-growing hedge of plants that creates a filter rather than a solid barrier is advised. An evergreen such as *Cupressus lawsoniana* or *C. leylandii* is very efficient, the latter being extremely fast growing. Privet is also evergreen and forms a thick low hedge fairly swiftly. Blackcurrants make a fairly good hedge and also yield a valuable crop of fruit; though not evergreen, they provide good summer and autumn protection, like-wise basket willows which are very quick-growing and provide a good crop of wood for basket making each winter. Poplars are another choice, but ultimately growing very high should only be planted where a very tall windbreak is required. Italian alders are widely used.

It must be emphasized that a filter effect is essential so that an air flow, albeit slower and warmer, is maintained.

Frost

We have learned the hard way that a pre-blossoming frost can be disastrous, a frost which strikes after bud-burst and when the young shoots are developing. This is the most usual cause of ovule sterility. Even low temperatures near to freezing can cause partial or even total sterility.

Temperature

Temperature during pollination and fertilization is absolutely crucial; apparently fertilization can only take place when the temperature is 10°C (50°F) or over. In Germany 55°F is considered essential. The lower the temperature the greater the decrease in the 'effective pollination period' recorded for each flower. In a year when cold wet conditions

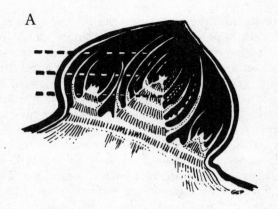

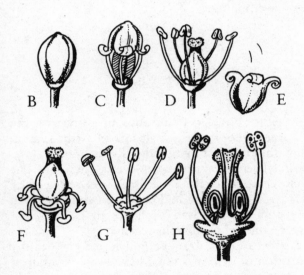

45   **A** Showing a section through a vine bud; the main cane is formed in the centre where the leaves and the embryo florets can be seen, at the side are the side shoots or sub-laterals.   **B** A single flower seen before flowering with the cap still firmly in place.   **C** The cap or corolla just about to be ejected by the developing stamens beneath.   **D** A normal vine flower, with well developed stigma and ovary and erect stamens, which expel pollen into the air and thus to the waiting ovary beneath; such flowers are self-fertile.   **E** The cap falls to the ground.   **F** A female flower, showing imperfect stamens which are less likely to be able to pollinate the ovary.   **G** A male flower, perfectly developed stamens but no stigma or ovary – therefore no grapes.   **H** A section through a single flower showing the pollen tubes and the awaiting ovary beneath.   **J** A section through a berry. The pips are seen in the pulp which is enclosed by the skin or epidermis.

prevail doggedly throughout the pollination period, the vines remain in flower longer in a vain hope of a fine day or two, whereas in a year when there is fine breezy weather during this period, the vines can flower, pollinate and set within five to seven days. Under good conditions a high proportion of berries in each bunch set and develop, in wet cold weather we find a low proportion of set berries, many are blind and never form and swell, suffering the condition known as millerandage, or 'hen and chickens'.

Research on varieties discovers certain vine varieties that are less vulnerable to cold wet weather during flowering, several will set a full crop regardless of outwardly impossible climatic conditions. Therefore potential growers have the opportunity of planting élite types of vine and thus avoiding many of the cultural problems outlined in this chapter. This work is covered in the chapter on vine varieties. Nevertheless, it is hoped that growers of all varieties will try all the aids and suggestions that can create more regular cropping.

Pollen

Pollen is the fine pale yellow powdery substance produced by the stamens. It becomes airborne, adheres to and is absorbed by the stigma, fertilizes the ovary and in due course the grape develops.

Pollen soon loses height even in a prevailing wind, therefore one would assume that the closer the vines the more likely they are to enjoy a full set, given good air circulation. The highest pollen concentration occurs in the afternoon; pollen is removed from the air by rain, but more is released within a few hours of the rain ceasing.

Remember that for a good supply of active pollen and for healthy receptive ovules, the nutrition of the vines must have been maintained and peaked as the flowering time approaches. In this way the flowers have the best possible chance of surviving unfavourable weather.

Pollinators

Work on apples has shown that some varieties of apple are sterile with their own pollen. These apples need pollen from other varieties to achieve a set. We also learn that certain varieties are better pollinators than others, and that it is vital to make sure that both regularly come into flower at exactly the same time so that the pollen is available on the day when needed, as pollen effectiveness may well decrease.

Trials have indicated that where pollinators are planted in a long line, hedgerow fashion, only the rows directly adjacent to the pollinators receive sufficient viable pollen to achieve a full set. Rows that are progressively further away set less and less well. Best results are produced where pollinators are planted at ratios of between 1–4 and 1–9 evenly throughout the whole plantation so that all trees have full access to plenty of pollen.

Vines are, we learn, self-fertile, which means vines will pollinate and fertilize with the pollen they produce themselves. Yet research has shown that berry size can be doubled when grapes are pollinated with pollen from other varieties. Also more berries per bunch tend to set. It is of course essential that the two or more varieties flower at the same time. Should a grower decide to plant a pollinator, there are two options open to him. He can plant a grape that can be harvested together with the main grape; the grapes must therefore be compatible and suited to the making of a blended wine. Certain grapes blend well with others, and arguably make a better wine than a single-grape wine.

Otherwise he must mark each row clearly with the vine variety, so the grape pickers have no difficulty in keeping the varieties separate at harvest. In this way all varieties will benefit from the pollen from each other, and the vineyard as a whole should be highly productive.

Trials on apples indicate that there is an incompatability between pollen from parent trees and their offspring, and vice versa. Whether this is so with vines remains to be seen – time will tell. In my trial $\frac{1}{2}$ acre here in Devon where I have planted up to 80 or 90 different vine varieties in 5s, 10s and 25s according to their possible potential, in the nine years, 1979 to 1987, every bunch on all varieties has set well with a full complement of berries, no coulure or millerandage, which backs up the strength of mixed pollen creating a total set, even in poor summers. No drop in potential has been noted between parent and offspring vines, either way.

Avoid planting vines that are prone to biennial cropping, vines that have a tendency to crop every other year; this obviously applies both to the major variety if any, and the pollinators or neighbouring main varieties.

Assisted Pollination

An age-old aid to flower set with fruit trees has been to shake or kick the trees or bushes on the day or days when they are in full flower. This fills the surrounding air with masses of pollen at the right moment, particularly effective if this day should be fine, dry and breezy, a perfect day for pollination.

Another method, and one not to be laughed at, is to arm as many people as possible each with two new clean feather dusters, and walking up and down each row, to dust gently the flowers of the major vine and the pollinator alternately – this will give a 100 per cent set if it can be done on the right day in the right weather, usually the fourth or fifth day the vines are in flower. Remember that indoor vines and indoor peaches are hand pollinated with a soft squirrel paint brush or better still, a rabbit paw. By so doing every single fruit is fertilized. I have found it very helpful to work among the vines, topping and sideshooting on the day the vines are actually pollinating; the extra movement helps to activate and spread the pollen grains from vine to vine.

The Value of Zinc

The inclusion of zinc in the form of Zineb in all sprays, which are applied to the vines every 10–14 days from budburst to flowering, together with sulphur, ensures that this vital chemical is present in sufficient quantity to meet the rising demand for it, which peaks at flowering. The presence of zinc goes far in the prevention of coulure and millerandage, conditions caused by nutritional deficiencies which can occur in any year, but are more likely, indeed often unavoidable with certain varieties when flowering coincides with abysmal weather conditions.

The most vital zinc spray is that applied just seven days before the vines come into flower. Should you calculate or guess this to occur on a certain day, and apply the spray accordingly seven days beforehand, and then the weather deteriorates, and flowering is postponed, should you have vine varieties that are prone to coulure or millerandage, then the only course is to go out and spray again. If your effort can save an aborted crop then this effort is well worth while.

Stopping or Topping the Vines

A highly successful aid to a good pollination is to pinch out or cut the growing tips of the fruiting laterals; again this must be done in the week immediately prior to flowering. This checks the upward thrust of growth, and diverts the energy of the plant into the flowering and fertilization process, an aid I have proved to be successful year after year. Swiss, French and American experts recommend this practice. Again, should the weather postpone flowering, then go through the vines again, especially those prone to flowering disorders, and nip out the tops once more. This can be done with secateurs, between finger and thumb, with a grass hook, an electric trimmer or a vineyard hedgecutter.

Some will argue that to stop the vines will encourage lateral or side-shoot growth to start. This will occur, but only sooner rather than later, a small price to pay for a good fruit set. Side shoots are later trimmed back once, maybe twice in a wet year, so that congestion is avoided and air-flow maintained. I find that I visit every vine once a fortnight during the growing season, and have found that to keep my cane height no higher than 1 m (3 ft) by trimming back on each of my visits I keep my vine rows a neat 30 cm (9–12 in) wide, allowing plenty of sun to fall on the developing grapes in each row from early morning to sunset, concentrating the vines' energy into grape production instead of creating yards of unnecessary extension growth. Keeping the tops trimmed gives me riper, mildew- and botrytis-free grapes, sweeter and cleaner than those grown in the vineyards where no growth control is practised.

This is no great involvement; assuming flowering to take place in early July, the vines are therefore topped the first time during the week prior to flowering, a second time in late July, a third time in early August, by which time the growth of the vine is beginning to slow up, and only in a very wet year might a fourth trim be needed in late August, after which extension growth is virtually zero.

Surely nothing is too much trouble if a good yield can be harvested in a year when weather conditions are difficult before and during the flowering period? We all lavish time, effort and money into our vineyards

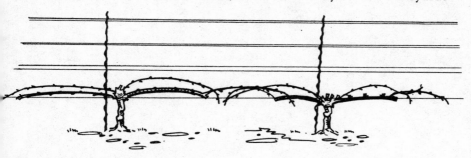

46 Haphazard four rod system used in some English vineyards in an attempt to soak up excess vigour – four fruiting canes from each vine often mostly composed of old wood due to lack of sound ripe young wood. Due to overcrowding and lack of air, pollination is poor and botrytis rife.

with costly fungicides and fertilizers, protective netting against birds, and we fit out expensive wineries to process the grapes, and all too often bring home miserable harvests of $\frac{1}{2}$–1 ton per acre, sometimes less. A better understanding of our vine's nutritional requirements, the function of pollination and the application of a little extra time and care at this crucial time of the whole season could perhaps result in a higher potential achieved by each vine and each acre on a regular basis. I hope that there might be at least just one snippet somewhere in this chapter that will help you, give you food for thought, an idea that you can research by yourself, for we are all learning all the time. Our knowledge at this time could be likened to the tip of an iceberg; we must all be open-minded and try new methods and new techniques each year until we achieve a greater measure of success, and we must share our successes and our failures with each other for the common good. Be ultra-careful not to miss the good moves you may make and build on these, and be energetic enough not to repeat mistakes, but discuss them with others and try to thrash out an answer.

Much vital information can be gleaned from Continental research, but a percentage of problems are those peculiar to England, our soils, our climate and the vine varieties we grow; and also to us. The new English winegrower is in a sense a pioneer; we must maintain an extrovert pioneering spirit, never be satisfied with second best, but always be looking towards bettering our effort and our unique product.

10
A Recommended Spraying Programme

Fungicides, Ancient and Modern

We must accept that the use of fungicides is vital to the health and productivity of the vine. Yet most fungicides have side effects which should be known to the grower. Our old friend, sulphur, has none, but the other age-old fungicide, Bordeaux mixture, in which the active ingredient is copper, will check or halt the development of the vine and the fruit by up to 10 days every time it is applied. Therefore, though we know that copper hardens and toughens the cane and leaves of the vine, and thus protects it from fungal attack, in England, where grapes only just ripen, it is not advisable to spray with copper in late years, or the grapes will stand no chance of ripening at all. In an early year, however, a copper spray in mid-August would be highly beneficial.

Most, if not all, of the modern fungicides actively encourage growth, so that each and every time they are applied one is feeding the vine as well as protecting it against mildew and/or botrytis. Fine if the vine shows a lack of vigour, but adding to the problem if one is trying to cope with the ultra-vigorous vine. In such a situation copper would be a wise move, perhaps in the form of Fungex marketed by Murphy, but only in an early or normal season, not in a late year.

Should a breakdown in control occur, revert to Elvaron at 0.1 per cent. It is safe to use Elvaron in the open vineyard, but under glass it displays phytotoxicity.

Daconil has a very depressing effect on fermentation, and Elvaron an even greater depressing effect. Growers are advised to spray no nearer than 21 days from harvest with *any* spray, including sulphur, for this also can prevent fermentation from beginning. By leaving 21 days it is to be hoped that the repressive nature of these sprays is reduced to negligible proportions.

Oidium and Peronospera

The principle behind forming a spray programme is to provide *preventive control* rather than wading in after mildew or botrytis has gained hold and trying to *correct the outbreak*. Once a fungal outbreak has occurred, given suitable climatic conditions it will spread like wildfire, and it is very *very* difficult to regain control over the problem.

Begin some two or three weeks after budburst in spring, spraying thereafter every 14 days with micronized wettable sulphur and Zineb. A spray every two or three weeks used to be recommended, but it has recently been realized that the effect of the spray wears off within 14 days, and that the development of mildew spores is also a mere 14 days from spore innoculation to outbreak proportions. Many growers use Daconil or Dithane in lieu of Zineb. These are fine products and equally effective, and in fact it is a good principle to vary the products used as a control so that spray immunity is not built up, and also no one chemical begins to become toxic to the vine. With chemical prices soaring like everything else, sulphur and Zineb have been chosen for their reasonable cost and their very considerable control over Oidium (powdery mildew) and Peronospera (downy mildew) respectively. Also Zineb has the added advantage in that it contributes greatly to the ability of the vine to hold its flowers through blossoming and thus encourages a good fruit set. Zinc, the base chemical of Zineb, is the significant factor here.

Botrytis

It has recently been discovered that strains of botrytis are becoming resistent to the three di-carb-oximides, Rovral, Ronilan and Sumisclex, the three relatively new chemicals in use on vines against botrytis. This happened all too recently when the then much heralded Benlate failed to hold botrytis on vines after a brilliant but fairly brief period of control.

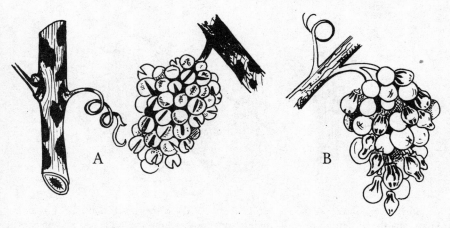

47 There are mildews which attack grape vines.
(A) *Oidium tuckeri* (*Uncinula necator*) known as powdery mildew or Oidium. The
    stems develop dark-grey mouldy patches, the grapes and leaves are affected by a
    fine light-grey powder, which causes the skins of the berries to harden, cease to
    swell and in consequence they split, and the Oidium then gains access to the berry
    interior. The grapes then cease to continue to ripen. Controlled by sulphur.
(B) The second, and less common mildew is known as *Peronospera* (*Plasmopara
    viticola*), called just Peronospera or downy mildew. It is first recognized when dark
    oily translucent patterns appear on the leaves. If allowed to continue, the fungus
    destroys the leaves which cease to nourish the grapes which in turn shrivel, then
    dry up or rot. Controlled by zinc, copper, maneb and other chemicals.

Therefore, in order that we do not lose control of botrytis in a given
growing season, it is recommended that we ring the changes with Rovral,
Bravo, Elvaron and Benlate. Since anti-botrytis chemicals tend to be
used just three, or at most four times a year, it is suggested that one
uses Elvaron or Daconil in the pre-blossom cocktail along with the other
six ingredients, Benlate in the post-blossoming spray together with
sulphur and Zineb, and Rovral in the pre-harvest spray, again with
sulphur and Zineb, so that the botrytis does not have a chance to build
up a resistance to any one chemical.

How long this system will stave off the inevitable evil day when
botrytis becomes totally immune to the present range of deterrents we
do not know, but we can only hope that in the meantime one or
more new and highly effective, long-lasting products will have been
discovered, tested and marketed.

(See Appendix 13.)

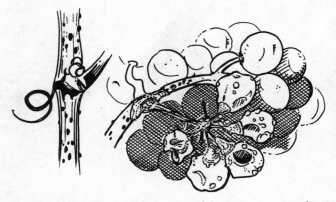

48 Botrytis, the most destructive of all enemies of the winegrower, makes its presence known by the formation of a grey mould on young sappy cane, on leaves and on the berries and bunch stems. The rot quickly cuts through the branch stems, causing berries and entire branches to drop. The drawing shows an affected branch, with botrytis on both stem and berries, some berries having dropped. Cane affected by over-wintering botrytis is a deadly white colour, with the telltale spots of botrytis spores as shown in the drawing.

Warning

Do not spray the vines with fungicides during the heat of the day if the weather is very hot. Sometimes the vine leaves will be burnt by certain chemicals if applied in hot weather, so spray in the morning or in the cool of the evening. Secondly, for applying most chemicals it is recommended that the operator should wear really adequate protective clothing so that no spray comes into contact with the skin. A lightweight green jacket and trousers set, sold to dairymen at farm sale centres, is excellent. Also wear good gum boots, and a mask if spraying high.

Mixing Sprays

All the chemicals listed are compatible one with another in the combinations given. Do not mix chemicals with others not listed without checking with the manufacturers first; this applies equally to fungicides, herbicides and insecticides.

To fill a spray container, first half fill with water, then mix the chemicals together with sufficient water to form a cream, pour the mixture into the sprayer and then top up with the rest of the water. Do not mix and fill the sprayer until you are ready to spray, otherwise the chemicals could well settle to the bottom or separate from one another. Keep on the move to keep the ingredients in suspension.

A Winter Wash

A spray with 2 per cent tar oil applied from mid-December until mid-January will clear the vine of harmful overwintering insects and fungal spores. Unfortunately tar oil also destroys any beneficial insects that might be overwintering on the vines. Tar oil can only be applied to vines during the specified period when the vines are fully dormant, if used later the fruit buds could well be severely damaged. This product is also of great value on glasshouse vines where it can only be used during the month of December. Indoor vines suffer to a far greater degree from insect pests.

Spring Wash

An April spray with copper, with or without sulphur and Zineb, is of considerable value in eradicating the spores of Phomopsis as well as mildew and botrytis spores, thus giving the vines a clean start to the new season. Phomopsis, or 'dead arm', is identified when the vine canes in spring are deathly white in colour, the surface of the cane being covered in tiny brown or black spots; these are the dormant phomopsis spores. Where possible infected canes should be totally removed during winter pruning and burnt immediately.

Standard Spray Base

Spray the vines every 14 days with micronized wettable sulphur and Zineb, a product made from zinc. Use 40 oz of sulphur and 20 oz of Zineb for a 50-gallon sprayer tank, and 2 oz sulphur and 1 oz of Zineb for a 3-gallon knapsack sprayer. Repeat the above spray every 14 days if possible and if the weather allows, until blossoming or flowering is imminent. At this juncture the first spray against botrytis is added to the base spray, plus four other chemicals, the spray cocktail being designed to bring the vine into maximum nutritional condition, by elimination of any deficiencies, in order to encourage a quick and total set of every berry in every bunch. Please refer to Chapter 9 where the reasons for and effects achieved by this specially formulated pre-blossoming spray are explained in fuller detail.

Pre-blossoming Spray

To a 3-gallon knapsack sprayer ...
2 oz sulphur, 1 oz Zineb, 1 oz Elvaron or Bravo, 1 oz Fungez, 1 oz

magnesium sulphate, 1 oz Solubor, and 1 oz Marinure liquid seaweed foliar feed.

Pay extra attention to spraying every embryo bunch and the undersides of the leaves, for it is through the breathing holes or pores on the underneath of the leaves that fungal spores gain entry.

Post-blossom Spray

Again make sure that every minute bunch is drenched with spray, for within a few days after berry set the berries swell so rapidly and begin to touch one another so that it all too soon becomes impossible to coat the interior of the bunch. Use 2 oz sulphur together with 1 oz of Zineb and 1 oz of Benlate per 3 gallons of water; this can be applied once the berries have pollinated, or from 70 per cent caps off. Again pay attention to coating the leaf undersides.

Continue fortnightly with the base spray until three weeks prior to harvest. The proposed harvest date is fairly accurately worked out when one realizes that different vine varieties require a certain number of days from berry set to ripeness, and harvest. Madeleine Sylvaner, the first to ripen, needs only 60 days, Siegerrebe needs 65 days, Madeleine Angevine needs some 70 days, Müller Thurgau requires 90 days and Riesling takes some 110 days. The vines must not be sprayed closer than 3 weeks before harvest, as the chemicals used would have a depressing effect on fermentation, and some taint may remain in the wine through to bottling.

Pre-harvest Spray

To our base spray of sulphur and Zineb add Rovral; 2 oz sulphur, 1 oz Zineb and 1 oz Rovral to each 3 gallons of water. Again drench all the bunches and the leaf undersides, particularly those leaves in close proximity to the fast-developing fruit to protect them through the final four or five weeks up to harvest. Due to the deteriorating weather conditions in October, cooler days and nights, the possibility of torrential rain and high humidity, they are more at risk at this time than at any other.

Certain chemicals, Bravo, Benlate and Elvaron in particular, are residual in wine and can be detected in a finished wine if used near to harvest.

If vines have had fungal problems during the growing season, a spray after harvest with Bordeaux mixture or Murphy's Fungex, both copper based, will clean the vines and help to harden the leaves, and more especially the canes, before winter.

A Cautionary Tale – Herbicides or Weedkillers

Weeds will appear in the months following planting, and can be a fearful nuisance and worry. Roundup, marketed by Monsanto, is your best friend here, for though expensive it goes a long way and is a total killer of anything green it is sprayed upon. Obviously once the vines are in leaf they must be protected, either by polythene sleeve cones, or very careful application with a hood on your knapsack sprayer lance. When spraying with herbicide do not drench the plants until the liquid pours off them, but use minimum pressure so that the nozzle emits a fine gentle mist. Remember that a few droplets on each weed is quite sufficient to kill.

Thereafter if any pernicious weeds such as thistle or docks appear, just go through the vineyard from time to time and spot-spray the culprits. In the fullness of time the vineyard becomes progressively cleaner and less of a problem. Should some such weed as bindweed appear, as it will often do on ground kept clean with herbicides, then again Roundup will squash this invasive monster.

Should you wish to clean up a light covering of small annual weeds, such a groundsel, chickweed, scarlet pimpernel and light annual grasses, then a very light spring clean spray through with paraquat mixed with Simazine will clean up the ground within days, the former burning off the above-ground greenery, and the Simazine spreading a film on the soil through which light annual weeds cannot germinate.

Caution

Never apply any herbicide during very hot still weather, during the hottest time of day, for certain chemicals, notably the more noxious such as hormone weedkillers and the lethal 245T, can vaporize and drift in cloud form through the vines and any other plant or crop area and can kill everything in their path. The winegrower is less likely to be the culprit here than farming neighbours spraying their headlands, or spraying over grassland or stubble prior to ploughing and re-seeding.

Spray damage to vines need not necessarily have been caused by an immediate neighbour, though it is more than likely to be so. In certain weather, wind and temperature conditions, spray droplets can be carried miles, either in a fresh damp wind or in a driving drizzle, and affect tender susceptible plants downwind wherever the poison-laden air next happens to meet a land mass.

The lesson to be learned here is never to use any highly toxic chemicals yourself, and to warn all farming neighbours, even gardeners, any of whom might use weedkillers in fields, on hedgerow weeds, or on paths, of the risk to your vines. Also mention very tactfully, just in passing, that three or more successful actions have been taken against people whose spraying activities have damaged vineyards, and therefore a legal precedent has been made.

A final point, always remember to wear really adequate protective clothing when mixing and applying herbicides; good boots, protective leggings and jacket, rubber gloves, and a deflective mask; never breathe in the vapour or allow chemical to be spilt on any skin. Should you accidentally get any on your skin, wash it off immediately. The same precautions should very especially apply to insecticides, though these are rarely used in vineyards as thankfully we have few insect pests.

Warning

Many growers, both on the Continent and in England, are becoming more concerned by the possible effects of continuous herbicide control over vineyard weeds. In wet years in particular certain chemicals, once applied, tend to wash into the rooting area very swiftly, and the vines may react by taking on a chloritic appearance, or appear to be withdrawing into themselves, producing little new growth and have to be cut back to a single spur in an effort to make them attempt to start living a normal life once more.

An eminent Alsatian grower, president of the association governing all growers in Alsace, told me that he considered we were building up a 60 cm (2 ft) or deeper area of poisoned soil, and in due course would find ourselves in very considerable trouble. He pointed out that he had no intention of finding himself in this situation.

I am informed of the existence of a forest in South Wales that has been kept clean of weeds with herbicides for many years, and that the poison build-up is now so great that the ground is in fact dead, and all attempts to replant this area with young trees fail year after year.

One must point out here that there are many herbicides on the market, some more toxic than others, some with long-lasting effects, some that are safe if used alone but rendered highly toxic if another herbicide is used either with them or applied afterwards. It is claimed that some herbicides are rendered harmless once they touch the ground.

However, I feel that growers should be made aware of the possible problems of relying totally on weedkillers to keep their vineyards clean. It may be cheaper on labour time, and at first sight a quick and easy answer to a major problem. I must also point out that many herbicides do not need to be applied quite as heavily as might seem necessary; a very light spray, just a droplet or two on each plant is often all that is required.

Safe use of Pesticides, Herbicides and Fungicides

On 1 January 1988 certain rules and regulations came into force for all users of pesticides, herbicides and fungicides. All users will have to have a fireproof, spillproof lock-up in which to keep their chemicals, and a separate area where protective clothing used for spraying may be kept. Employers should provide full protective gear for themselves and their employees, from goggles, plastic face visor, mouth and nose respirator, rubber gloves, wellington boots and overalls for use when mixing, applying and cleaning equipment afterwards.

Few of the chemicals we use are toxic, we use few if any insecticides, but certain people are more sensitive and therefore affected by certain materials and could suffer from asthma or eczema. All users should however make themselves aware of the degree of toxicity of the materials they use, and read the labels carefully on each pack where advice should be given on mixing, safety in use and disposal.

A record book must be kept, noting dates of application, weather at the time, and chemicals used, so that when an ADAS officer calls he can be shown the chemical store, clothing and the record book. It is advisable that at least one person from each vineyard should attend an ADAS 'Safe use of Pesticides' course, and obtain a certificate of competance.

To sum up the three major spray Applications:

	For 300 litre tank (50 gallons)	For 15 litre knapsack (3 gallons)
Pre-blossom Spray	40 oz Sulphur	2 oz Sulphur
	20 oz Zinc (Zineb)	1 oz Zineb
	20 oz Magnesium sulph.	1 oz Magnesium sulph.
	20 oz *Elvaron or Bravo*	1 oz *Elvaron or Bravo*
	20 oz Copper (Fungex)	1 oz Fungex
	10 oz Boron (Solubor)	$\frac{1}{2}$ oz Solubor
	20 oz Marinure	1 oz Marinure
Post-blossom Spray	40 oz Sulphur	2 oz Sulphur
	20 oz Zineb	1 oz Zineb
	20 oz *Benlate*	1 oz *Benlate*
Pre-harvest Spray	40 oz Sulphur	2 oz Sulphur
	20 oz Zineb	1 oz Zineb
	20 oz *Rovral*	1 oz *Rovral*
	10 oz Copper*	$\frac{1}{2}$ oz Copper*

NB. The Copper* hardens the grape stems and grape skins and thus goes far in preventing botrytis etc attacking the ripening grapes.

Italics = specific against Botrytis.

11
Insect Pests and Virus Problems

There are comparatively few insect pests that attack vines and grapes in Britain. The Pyrale, Eudemis and Cochylis caterpillars which are such a major curse in Continental vineyards, are fortunately not endemic to Britain.

Red Spider

Starting with the least problematical and most easily eradicated pest first, outdoor vines are sometimes invaded by the red spider mite, normally a pest associated with glass-house crops, such as peaches, nectarines and cucumbers. When really established in a glasshouse, red spider is very difficult to kill. The safe benign insecticides such as derris and pyrethrum will not affect them, and the problems of using the more drastic insecticides to kill a pest on edible crops need very careful research. Gamma BHC cannot be used on grape vines after flowering; it cannot be used on cucumbers at any time, being very poisonous to man and to all domestic pets. In the 1960s a predator of the red spider was discovered, researched and multiplied, and is now available to growers today; it can only be introduced when the temperature is consistently above a certain level, below which these predators would perish. This is certainly the safest and most successful method of dealing with red spider under glass, providing conditions are right. They will consume all the red spider and then die.

In the open vineyard a spray of Malathion is the best control, maybe two sprays will be needed to cope with a later hatching batch of red spider. Remember that malathion is highly poisonous to the operator, and that full protective gear should be worn so that *all* the skin is adequately covered, and also one of the mouth and nose masks worn to protect the face and lungs.

Do not be misled into thinking that the red velvet mite is red spider – the velvet mite is often to be seen in profusion on walls, stone patios, anywhere hot and dry, and is a brilliant red colour, easily visible and very active. This mite is harmless. The red spider mite is much smaller, is brown in colour, and infests the underside of leaves, moves slowly, and is identified by the upper side of the leaves of the affected plant turning a pale silver-yellow colour due to the tremendous sap-sucking capacity of the thousands of red spiders. An eye-glass will reveal the full extent of the infestation. If left unchecked, red spider will kill indoor fruit trees.

Red spider like a hot dry atmosphere, so should not be a problem in the vineyard in a wet year, but, under glass, keep the plants sprayed with the hose daily, and keep the borders and floors damp. It is rarely found in the open.

Vine Scale

The vine scale can be quite a serious pest to wall or indoor vines. They are browny-grey in colour, of an elongated oval shape, and are most noticeable when the female dies, having previously laid her eggs, and leaves her body as a protection over the eggs. At this stage in mid- to late-spring, they are easily seen owing to the white cottony substance surrounding the female's shell, which, when removed from the vine, reveals a reddish interior.

The keen vinery gardener will watch his vines' progress very frequently and examine his vines closely from time to time, keeping a keen look-out for this and other pests.

The scale is most likely to be eliminated by an application of 5 per cent tar oil in late December or early January; do not apply either before or after this date, for this period is the only time of the year when an indoor vine can be said to be dormant. Paint the tar oil solution on to every square inch of vine, taking extra care around all the buds, cracks and crevices.

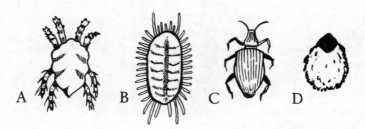

49 Other pests of the vine. **A** The red spider, a highly debilitating pest of the glasshouse, sometimes invading the open vineyard. **B** Mealy bug, a bark sap-sucking pest making the indoor vine weak and unproductive. **C** The vine weevil, which feeds on the roots of the indoor vine. **D** Vine scale.

The best method of control is first to scrape all the old bark off indoor vines each winter, doing so carefully in order that the smooth new wood is not scratched, and then apply the tar oil solution. The insects will, therefore, have no cover under which to hide and evade detection.

If the vine scale is discovered in the growing season, it should be removed carefully with a knife blade or the thumb nail, and destroyed. There is no spray treatment that is strong enough to penetrate these tough customers and is safe to use on a vine in the growing season, particularly if it is carrying bunches of grapes for eating or wine. For identification note the drawing of the vine scale.

The Vine Weevil

This insect used to be a serious pest in glass vineries, but since a vinery is a rarity nowadays, the vine weevil has apparently taken to the big outdoors, and inhabits waste rough ground. It can, therefore, attack both indoor and outdoor vines.

The vine weevil (see drawing), is a menace both in its grub form, when it is a creamy white maggot, about $\frac{1}{3}-\frac{1}{2}$ inch long with a brown head, and in the weevil form, when it is $\frac{1}{2}$ inch long, dull grey-black in colour, and spends the nights in the vine foliage, usually returning by day down to the soil. It moves fast and is to be seen on the underside and upperside of the leaves, and on the rods, and under glass is often to be found on the walls and woodwork.

Signs of the vine weevil's presence are indicated by the edges of the leaves being eaten away, little black specks on the leaves – these are the weevil's droppings, and on closer inspection, of course, the weevil itself, very readily visible.

The indoor vine will also show signs of lack of vigour; this is the effect of the maggot eating the roots. Young vines are particularly vulnerable, and can easily die.

Again the vine weevil is unharmed by such insecticides as pyrethrum or derris, and the grower must exercise great care over which remedy he uses, as the grapes are destined for human consumption. I am told that a dusting of French chalk where the vine enters the soil – across which the weevil must walk as he descends – will kill him. Also in a vinery known to house this pest, French Chalk should be dug into the soil in spring when the soil is scraped away prior to applying the spring dressing of manure, bonemeal, hoof and horn, and sulphate of potash.

An outbreak can be controlled by using Gamma French chalk in the manner described, and also by going over the vines both by day and at night with a torch, and taking the weevils off the foliage and killing them.

Great care should be exercised in the use of these chemicals; never allow them to touch your skin, or that of your animals; wear a mask so that no powder or vapour is inhaled; never use them near fish, or near any extra-tender sensitive fleshy plants such as tomatoes, cucumbers, peppers, etc., or near any developing fruit or vegetables you propose to eat.

Erineum Mite

The erineum mite causes green blisters on the upper side of affected vine leaves, and in the indentations on the underside of these leaves will be seen a white down in which the mite lays its eggs. It does not generally cause enough of a problem to require a spray of pesticide. Be careful not to confuse this comparatively harmless mite with phylloxera.

Phylloxera (The Grape Louse)

Phylloxera, introduced into Europe from the United States in 1863, slowly but surely laid waste almost all the vineyards in Europe, ruining the winegrowing economy. The phylloxera, or *Phylloxera vitifoli*, more usually known as *Phylloxera vastatrix*, is an aphid, and during its life-cycle lives on the roots of the vine as well as on the leaves, stems and flowers. The drawings show the root galls and leaf galls of this pest, and a likeness of the aphid.

This pest apparently injects a poison into the roots of the vine, the European vines cannot take this treatment, and fold up and die. The native American vines, being so much more vigorous, both above and below ground, and having a vast fibrous root system anyway, seem immune to the poison, and, when a root is severed, throw out many new roots from the wound. The European vine, on the other hand, forms three or four major roots from the base of its stem, roots which thrust deep before dividing and, therefore, when one or two of these main roots are eaten through the vine is immediately seriously debilitated. The only situation in which European vines are immune is when they are planted in sandy soil, or in a river-bank site when the soil is often in a semi-waterlogged condition. The phylloxera cannot exist in either.

Also the beast apparently likes the flavour of the foliage of its native host, and thus concentrates less on the roots, whereas it dislikes the foliage of the European Vinifera, and concentrates its voracious appetite

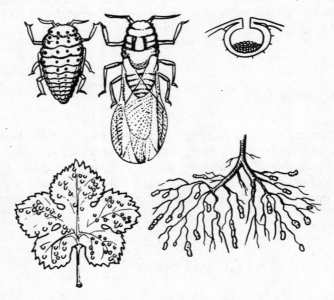

50 The *Phylloxera vastatrix* in its various forms; first the wingless female from the vine root, secondly the winged female, the flying form. Thirdly a section through a root gall showing the eggs. Next shows the galls on the underside of the leaf, and lastly nodosites caused by this most deadly parasite on the roots of the vine.

on the roots. Therefore, the European Vine suffers to a greater degree, and usually fatally.

Since phylloxera has been discovered in at least four vineyards very recently in England, it rests with the grower as well as the importer to check carefully where those vines come from and enquire into the precautions taken to prevent the introduction of pests and diseases into our vineyards. Phylloxera is a notifiable pest, and could result in part if not all of a vineyard being grubbed. Above all avoid accepting 'Kartonagen' vines, vines imported in cardboard tubes full of a rooting medium, for this soil-substitute could harbour eggs.

To attempt to make really sure, a grower should rinse newly-imported vines in a solution of insecticide, before planting. Lindane would be the most effective chemical – German research has been done on this, so this is good advice. To dip the tops, (not roots) in a solution of lime sulphur would ensure that one was not introducing any mildew or botrytis in overwintering form. Tar oil at 2 per cent solution is an excellent winter wash, but can only be used from mid-December to mid-January, otherwise it will damage the vine buds. Tar oil can only be used when a plant is totally dormant.

There is no compensation from the Ministry of Agriculture should an outbreak occur, so examine newly-arrived grafted vines well for swellings on the roots, and also think very seriously about insuring your vineyards against phylloxera infestation, for should an outbreak occur the powers that be may well decide to grub up the vineyard and destroy the vines.

The presence of phylloxera first shows in summer. The leaves of an affected vine take on a red colour, and by the end of August the fruit fails to develop and dries up. On examining the roots one will see some yellow aphids, and there will be swellings on the roots. By winter the laterals will be brittle and dry, the vine is dying and will have died by the following summer. When any animal or plant dies, its parasites depart immediately. Phylloxera is no different – none are found on the roots of vine that has died.

To conclude, do not become neurotic about this pest, infestation is extremely unlikely. Vines can and do fade and die for no visible reason, often reckoned to be waterlogged roots. If galls are discovered on the leaves, if they are hard on the top of the leaf and extend under the leaf it is the gall of the vine leaf midge. The phylloxera gall is on the underside of the leaf, covered in coarse hairs, and has an entrance slit in from the surface, and would contain one or two legged aphids.

Clear Droplets on Leaves and Canes

When small transparent globules are discovered on the edges of the vine leaves and on the younger green cane, mostly in spring and on new growth, this is not a disease or a pest, but merely the vine ridding itself of excess moisture. This situation will right itself as the vine growth extends, and the vine is able to cope with all the moisture taken up by the roots.

Virus Conditions

Though not a pest, but an inbuilt or contracted condition, it seems a good place to include a paragraph or two about virus diseases, since they can be spread from vine to vine by insects. There are several virus conditions from which the vine suffers, but only three which need concern the British grower.

51 The vinegrower's friends. The larva, pupa and adult ladybird: larva and pupa are a dull grey-black, with pale yellow markings.

It would pay growers to be more careful about the source of the vines they order from the Continent, for there are an equally large collection of vine nurserymen with less stringent principles as there are top-class producers, as indeed there are in any walk of life. Another important point is that one must be equally insistent on trying to plant only virus-free stock, for should vines carry any virus, they cannot but perform at a much less than full cropping ratio, and will produce less sugar than grapes from virus-free vines. Also, insects can carry virus from infected to virus-free stock, be they underground eelworms or flying or hopping leaf eating insects.

The Germans are researching the problem very intensively, and can now offer proven virus-free vines. The French are not anywhere near on top of the problem yet, indeed most of the great winefields are affected by virus, Burgundy and Bordeaux in particular. It is virtually impossible to stamp it out, for as soon as a grower grubs and replants his vineyard with virus-free vines, they are re-infected from their neighbours on all sides. A heartbreaking situation – with no solution.

One should never propagate from vines affected by virus. One nursery in England used to regularly offer rooted Chardonnay vines affected with leaf roll virus which is extremely naughty, as this action must have spread this virus to many hundreds of sites.

Leaf Roll Virus (*Not* transferred from one vine to another)

The least serious disease is leaf roll virus, which shows during the late summer. The lower leaves of the vine yellow, and the outside edges of the leaves roll inwards in a fairly loose roll. This occurs before normal autumnal yellowing of the lower leaves. Leaf roll virus results in lower yield and lower grape sugar assimilation. The vines should not be used for propagation, and should be dug up carefully to try to remove all of the root system, and then burnt. New vines may be replanted immediately in the gaps.

Fan Leaf Virus (*Court Nouie*)

Fan leaf virus is a far more serious affair, in that the vine with this virus degenerates, and it is highly contagious to other vines, spread by insect vectors. This virus is identified by the leaves failing to develop to their normal size, and distorting to look like a frilly-edged fan. The internodes fail to extend fully, and develop in a shortened zig-zag fashion, hence the French name for this disease, *Court Nouie*, or short joint. The vines must be dug up, again trying to remove all the root system, and burnt, and no vine should occupy the area for many years as any root left in the soil can re-infect a new planting, and the virus will live for years. There is a suspicion that *Court Nouie* has a direct link with phylloxera.

Spray drift from hormone or other noxious weed killers can cause leaf distortion similar to fan leaf, a condition that will right itself in time if the outbreak has not been sufficient to kill the vine. Remember that spray drift would follow spray being used nearby, and a large number of vines could be affected, so again do not panic, but look for the more likely cause before suspecting the worst. Spray drift *can* be carried several miles on a strong wind, though it is more likely to have been used nearby, and to windward of the affected area in the vineyard.

There have been two instances where vine growers have won their cases against neighbours who have damaged their vines with spray drift. Therefore, a precedent has been made and compensation can be claimed and awarded.

Mosaic Virus

The next virus is Mosaic Virus, identified by *one* side of each leaf being slightly distorted, less well endowed, smaller; all the leaves are smaller than usual, and have a yellowing tinge. This is again a debilitating condition, the vines will not function or crop to anywhere near full capacity and they should be grubbed and burned immediately. Do not replant directly into ground vacated by Mosaic Virus affected vines.

With time, a grower who really cares for his vines, and is in the vineyard every day, will begin to notice the slightest sign of ill health, infestation by insect pests, also of lack of vigour, deficiency and any mineral imbalance, and also given time will be able to identify the problem and know which remedial action to take. Always look for the simple answer and remedy first, do *not* panic; the list of horrors looks pretty daunting but most problems are comparatively rare. The problems have to be listed and described in order that a grower may be able to run down and identify the trouble and quickly take the correct course of action.

Entipiose

Etipiose is a virus which causes a vine to display poor vigour early in the season, and then suddenly all the leaves brown and die, and the vine dies in July or August. Dig the vine up and burn it, and do not replant in that situation for 2–3 years. The virus is becoming a very serious problem in Europe, and large areas of vines are becoming devastated.

12

The Bird and Wasp Problem

Provided the grower can keep rabbits and deer from eating his vines by means of a protective outer fencing, the vineyard remains relatively free from predators until the grapes begin to ripen in late summer. The annoying and costly factor here is that both birds and wasps will attack and consume the grapes, the entire crop if left unheeded, well before they are ripe enough to harvest. Therefore, on most sites steps have to be taken to protect the grapes from attack.

On the Continent the problem rarely arises, if it does it does to a far lesser degree. The winegrowing areas there are vast, covering many thousands of acres in many cases, so that the birds make little or no impression, whereas in Britain a single vineyard of a few acres stands out as a glaring invitation to all the blackbirds in the entire district. Secondly on the Continent there is no law and few scruples against shooting or trapping birds, so the grape grower is doubly protected. The French in particular are renowned for their love of shooting anything that moves, song birds included.

However, on the Continent certain areas do have problems with birds. In the Champagne areas the growers use brightly coloured plastic sacks, which they cut into strips long-ways on, leaving an inch or two uncut at the top, so that the sack has the appearance of a plastic curtain such as one might see at the entrance of a downtown café or barber's shop. The sack is then suspended between two tall poles on a length of nylon cord, and it dances and swirls in the slightest breeze.

In Germany the early-ripening grapes are protected against bird attack by running lengths of plastic netting down the entire run of each row; the netting, about 1 m in depth, is attached above and below the area in which the grapes are borne, thus enclosing this area within a protective envelope. I have taken this idea one step further in my vineyard in Devon, by purchasing netting sufficiently fine to defeat both birds and wasps, the latter being attracted to my early-ripening Siegerrebe and other early grapes, due to their glorious aroma. The netting is 1 m deep, and 30 m long, and two strips are used for each row, being attached, with paper or plastic covered wire plant ties, one to the other above the second wire through the fruiting rods. It is then 'moored' to the ground either side of each row of vines by stones, and it therefore forms a long tent-shaped structure, tied round the end posts, and neither wasp nor bird can gain entrance. An added bonus is that when one rolls the nets up during harvest, there are no inebriated wasps waiting to sting the fingers of the unwary grape pickers.

The nets need to be put on after the last spray, about three weeks before harvest, so that the precious crop, which has taken so much time and effort to bring to this stage, can be picked sound and in its entirety. One has the added advantage in that should the October weather be really good the grapes can be left on the vine to become superbly ripe without fear of any damage.

Many English vineyards are completely netted over like a vast fruit cage; for many, where there is sufficient manpower to sew the giant nets together and haul them into place, this is the best method. Once in position, usually supported by cross wires run across the top of the trellis posts 2 m above ground level, the grape pickers can move about with ease without having to be permanently bent double. Obviously the vineyard will have to be protected at the ends and sides as well as above.

Certain nets are sensitive to the sun and have a built-in obsolescence, nets of Ulstron and polythene for example. The best nets are made of plastic, and will, with care, last for a great many years.

In Germany starlings are the main problem. Long, long lengths of yellow plastic strip are strung above the vineyards, the same material as the orange plastic strip used by council roadmen in Britain to surround and show up areas under repair. Apparently the colour yellow is disliked by the starlings, and the plastic tape, which is twisted for extra effect and moves and dances to every breath of wind, is really effective.

In Britain several vineyards use the Av-Alarm, a battery-operated device that emits, at intervals, ear-splitting oscillating sounds that are so disturbing to the hearing of the birds that they keep well out of range. This instrument could only be used in vineyards well away from human habitation. Another sound device has been introduced that repeats the alarm call of blackbirds at intervals, which is another good principle. One hopes the vinegrower remains sane!

One can also use rope bangers, designed to scare pigeons and rooks from farmers' crops. There are also two different painted metal bird scares, one fairly substantial, standing on a tall post, the other much like a car fan, the vanes painted red and white alternately, and both are wind operated.

Several growers have found Croptect Humming Line stretched between the tops of six foot bamboos lashed to trellis endposts to be effective in keeping birds away. The tape emits a high pitched hum with every breath of air. The very realistic plastic kestrels are an excellent bird deterrent, whether suspended on top of a pliable fibre glass rod, or suspended between two high bamboos along a length of fine nylon twine. Move daily.

There are therefore, quite a fair collection of aids that can be adopted as an alternative to netting. Backed up by a dawn patrol with shotgun and dog, and using a variety of bird-scaring devices, changed frequently so that the predating birds never become used to any one deterrent, the grower has a fair chance of protecting the crop of grapes and of avoiding the use of netting.

There is, of course, no sure substitute for netting-in the entire vineyard, or netting each row. Birds quickly become used to scarers, and unless one rings the changes frequently they can cause havoc in a very short time. Therefore, unless the grower is on hand at all times during the last month leading up to harvest, the only insurance against damage is effective netting.

Should wasps be a considerable threat, the first step is to discover the wasp nests. By walking the area between the vineyard and any likely grassy banks or hedgerows, one has a fair chance of seeing the wasps flying into their homes as dusk approaches. If the entrance to the nest is discovered, one can pour paraffin into the hole at night, after having first dampened the surrounding area to prevent any risk of fire, and then drop a match down the hole. The wasp nest is not unlike a spherical bundle of paper, and will instantly burn up, destroying the occupants. It is no good burning the nest in the day as all the wasps will be out and about.

Place narrow-necked jars half-full of ordinary beer along the perimeter of the vineyard nearer the banks where the wasps are likely to live – these will attract the wasps before they reach the grapes. Some say cider is better than beer, others use honey or jam – but beer is hard to beat. Empty and refill frequently because the attractive aroma of fresh beer or cider soon lessens.

Should wasps be a major problem, and the grower wish to crop early-ripening grapes to be sure of a really viable crop each and every year, then he should net each row with net fine enough to keep wasps out – clipped together with twistits above the middle wire, anchor to the ground with stones, and your grapes will be completely protected.

To sum up, keep a keen eye on the movements of the birds as the grapes approach ripeness, and be prepared with one deterrent system or another to protect the crop before any damage occurs. Realize that protection will be a necessity, have it to hand in good time to avoid the inevitable panic-buying rush at the last minute.

13

White Wine Production

There are two main categories of vine grower; first there are those whose satisfaction lies in seeing the whole process through on their own premises, following the growing of the grapes with the making of the wine. The wine, the end product of a full 12 months effort, is therefore able to be described on the label as 'estate grown and bottled'. There is a certain pride in producing one's own wine, and it is particularly satisfying should that wine earn widespread customer approval and demand, and also perhaps do really well in national and international competition.

Other growers are perfectly content to commission others to make their wine for them, whether they choose large organizations like the Three Choirs Vineyard, Newent, Glos, or opt to have the wine made in local wineries, where the resident grower may offer his facilities and expertise to several other growers in the vicinity. The wine is then fermented, matured, filtered and bottled, and returned labelled, corked and capsuled to the grower – an excellent service.

There are those who are quite content never to make their own wine, but to have it made professionally for them every year. Others, new to growing wine, opt to take advantage of such a service until such time as they can afford to equip a winery of their own, or until they feel sufficiently confident to tackle the processes and chemistry involved in making fine wine. This allows for total expenditure to be spread over a longer period and some returns to be made from the sales of their wine before embarking on the second phase of expense in setting up a winery.

Whichever course a grower decides upon, there is the actual physical problem to overcome of transporting the grapes from the vineyard to the winery in a sound condition. To a winery on or near the vineyard the task is an easy one, but if the grapes are to be delivered for processing some 50, 100 or 200 miles away, then the problem of containers arises.

In Champagne the grapes are picked into wooden trugs and are transported in large wicker baskets from the vineyard to the press house. Some English growers transport tons of grapes packed into wooden tomato boxes, ideal because they stand well above one another when stacked, and allow the air to circulate. Others use the Allibert plastic crates similar to milk crates as these also stack well and encourage adequate air access. Do not make the mistake of transporting your grapes in plastic sacks or plastic dustbins for any distance, for the mass of fruit matter will begin to heat like a compost heap, and begin to rot and deteriorate very fast indeed. Many have made this mistake, and the wine carries a taint, an off-flavour that cannot be removed. Also do not use the modern grey fibre glass cold water tanks for transporting, for they can also taint the grapes irreparably. Use no metal other than stainless steel.

Most English growers who process on their own premises pick into taint-free plastic buckets, tipping the grapes into taint-free plastic crates placed in a linkbox or on a trailer behind a tractor, and the grapes are then taken immediately to be processed. Any delay between picking and processing and the grapes will begin to deteriorate.

Yeast

Ten or more years ago research was being done on selecting strains of wine yeast capable of starting and maintaining wine fermentation at a very low temperature. This process was pioneered at the German State wine Institute at Neiderhausen in the Nahe valley where it is taken to its furthest extreme; the fermentation cellar is maintained at 0° Centigrade, the action of fermentation keeps the wine at 4°C, thus prolonging the ferment for many weeks, even months. The more delicate aromas and flavours are therefore retained, and *not* boiled away as they are during a swift vigorous fermentation. The wine is subsequently kept cold through maturation and bottling, and retains the most exquisite youthful freshness throughout bottle life, often with a touch of spritz or effervescence which is dissolved carbon dioxide within the wine.

Such a yeast is SIHA, selected by Professor Fritz Zimmerman of Darmstadt University, a remarkable yeast. Marketed in $\frac{1}{2}$ kilo vacuum packs in granular form, simply mix the required amount of yeast with a little grape juice half an hour before inoculation, when it is poured into the vat. It encourages a quiet steady bottom fermentation with just a rim of bubbles around the edge of the vat, ferments to dryness, and settles to a firm cream cheese consistency on the bottom of the vat, with no unstable flocculent layer, enabling one to pump off the clear wine, leaving less than an egg-cup full of wine in the process. And above all, it will maintain fermentation at a mere 5°C–7°C. Another good yeast is the Swiss Novo Yeast.

The cool of cold fermentation process is now practised world-wide, in California and Oregon, in Australia and New Zealand, also in France, Germany and Luxembourg, and parts of Spain and Italy.

Milling and Pressing

Weighing

The grapes should be weighed before being processed, so that the total yield can be assessed, and when the grapes have been pressed one can calculate the extract per kilo and per tonne. In a good year when the grapes are really ripe the extraction will be high, but in a poor year when the grapes are small and hard the extract will be low. Many growers find old sack weighing machines at farm sales which are fine for weighing plastic crates full of grapes; on a smaller scale a hanging weighing machine will cope quite adequately with buckets of grapes.

Milling

Before grapes can be pressed to extract the juice, they first have to be milled to break the skins. The traditional age-old method was to tread the grapes in great half casks. A gang of men, with linked arms, trod in unison until all the berries were burst. This method was perfect, since the gentle crushing action of feet did not break the grape pips and release the unwanted acid oils into the wine. Treading is still practised in the more primitive areas of France, and doubtless in other countries, indeed it is practised in several of the smaller Burgundy establishments where traditional methods are still employed. In one winery I visited, the men wore bathing trunks, and were submerged in the must up to the level of their chests, their bodies stained a glorious deep, deep red colour.

Traditional methods were followed in the making of this wine, a slower cooler fermentation than that used by most of the famous, large high-powered establishments, the wine being bottled as late as two-years-old, compared to the modern approach of hastening maturity and achieving early stability, by pasteurization, and bottling and selling the wine when only a year old. More of this later.

To return to milling, there are many milling machines on the market today, ranging from the cheaper Italian hand-cranked or power-driven models, to the super stainless steel or enamelled French and German efforts. The most expensive are incorporated in a stainless steel harvest trailer, so that the grapes are milled at the flick of a switch, and can be piped automatically through a wide-gauge corrugated polythene delivery pipe directly into the wine press. This is automation at its best, and eliminates double handling.

De-Stemming

For white-wine production, modern milling machines can be bought with an attached de-stemmer, which removes bunch stems from the grape pulp as an integral function, a necessity with grape varieties already high in acids and tannin. For those grape varieties less endowed with natural acid and tannin, it pays to leave a percentage of the stems in the must for pressing. In a year when the grapes are *superbly* ripe, and the acid content is really low, leave all the stems in partially to rectify this omission. The stems allow a better must extraction in the wine press.

In the Champagne vineyards, where the newly-picked grapes are checked by gangs of women before going to the wine press, they use a slatted wooden rack over which the grape bunches are rubbed – the crushed berries fall through into a tub below, and the separated stems are then discarded.

To sum up here, it is recommended that, for the delicate style of white wines English grapes tend to make, we practise de-stemming prior to pressing. This eliminates the harsh bitter flavour associated with excess tannin in our more delicate flowery wines. These wines are not designed or destined for a lengthy bottle life. It is essential that we strive to preserve that which is most attractive in our wines, an elusive flowery fragrance.

Wine presses

The grapes are next transferred to the wine press. There are a wide range of presses on the market today, presses to suit all sizes of vineyard, and many different methods of operation. Beginning with the ever-popular centre screw press, Italy exports a wide range, of many different sizes, to Britain. These presses are fine provided they are maintained well. The base tray and legs should be cleaned down well with sand paper, and painted with Hammerite, which is non toxic to the grape juice, and also gives the best wear, but must be applied some weeks before needed to allow it to harden. Every few years dismantle the hardwood basket, first numbering the staves to correspond with the steel bands, sand them down really well, and varnish with several coats of Crown polyurethane varnish before putting it together.

The next step up is the horizontal wine press. The well-known French Vaslin press is available in many sizes, from the small manually-operated model to fully automatic presses of truly vast dimensions. The principle of the Vaslin press is to squeeze the must towards one end of the interior of the horizontal cylinder by means of a rotating screw which pulls a round plate towards the opposite end. When it is decided to break up the cake of pulp, the plate returns to the further end, and a series of chains breaks up the grape skins and pulp in readiness for a second pressing. The mechanism is operated by electric motor, and the function can be manually or automatically selected, according to the model.

An alternative is the Howard wine press, which operates on similar lines, and is gaining a big following with British growers.

The German Wilmes press (pronounced Vilms) employs a different principle whereby the grapes are pressed against the sides of a perforated horizontal cylindrical drum by inflating with compressed air a rubber bladder in the centre of the cylinder. The makers and many users claim that the Wilmes press is far kinder on the grape pulp, and, because the action is so gentle, produces a must with fewer off-flavours.

Pressing

Transfer the milled grapes immediately to the wine press so that the grapes are exposed to the air for the shortest possible time. Prolonged exposure to the air should be avoided so that oxidation and the attentions of the acetic-acid fruit fly can be avoided. More particularly with white wines the speed of the operation is all important as wine is delicate and highly vulnerable at this stage. This is more critical still if a grower is using black grapes for white wine, for if there is any delay the black skins will begin to stain the grape pulp and juice, and the wine will be a dirty pink colour.

An important point I learned both in Champagne and Alsace – at the Krug establishment on Rheims and the Joseph Meyer winery at Wintzenhaim near Colmar respectively – was that, in making a fine classic wine devoid of off-flavours and harsh tannins, they do not squeeze every last drop of juice out of the crushed grapes. Given that an automatic wine press has a dial numbered from one to ten, denoting that a degree of extraction can be preset, these top winemakers and others of a similar persuasion only exert a pressure of up to five or six on their grapes.

In making Champagne, only a free-run juice and that from the first two or three light pressings, called the première Cuvée, is used for vintage of classic wines.

The huge round Champagne presses, no more than 600 cm high, and more than 3 m in diameter, hold about 4000 kilos of grapes, and only the first 2666 litres of extracted juice can be made into Champagne. This may be achieved in just two or three pressings of each load, the first 1000 litres of the Vin de Cuvée are known as the première Cuvée, and the last 400 litres form the Troisième Cuvée. The Vin de Cuvée is used for the best Champagnes.

The juice extracted from these three pressings is better constructed chemically than that from later pressings, being high in sugars and acid. It also contains most of the yeast cells, and less colour taint than later pressings. Each successive pressing yields a juice of progressively lower quality.

The next pressing, yielding 666 litres, is known as the Vin de Taille. The first 200 litres are the première taille, the following 200 litres the deuxième taille, and the final 266 litres form the troisième taille. This would already indicate the pulp has been pressed and turned to less than six times.

Most top Champagne houses sell these last three pressings to the makers of lesser-quality wedding Champagne, to be sold under the labels of the buyers, hotels, restaurants, chain stores etc. Sometimes the pulp is then removed to a stronger press, and the resultant juice is made into a still wine for the staff, or sold off as Vin Ordinaire, being somewhat bitter and low in acid and, therefore, lacking keeping power. Alternatively the pulp is sold off to the local distillery.

The first three pressings are, as explained, comparatively gentle and slow to ensure a fine quality juice. The total process of the six pressings and subsequent breaking up of the pulp before it can be re-pressed – a process known as *retroussage* – takes from three to six hours according to the efficiency or antiquity of the wine presses.

I think that we might well take note of this practice, for, in certain years, many British growers are forced to cope with rather unripe acid tannic grapes, and we could perhaps concentrate on converting three-quarters of our yield into our quality wines, and creating a lesser wine from the final pressing, perhaps even having a shot at making a sparkling wine with the lesser quality juice. In this way we could produce a more consistent quality in our wines each year.

It also occurs to me that the time is fast coming when a distillery could, perhaps, be set up in each area of Britain, a concern that could buy up all the dry grape pulp from all the growers in the area, and make a local grape spirit as they do in France and Germany.

In France they call their local grape brandies *Marc* (pronounced Mar), *Marc de Bourgogne*, *Marc de Champagne* for example, and although such an enterprise would not yet offer the English distiller a living, it would certainly fit into a programme of various other enterprises. Naturally the permission and advice of the Customs and Excise office would have to be sought before making any marc, emphasis being made that this valuable product has in this country to date been converted into compost, whereas, by creating a further saleable product, the Customs and Excise office would earn an attractive income each year.

Pumping the juice is avoided in several of the very top French wineries. They maintain that the less a wine is knocked about the better it will be. They transfer their must or wine from one process to another by gravity wherever possible, but of course have the added advantage of a winery built on several levels, with cellarage at the lowest level.

When planning a winery, whether putting up a completely new building or renovating an existing building, try to see your way to providing two levels so that you can take advantage of the force of gravity for moving your wine. A winegrower I visit in Germany had made truly brilliant use of various levels. The winery was built into a hill which lent itself to the use of three levels. The grapes arrived in an enamelled container on a tractor trailer. An electric hoist attached to a bar on the ceiling had a chain and hook suspended from it, and was connected to the far side of the container. The grapes were tipped into the crusher hopper which was let into the floor. The pulped grapes fell from the electrically-operated crusher straight into the open horizontal press standing below. A man standing inside the wine press forked the grape pulp into all corners of the wine press to ensure it was evenly packed.

When full, the automatic press crushed the must thoroughly, and the grape juice ran down polythene pipes by gravity into settling tanks on a lower floor, where it was sulphited and left to rest overnight to settle out. The whole operation was managed by just the two men, one driving the tractor and tipping the grapes into the hopper, the second packing the wine press with the pulp, demonstrating an inspired use of the three levels to cut down on manpower, and to allow the grapes and juice to speed on their way by gravity. One must consider labour-saving methods today.

Today some winemakers treat the pulp with a pectin enzyme before pressing. The milled pulp is kept in bulk, dosed with a pectin enzyme, covered, and left overnight. The correct dosage is given on the pectin enzyme pack. Overnight the enzyme works on the pectin in the fruit, breaking it down, a process which results in a higher yield from the grapes when pressed.

The following morning start as early as possible pressing the grapes, and transferring the juice to the fermentation vessels. Pack the wine press firmly with the pulp, making sure that the basket or cylinder is packed evenly around the edges. Apply pressure slowly, for again this is conducive to a better yield.

Containers

White wine can be fermented and matured in a range of materials including glass, stainless steel, polyester resin and concrete tanks lined with tiles glazed in a glaze containing no lead. Casks are not usually recommended due to white wine tending to pick up an excess of tannin and, perhaps, oxidizing in the relatively small casks we would use. Should a grower particularly wish to use wood during some stage in the production of his white wines, then it is safer to do so during the first vigorous ferment, a process that can take from one to three weeks, rarely longer, and thence rack his now almost dry wine into glass or stainless steel to enter the next stage of production.

The reason for choosing the initial ferment as the time to cask a white wine is that a wine is virtually safe from bacterial spoilage during the massive vigour of the primary fermentation when the wine is giving off carbon dioxide at the rate of knots. When this excessive activity ceases, the young wine is again vulnerable to spoilage organisms, and must be closely contained in vessels that eliminate any possibility of oxidation.

At the House of Krug, makers of one of the best, if not *the* best Champagne, the first fermentation is conducted in 225-litre or 45-gallon casks. Quality control is of paramount importance at Krug, from the choice of grapes and right through each of the stages of production, and, therefore, with certain grape varieties and proposed wine styles, this practice would be worth trying.

As the white grape juice is expelled from the wine press, it is run by gravity, pumped or poured, into the waiting sterile settling vats or containers for the solids in suspension to precipitate. These particles of leaf, skin, stalk, pulp, earth and even parts of various insects, take from 6–24 hours to settle out. In general a 12-hour resting period is recommended, but Professor Huberty of the Remich Viticultural Research Institute in Luxembourg states that six hours is perfectly adequate and, due to the shorter exposure to these undesirable and possibly tainting influences, gives a superior wine. I find, however, that several grape varieties need at least 12 hours to drop their sediment.

Certain Continental winemakers bypass this settling-out stage by centrifuging the freshly sulphited juice straight from the wine press. This process rids the juice of all particles immediately and makes for a very clean fermentation.

Syphon or pump the now clear juice into prepared clean sterile vessels in readiness for the fermentation process, being careful to avoid stirring up the bitter sludge. This sediment is now thrown away.

Sulphiting and CO_2

The freshly pressed grape juice must immediately be sulphited to kill all undesirable bacterial organisms and also to stem all wild yeast spores. This juice is sterilized with wine sulphur at a ratio of from 5–20 gms per hectolitre, according to the degree of soundness of the grapes. (1 hectolitre is 22 gallons). I find that with early, botrytized soft grapes picked in warm weather, one needs 20 gms per 22 gallons, and, with really late-picked, sound, often hard, grapes, 5–10 gms per hectolitre is sufficient.

The wine sulphur kills off bacteria, moulds and unwanted wild yeasts, which if left to ferment the wine would do so, vigorously, until 5 per cent of alcohol had been reached, and the yeasts would then expire. So these wild yeasts are stunned, and rendered sterile in readiness for innoculation by a pure and actively working wine yeast.

Acquire a cylinder of CO_2 and cover the grape juice with a layer of CO_2. This keeps the juice free from contamination. Ideally, collect the juice from the press under a blanket of CO_2. Distillers M. G. Ltd., of Leafield Trading Estate, Corsham, Wiltshire, SM13 9UE, will deliver CO_2 cylinders weekly on receipt of order and remittance.

Method of Determining the Free and Total SO$_2$ in Wine Expressed in mg/1 SO$_2$

Apparatus

3 burettes with stand and clamps
1–10ml pipette
1–150ml Erlenmeyer flask

Reagents

Iodine solution (blue solution)
N/1 NaOH (sodium hydroxide)
25% H$_2$SO$_4$ (sulphuric acid)

Method for Free SO$_2$ (H$_2$SO$_3$)

Pipette 10ml of wine into the Erlenmeyer flask, taking care not to splash the wine.
Titrate to a light-blue colour with iodine solution.

Method for Total SO$_2$ (H$_2$SO$_3$)

Measure 5 ml N/1 NaOH solution into the Erlenmeyer flask and add 10 ml of wine. Shake gently, and allow to rest for 15 mins. Next add 2 ml H$_2$SO$_4$, and then titrate with iodine solution to a light-blue colour.

Calculations

Each ml of iodine solution required $\times$ 10 = mg/litre SO$_2$.
It is recommended that the free SO$_2$ is adjusted to 30ppm when the wine is bottled for stable dry wines, and adjusted to 50–80 ppm for sweet wines.

Adjusting the Specific Gravity or Density

Rack the now-cleared juice off the sludge and then adjust the gravity with the required amount of sugar to bring the level at which you wish to begin the fermentation. A recommended figure for white wines would be a gravity of between 75 and 80, resulting in a final alcohol potential of between 9.5 and 10. White wines do not need to be too alcoholic, but must contain sufficient alcohol to show off or enhance the flavour and character of the wine, and to act as an adequate preservative.

To test the gravity of the grape juice, a graduated float or hydrometer is needed, which is easily read if suspended in wine in a trial jar. Then consult the table (p. 221) to compare the readings obtained and the more easily to ascertain any adjustments that might prove necessary.

A word of encouragement here which is especially applicable in a poor year and to those growers who are despondent about consistently lowish gravity readings with certain grape varieties. Jean Meyer of Wintzenheim near Colmar in Alsace, the son of Jos. Meyer, growers and winemakers of the highest order, told me that he preferred to make wine from grapes of moderate rather than magnificent summers. The balance of the grapes made for wines that were easier to make and the higher acidity of a moderate season resulted in better balanced wines that would enjoy a long and successful bottle life. An initial acidity of 10, 11 or even 12 is not too high, for it will naturally reduce to 6 or 7, perfect for the crisp flowery clean wines for which we are renowned. A higher acidity than 12 should be lowered, either before fermentation with Acidex, or after fermentation with precipitated chalk.

Certain English growers have proved that it is possible to make fine wines which began life with a gravity as low as 50, the lowest gravity permitted by the powers that be for making wine to be offered for sale.

Therefore, a grower must keep a vigilant watch on rising gravities and, more important, on lowering acidity in earlier ripening grapes in good and in heatwave summers. A day arrives beyond which it is not advisable to leave the grapes on the vines, for the grower will then have too low an acidity to make a sound wine. One is not allowed to add acid to a wine, so one has to rely on using the natural acidity. The only alternative to this problem should one wish to leave the grapes on the vines to reach an astronomic density, is to grow another grape renowned for a high acidity, such as Chardonnay, or Seyval. These grapes are blended in at harvest at a proportion of no more than 15 per cent if one wishes to name one's wine by the variety of the master grape. Should a grower wish to blend in more than 15 per cent, then the label should state the names of the two grapes in order of precedence.

To sum up here, it is vitally important to pick for acidity rather than sugar, with early ripening grapes in particular; these varieties tend to assimilate sugar very fast, and equally to lose acid very rapidly. Therefore it follows that a good winemaker does not consider a very high gravity to be of prime importance for he knows he will make a superior wine if he has grapes of an adequate acidity on which to ply his skills. Müller Thurgau loses acidity very fast, and so must be watched with care. Siegerrebe, Madeleine Sylvaner, Madeleine Angevine and Ortega must also be monitored frequently for the same reason.

To convert readings from the refractometer to density, specific gravity or oechsle, multiply the refractometer reading by 4, then add 2 for readings below 17.0, add 3 for readings between 17.0 and 18.8 and add 4 for readings from 19.0 upwards.

Adjusting Acidity

It is also extremely important at this stage to determine the acidity of the must. Should the must be too acid, the acidity can be lowered prior to fermentation with Acidex, or after the fermentation at the first racking with precipitated chalk.

A certain degree of acidity is essential to the creation of a sound drinkable wine; sufficient acidity and tannin in a wine guarantee a long and sustained life in bottle. Wines lacking in both these elements tend towards a soft, flabby, almost salty flavour, and a very short bottle life.

Again here, a light delicate wine would not be able to carry a high acidity, but to the heavier stronger wines a healthy acid content is a necessity for sound and stable longevity.

Most white and red grapes grown in English vineyards tend to have sufficient or overmuch acidity, so the problem of too low an acidity rarely happens. Should it arise, the best move is to blend in a low percentage of very acid must from other grapes.

The total acidity is shown by titration; total acidity is a combination of tartaric and malic acids. To determine the acidity a simple titration set is needed, the kit consisting of:

Apparatus	*Regaents*
25-ml pipette	N/3 Sodium Hydroxide (NaOH)
50-ml burette	Litmus paper
150-ml beaker	
glass rod	

Testing method
Fill the burette with sodium hydroxide, checking that the stopcock is working; note the level of the NaOH in the burette.
Pipette 25ml of wine into the beaker.
Titrate with N/3 Sodium hydroxide to neutral, using litmus paper as an indicator.

Calculation
1 ml of N/3 NaOH = 1 gm/litre acidity expressed as tartaric acid.

Degree comparisons – Refractometer – Alcohol Table

Specific Gravity (G.B.)	Oechsle Degrees (Germany)	Brix or Balling Degrees (U.S.A.)	Baumé Degrees (France)	Approximate Potential Alcohol % Vol.
1.045	45	11.25	6.3	5.3
1.050	50	12.50	7.0	6.1
1.055	55	13.75	7.7	6.9
1.060	60	15.00	8.4	7.7
1.065	65	16.25	9.1	8.5
1.070	70	17.50	9.8	9.3
1.075	75	18.75	10.5	10.1
1.080	80	20.00	11.2	10.9
1.085	85	21.25	11.9	11.7
1.090	90	22.50	12.6	12.5
1.095	95	23.75	13.3	13.3
1.100	100	25.00	14.0	14.1
1.105	105	26.25	14.7	14.9
1.110	110	27.50	15.4	15.7
1.115	115	28.75	16.1	16.5
1.120	120	30.00	16.8	17.3
1.125	125	31.25	17.5	18.1
1.130	130	32.50	18.2	18.9
1.135	135	33.75	18.9	19.7
1.140	140	35.00	19.6	20.5
1.145	145	36.25	20.3	21.3
1.150	150	37.50	21.0	22.1
1.155	155	38.75	21.7	22.9
1.160	160	40.00	22.4	23.7

White Wine Must Improvement to 80° Oechsle – 10.9% alcohol sugar additions relate to a volume of 100 litres of Must.

To determine how much sugar to add to your Must to raise it to a pre-determined figure, the following table will make the calculation easy to work out.

°Oe	Kg sugar (1 Kg = 2.2lb)	°Oe	Kg sugar (1 Kg = 2.2lb)	°Oe	Kg sugar (1 Kg = 2.2lb)
50	7.5	60	4.9	70	2.4
52	7.0	62	4.4	72	1.9
54	6.5	64	3.9	74	1.5
56	6.0	66	3.4	76	1.0
58	5.5	68	2.9	78	0.5

Correcting a High Acidity

Watch a wine with a high acidity carefully, comparing the initial acidity before fermentation to that at the end of the first fermentation. Watch carefully for a malolactic ferment, which can be induced by racking a wine followed by raising the temperature, with an immersion heater if necessary. Again note the drop caused by the malolactic fermentation, and if the acidity is still too high for bottling, i.e. *above* 7, then it may be reduced with precipitated chalk, calcium carbonate, and done a month or two before bottling.

Add 3 gm per gallon for each point to be reduced; for example to reduce from 7 to 6 add 3 gm per gallon, or to reduce from 9 to 6, add 9 gm per gallon.

Calcium carbonate when added to wine causes a major eruption, so therefore, before adding to the wine, reduce the volume by half.

An acidity of between 8–11 is desirable initially, since during fermentation the acidity drops naturally quite dramatically. Potentially harmful bacteria cannot, at such levels of acidity, harm young wines which, at this stage, is a safeguard to health.

Should the acidity be higher than 11 or 12, it can be lowered prior to fermentation with Acidex, or after fermentation with precipitated chalk.

To sum up here on progress to date; the newly-pressed juice, preferably protected under a blanket of CO_2, has been sterilized with sulphite or SO_2, and has had both the natural gravity and acidity of the juice ascertained and corrected if necessary.

Some winemakers next add Bentonite as a matter of course, to remove proteins which might at a later date cause a haze if they remain in suspension. Making wines under normal English winter conditions with low January temperatures will usually settle out any hazes, particularly if the wine is deliberately exposed to the frost for a few nights. Therefore, the addition of Bentonite and the vast sediment it creates by way of swelling to 16 times its original volume, which results in a waste of wine, would appear to be superfluous. However, if a winemaker finds his methods tend to leave him with wines with a protein haze, then by all means treat now with Bentonite, which is a volcanic ash or clay, a natural fining medium.

Using Bentonite

For a medium dosage add 100 to 150 grammes of Bentonite to each 100 litres of wine. Measure the amount of Bentonite needed for the wine to be treated, and mix it to a medium cream with warm water. Put this mixture into the blender on your food mixer, and blend for half an hour. If it becomes too stiff, add more warm water. This goes a long way to ensuring that the Bentonite initially absorbs water so that when it is added to the wine it will thus absorb less precious wine. Make sure the consistency is quite thin, stir into the wine really well.

The substance will absorb protein solids as it gently precipitates down through the wine, and should settle out in some 6–8 days.

100–150 gms per 100 litres = 22 gallons
50–75 gms per 50 litres = 11 gallons
25–37 gms per 25 litres = 5.5 gallons

Yeasting

Using modern granulated cool temperature wine yeasts, pour the recommended amount into a previously sterilized jug containing half a pint of grape juice. Mix well and allow to stand for half an hour before inoculating the must. Fermentation should begin within some twelve to twenty-four hours, maybe longer if the temperature is cool or cold.

Fermentation Too Cool

If fermentation refuses to begin, it is almost always due to the must being too cold. It is totally impractical to heat the winery and the must; therefore an immersion heater can be used to heat the must, set to about 20°C, or 70°F. A further way of rectifying this problem is to remove a fair percentage of the juice, heat it in non-ferrous containers, use stainless steel or Teflon, and return the warm juice to the bulk of the wine. Do not bring the juice anyway near to boiling point. This will nearly always start the ferment. As a final resort, bakers' yeast can be added to a recalcitrant must that stubbornly refuses to begin to ferment.

Overheating

A problem that is rarely likely to occur is that of overheating of the must. Should this happen, immediate steps must be taken to avoid spoilage. In the Champagne house of Pol Roger, they have irrigation laid on that runs cold water from top to bottom of the outside of the giant stainless steel vats to prevent the young wine overheating. This is not always possible in a smaller winery.

Should red wine, fermenting on the pulp, begin to overheat, the only course is to take several bucket loads out of the mass to reduce the volume and thereby reduce the temperature. Return when cool. Liquid red or white wine can be cooled by pumping it out of the vat in a plastic pipe, running the pipe through a tank of cold water, and returning the wine to the vat via the pipe. Alternatively run a plastic pipe through the vat and pump cold water through it until the temperature is lowered.

Notes on Fermentation

Grape wine ferments out quickly, often in as few as five to seven days. Obviously temperature plays an important part here. The finest wines, both red and white, are, however, created by means of a cool, slow, steady fermentation, and one should strive to create a steady cool atmosphere for fermentation, which is best if it can be prolonged for four, five or six weeks. A hot fermentation boils away the finer, more delicate bouquets and flavours.

Problems

There can be too great a concentration of sulphur from the grape skins left from the final spraying of the vines. This material will gravitate to the bottom of the tank within twenty-four hours, when the wine may be racked. The removal of the must from the sulphur and the added aeration should now enable fermentation to begin.

Wine musts with excessively high acidity from late ripening grapes in moderate and poor summers will often fail to ferment without some reduction of this acidity. Musts with acidities in excess of 12 or 14 expressed as tartaric can be a problem. Sometimes an acid reading is as high as 16 or 18, which will definitely need reducing. Chardonnay in particular is especially difficult to start if it has a high reading. Read notes on Acidex and precipitated chalk for reducing acidity.

Wine yeasts must be fresh and of the current season to encourage an early fermentation. Do not be tempted to keep opened packs of wine yeast from one year to the next.

This low temperature is maintained through maturing to bottling, and by virtue of the dissolved carbonate within the wine and the physical and chemical differences brought about by this method, the wine retains the original bouquet, freshness and youthful prickly attributes of a very young wine in bottle. The wines made in this manner are quite outstanding, and we English winegrowers could well adopt these principles into our winemaking.

Attention must be paid to topping the vats up every four days as wine constantly loses volume due to the evacuation of the carbonic gas, in order that no access is afforded to bacterial attack in the air space. Alternatively, keep the air space filled with a blanket of CO_2.

The wine should be chilled the minute the first fermentation ceases which causes the finished yeast cells to settle out, quelling the action of any harmful bacteria and halting fermentation. The young wine must now be racked off the sediment, syphoning the wine from the dead yeast cells and micro-organisms which can cause off-flavours if the wine is not quickly removed. Fill the container right up to the top, fitting an air lock in case there is any more activity. When this activity ceases, the air lock can be removed, and a solid cork bung fitted firmly. Raise the free SO_2 to 30 ppm after each racking.

Malolactic Fermentation

Most wines will undergo a malolactic fermentation naturally. The vigour of the primary fermentation ceases, having converted most of the grape sugar into alcohol. The new wine is still muddy, yeasty and opaque, and still has solid matter to precipitate before it is ready for filtering and bottling.

With high acid wines the malolactic ferment is encouraged, indeed welcomed, as it reduces the acidity to a manageable level and has a mellowing, softening effect on young harsh wines. Those wines which began life with a low acidity, however, should be prevented from a malolactic fermentation, for it will tend to remove the little acidity that remains after the first fermentation, and render such wines soft, flabby and rob them of any reasonable length of bottle life. Hence the need for a very careful watch on fast-ripening grapes, so that the acidity does not drop too low, for the action of fermentation further reduces the acidity and the wine will be rendered soft and characterless. This problem is only likely to occur with very early-ripening grapes, and with a broader spectrum of grapes in a heatwave summer/autumn.

A closer understanding of the chemical changes that occur within the malolactic ferment should be considered. The malolactic occurs within the secondary fermentation, the latter encompassing a slow and steady clearing of the particles and hazes within the wine. The malolactic area is concerned with the various acids within the wine.

Grape must contains two predominant organic acids, namely tartaric acid and malic acid. Tartaric acid is peculiar to the grape alone, whereas the malic acid is found in many other fruits. There is a high count of malic acid in unripe grapes, and a low count in ripe grapes, but the tartaric acid is a stable feature and does not alter in the grapes as they ripen.

As the primary fermentation proceeds, a certain family of bacteria gradually build up and when a cracking point is reached, they suddenly attack the malic acid in the new wine, changing it to the much weaker lactic acid, without altering the tartaric acid. This action brings about a sharp reduction in the total acidity, downgrading the original degree of malic acid by half. The outward signs are a renewed activity as carbon dioxide (CO_2) is given off as the last remnants of sugar are fermented out, a marked clearing of the wine, and a deposit of potassium bitartrate crystals around the sides of the vessel.

To induce this reaction in a wine, rack the young wine off the sediment at the cessation of the primary ferment and move the wine to a warmer situation. The aeration, turbulence and warming are usually sufficient to trigger off the malolactic ferment sooner or later in the majority of wines. Should this action fail to encourage the desired effect, a malolactic ferment will occur naturally in June. A wine that has too great an acidity can inhibit the malolactic ferment, and this acidity may have to be reduced with precipitated chalk to a level where the malolactic can function and take over the good work. Beware of over reducing here, for precipitated chalk reacts on the tartaric rather than the malic acid, which might render the wine totally devoid of both acids after the malolactic ferment, which could be a disaster.

Therefore, never add more than 1 gm of precipitated chalk per litre of wine, remembering never to add the precipitated chalk to a wine container more than two-thirds full, for the lively eruption that occurs will cause the wine to overflow and be lost.

Aim to arrive at a final acidity of between 6 and 7, which is both an adequate preservative and sufficient to render the wine pleasing to the taste with a good balance of acidity.

To recap, wine with an initial acidity of 10 will usually cope with these processes naturally and without any assistance, and will arrive at a final acidity of between 6 and 7 which is both an adequate preservative, and is sufficient to endow a wine with a perfect balance of acidity to show off the flavour and character. Grape musts with an initial acidity higher than 11 or 12 will more than likely have to be corrected, either at the outset with Acidex, or, after the first ferment, with precipitated chalk as has already been described.

A second racking must be undertaken a month later, when another light sediment will have fallen. Again, top the containers right up to the brim and bung up the vessels firmly. To expose the wine to extreme cold and frost during early January will render most wines brilliantly clear, as cold will hasten the last minute stubborn particles and hazes in suspension to drop.

Advice from Messieurs Remi Krug of Krug Champagne and Jean Meyer of Jos. Meyer, winegrowers of Wintzenheim near Colmar in Alsace, is that, whenever possible, one should transfer wine from one vat to another by gravity rather than by pumping. A great advantage to a winemaking concern is two or more floor levels, so that the wine can be transferred by gravity.

Notes on Bottling

Dr Hans Ambrosi, principal of the whole massive area of State vineyards in the Rheingau, and also of the recently much enlarged State winery at Eltville, was most insistent that English vines should be bottled in January, so that the youthful fruity bouquet and fresh grapy flavour would be retained in the wine. It is, therefore, highly recommended that we bottle before the weather warms up in the spring, and, providing the winemaker has racked monthly and the wine has fermented out, is stable and has cleared well, then there is nothing to gain by postponing bottling.

The great wines of Chablis, made from the Chardonnay grape grown in the classic Vaudesir vineyards, are maintained in bulk after fermentation and bottled at a year old. This later bottling is obviously directly related to the overall life of the wine, the Chardonnay being a wine with a far longer bottle life than the softer German wines.

Almost all Alsatian winegrowers make no less than seven wines from seven different vine varieties, because everyone else does. The quality of these wines varies from commonplace to exquisite, the more ordinary are bottled early in March and the most elegant are bottled last, often as late as September. The top Alsatian growers such as the Meyers of Wintzenheim, keep their wines for a further year in bottle before selling. The better Alsatian wines possess great substance and richness, and improve in bottle for a further six to eight years before going over the top.

Sweet or Sussreserve

It is a recognized practice in Germany to add süss, or sweet reserve, to the lower grades of wines, wines that otherwise would be too rough and acidic for the German taste. This practice is limited to all wines of less than qualitatswein standard.

Sweet reserve is unfermented grape juice, which is added to wines in need of softening, immediately prior to bottling. This material is crushed and pressed, and then sulphited, and is maintained in sterile conditions within sealed tanks under pressure with CO_2. It is usually made from grapes that have a high natural sugar content, a low acidity and a bland adaptable flavour, so that it can be added to any wine type and not interfere with the flavour or character of the wine. Ortega is just such a grape and, having an early ripening habit, is much used since it can be harvested, milled, pressed and contained well in advance of the main harvest of Riesling and other popular varietal grapes. Morio Muscat is another grape used for Sussreserve, having a strong muscat, even catty flavour; it has the added use of injecting a degree of taste or character into a bland plain wine.

It is German practice to subject wines in need of such treatment – the German preference is for sweeter heavier white wines than is the cultivated English taste, wines within the lower quality structure – to test and match up such wines with several varieties and percentages of sussreserve in January or February. The wines are then blended in with the chosen sussreserve; being well sulphured this would remove any chance of fermentation. They are sterile bottled immediately, so that all yeasts and bacteria are totally eliminated, the filter and all equipment used, plus the bottles and corks, being sterilized with a 2 per cent solution of SO_2. This is essential, for if any yeast cells were to be passed into the wine containing the unfermented süssreserve, fermentation could begin, corks would blow, bottles burst and reputations be lost.

Remember this is a German practice, designed basically to render smooth and moderately sweet the lowest denomination group of wine, a practice that would doubtless benefit English wines in a poor wet year, but, hopefully, be unnecessary in a good year. In other words, it is used to mask certain defects or deficiencies.

EEC law demands that we use blend wines of these low grades with suss produced within our own particular area, i.e. northern Germany and northern France. If you purchase German sussreserve, order early and choose a variety to match your wine type, M.T. for M.T., Bacchus for Siegerrebe or Schönburger, Riesling for Kerner, Scheurebe, etc. Why not grow, press, SO_2, filter and deep freeze your own?

The elusive fragrant flowery bouquet and the comparatively light delicate fruity acidity can be totally swamped by an overall smooth soft flavour of some unrecognizable and totally un-English grape juice.

This practice is not being condemned; it obviously has a beneficial part to play with a poor thin sour wine of a bad year. Why not have one's wine professionally assessed by a German expert who could advise and supply a süssreserve of similar style and of a type chosen to enhance and not overbalance the original wine. Alternatively, why not grow your own grapes to fulfil this very purpose, and contain the juice in a sterile situation under CO_2 pressure until needed – if it is not, it can always be sold to a less fortunate grower.

Most German vineyards are planted with an area of 10 per cent of grapes for this very purpose, Ortega or Reichensteiner – both early-ripening, both attain a high sugar content, Reichensteiner a fair acidity as well.

One last warning; do not add too much süssreserve to your wine, for you are in effect diluting the alcohol content by some 5 per cent, 10 per cent or even 15 per cent, which can seriously wreck the balance of the wine. Such a practice can render a wine flat, dumb and plain uninteresting – quite apart from reducing its bottle life by having diluted the alcohol, tannin and acidity, the three components essential as preservatives. Obviously sussreserve needs much thought and very careful application, for correctly applied it can enhance a less than perfect wine, but applied without care and delicacy it can swamp the character, balance and identity of English wine.

Filtration and Bottling Equipment

To render a wine stable, sound and crystal clear, it must be run through one form of filter or another before being bottled. When offering a product such as wine for sale to the general public, one must be totally sure that there are no floaters in the wine, nor any yeast cells that could start the wine fermenting again, making it frothy, bubbly and subsequently blowing out the corks and ruining the grower's reputation.

Therefore, the wine must be filtered. There are basically three types of filter: the sheet filter where the wine is forced through cellulose or asbestos sheets held by plates like toast in a toast rack, the millipore filter, and the membrane filter; the latter seems to be the most efficient.

Whatever type of filter is used, the operator must be made aware of the fact that this unit must have immense care taken over cleaning and sterilizing before use. Hose unions, various junctions and the plastic hoses themselves are perfect hosts to trapped bacteria which could spoil a perfectly sound healthy wine.

The best cleansing is to purge the filter with nitrogen. Steam sterilizing is also most effective – steam at 10 lb p.s.i. for 30 minutes. A chlorine solution is another possibility. All should be forced through the filter backwards. Before use, flush the filter first with 2% SO_2, then with cold water, each for half an hour, with the filter pads in place. Obviously the first two or three bottles of wine will be severely diluted with water and must be discarded.

The next essential is a bottle filler, a simple piece of equipment into which the wine flows direct from the filter under some pressure via a plastic hose, and is dispersed through two to four heads or tubes into the bottles. The heads are valve-operated, so that they only function when a bottle is pressed upwards over the outlets. One person can easily operate this machine alone.

The filled bottles are passed to the operator of the corking machine, which can vary from a simple but efficient hand corking machine, or a semi-automatic affair with the corks dispensed into the plunger aperture from a hopper and banged home at the press of a button, to a fully automatic one that corks the bottles as they pass underneath on a roller line. Again, this machine must be cleaned and sterilized.

If the bottles are to be laid away in a cellar proper, do not fit capsules or labels to the bottles until they are brought out to be sold, otherwise the labels could well peel off or become stained in the damp atmosphere. The wine should be able to breathe to enable it to recover from the traumatic shock of having been filtered and bottled, and, therefore, it is recommended that the winemaker postpones capsuling and labelling until the wine has to be made ready for sale. It can breathe if necessary through the cork to continue the steady improvement process.

Bottled wine must be stored on its side in a cool even temperature, so that the small air bubble is not in contact with the cork. The cork is thus kept damp and healthy and will not dry out and emit air and subsequent spoilage into the wine.

For the Smaller Vineyard

There is a very efficient mini-filter on the market that is perfectly adequate for the grower of several dozen, or even a hundred or two vines. It consists of a 1-gallon plastic container with a pump fitted on top. The wine is pumped outward by air displacement and through a single pad filter into a demijohn or direct into bottles.

The Bottling Process

As with all winemaking processes, a sound preparation of all equipment before beginning is a necessity. Should reused bottles be contemplated, these must be more than thoroughly washed to ensure absolute cleanliness. Use a hot soda solution followed by a mild chlorine (chempro) solution, using a brush bottle-washing machine. Every vestige of label and glue must be removed. For the professional grower of some scale, new bottles can be delivered in pallets of *c* 675, shrink-wrapped in polythene sheeting, set on a wooden pallet. These, therefore, only require a sterilizing rinse and drain before being filled. Hand-washed bottles must, likewise, be sterilized before use with a mild solution of sulphite, or on a sterinal sterilizer.

Most winemakers make or buy a large low trolley on four wheels with a base with, say, 100 holes to take 100 newly-sterilized bottles set upside down to drain, so that they have a good supply to hand when bottling commences. It would pay to have one person manning the bottle filling operation, another the corker, a third taking the full bottles to the cellar and a fourth sterilizing bottles and re-charging the bottle trolley for the person bottling the wine.

The smaller grower will need a binning area within the cellar to store the wine bottles away, planned with space economy and accessibility in mind. Really large growers should consider the modern metal mesh containers, each holding 250–500 bottles and set on a pallet, so that bottled wine can be bulk-handled by fork lift truck to cut down on man-handling, time and space.

Corks

Never be tempted into buying cheap corks. Several English growers do so, and the chances of bacterial contamination, and, indeed, weeping bottles, if not total loss of corks, can ruin a good reputation, all the more tragic if the wine is really first-rate.

There are two top-rate cork merchants in London who sell some four or six grades of corks. There is a slight price difference between the cheapest and the best, 4p each and 7p each respectively. Ask for samples and compare them. The best are blemish free, with a lovely tight smooth grain. The manufacturers offer excellent extra services of waxing the corks and sterilizing them with SO_2, these processes giving the corks a greatly extended bottle life. Lastly they will brand them with the name of the grower, the wine or vineyard, plus the address, or, alternatively, his registered number. Personalized waxed high-quality corks are an outward indication of the care and pride a grower takes in his wine and helps to make the wine more attractive.

Capsules

Lead capsules give wine a really professional finish. These require a spin-on capsuler to affix them without creases and bumps. For the private grower there is available, in a variety of colours, a range of plastic and shrink-on viscose capsules which also give a good seal to the bottle and keep the cork in good order.

Labels

A label is a great selling point of a wine, probably the greatest possible influence on the buyer. The name of the wine must be displayed in large letters, be of easily read print, so that it can be read and recognized some ten or more feet away from the prospective buyer. Avoid difficult Gothic print and avoid an unwieldy ugly name that is difficult to remember.

Study other labels and try to list the factors that make some really attractive and others total failures. The more simple and uncluttered the design, the better the label.

A good selling point is to feature the town, if famous, or the county in which the wine is grown. Buyers like to identify with a county or town in which they live, have visited, or have a relation living. Therefore, this should feature on the label. Certain counties have instant appeal, especially those associated with holiday areas such as Devon, Cornwall, Dorset and Somerset.

Should there be a well-known land mark or geological feature, or a famous building in your immediate vicinity, this creates an immediate recognition or bond with the buyer and is of greater impact than Oak Tree Farm, or Lower-Nether-Wapping etc. If, however, you have no outstanding or well-known feature in the area, then, of course, you can do no better than to name your wine after your house or village, whichever is the more attractive and suitable.

There is a strict ruling that lays down the size of the label, the size of the print, the wording and descriptions one must include on the label, which one must study and abide by or the label will be disallowed. The law has tightened in as much as the stated contents on the label must tally with the actual volume of wine; as well as being no less, there must be no more. There is a new ruling that we must bottle into 75 cl bottles after 1 May 1989, and also that from this date we must state the alcohol content on the label, accurate to .5 of a degree. We are however allowed to use up old labels until they run out. If you need any further advice, consult the Wine Standards Board.

Obviously all these factors apply only if a grower is actually selling wine.

Concluding Notes

Dry white wines must be sulphured to contain 30 ppm before bottling, and red wine adjusted to 30 ppm. This both stuns the yeast cells and aids a long bottle life without oxidation. Test the wine for free SO_2 content, using the instructions given on p. 218. Then add the required amount of sulphur to bring the wine to the correct level. Once this is done, retest, for readjustment may be needed. Do not over-sulphur, or the wine will stink of sulphur for a long time. Sweet wines should contain 50 ppm of sulphur to be sure of long term stability.

Skin Contact

Winemakers are experimenting with leaving all or part of their newly crushed grapes on their skins for 5, 10, or 25 hours to extract more intense flavours and colour from the skins that would be lost if the pulp were to be pressed out immediately. This is particularly valuable for the more aromatic wines, Gewurztraminer, Siegerrebe, Schonburger and Bacchus, and helps to create wines with more character and complexity. Perhaps not to be recommended for the lighter, crisp delicate types of wine, for these qualities would be swamped by over dominant flavour.

Experiment skin contact with 5, 10 or 25 per cent of the pulp rather than risking the total crop. Take these wines through to their conclusion before assessing and evaluating their respective merits to give a guideline for future practice. They can be blended into one another before bottling if necessary.

14

Red Wine Production

The production of red wine on a commercial scale is an enterprise that should not be undertaken lightly. In fact, without an absolutely perfect site for the vines, it should not be undertaken at all. The making of really drinkable red wine requires that one can ripen the black grapes fully. Therefore, in addition to an ideal site, vines capable of ripening their grapes in a mere average English summer are the second essential.

The third point to be made is that there are very few black grape varieties that make a good wine on their own in England. Therefore, to create a wine with good colour, body and long bottle life, the planting commitment should be divided between two or three varieties of vine. When planting privately, the same principles should be observed.

The English grower is too concerned with trying to make single grape wines to pay sufficient attention to the fact that blends are often by far superior. One has only to look to the way in which red Bordeaux wines are grown and made. Red Bordeaux is created from no fewer than three or four grapes, namely the Cabernet Sauvignon, which donates elegance, style and tremendous longevity to the wine, Merlot, which provides fullness and softness, and a smattering of Petit Verdot, which gives red Bordeaux that fascinating and unmistakable nose or bouquet. Alone each would produce a wine, but blended together they create a wine of majestic elegant proportions. Cabernet Franc and Malbec are also grown.

When winegrowing was re-kindled in England in the 1940s, Pirovano 14, Brant, Baco 1 and Seibel 13053 were the only vines available for planting for red wine, plus the Wrotham Pinot, an Anglicized sport of the Pinot Noir discovered on a cottage wall in Kent – a vine possibly introduced by the Romans nearly 2,000 years ago.

The wines from these grapes were frankly rough, often obviously hybridy and lacked any semblance of quality. And, more often than not, the result was a rosé rather than a red wine. We had not yet found the answer.

In the 1960s, I planted a trial vineyard where I had all the vines that were available at that time in England. As well as the aforementioned varieties, I had Foch, Joffre, Leon Millot, Oberlin 595, Triomphe d'Alsace, all hybrids bred in Alsace in the latter part of the last century. Pinot Noir and Gamay also had their place, plus Baco 1, Portuguese Blue, and three of the Russian Aumurensis Pinot Noir crosses – Gagarin Blue, Kubishevski and Teveshkova.

Seibel 13053 yielded a good crop of tiny grapes, making wine of a distinctive and harsh hybrid flavour. Pirovano 14 was a shy light cropper without wall or cloche protection. Baco 1 produced a coarse astringent wine. Pinot Noir ripened late and bore a light crop of quality grapes that produced a wine so barely reminiscent of that of its native heath that it is not really viable except on a superb hot site on limestone soil. Portuguese Blue is a rampant vine of Austrian origin and produces a wine of really low quality. The Russian vines remain of interest – Kubishevski is a very strong grower and produces lovely open bunches of early-ripening black grapes; Gagarin Blue displays similar attributes and is enjoying much renewed interest in Britain today.

After having earlier dismissed any vine that was a hybrid, due to vineyards in France being denied Appellation Contrôlée status if they grew hybrids – and we would in due course look for an English equivalent system – the qualities of habit, wood-ripening and wine from the Alsatian hybrids soon re-kindled my interest.

In particular the Leon Millot and Triomphe d'Alsace displayed viable cropping tendencies and consistent early ripening, and the wines, given two years in bottle following eighteen months maturing in bulk, reached a hitherto unbelievable quality, colour, depth and style never before experienced with an English-grown red wine. We were approaching a breakthrough in the myth that red wine cannot be grown in England. The one snag is the necessary time spent maturing; when new these wines are raw, rough, an immature purple colour, and totally lacking in promise. The dramatic transformation that only time can bring to these wines, wines that are approaching their best from four years of age, would indicate that a grower would have stock tied up, slowly maturing, for three or four years before it would be fit to sell, which is a fairly daunting prospect.

However, once the initial wine is ready to sell, one would have properly aged, mature wine to sell each year henceforward, and the problem would be resolved.

To return to the prospect of blending grapes, the Germans have done much valuable research into producing tinting or colouring grapes recently, and have bred several that might well be of interest to the grower of red wine. One must look to a grape that will ripen alongside the main grape and can, therefore, be crushed and fermented with the main grape – these *teinturier* grapes have blood-red pulp and juice, and as little as 5–10 per cent is sufficient to ensure that the red wine will have a glorious deep colour. Dunkelfelder will provide a rich dark colour.

There are also serious trials being operated in Germany to breed a grape from at least one noble parent, producing this dark-red pulp and juice, that will make a sound balanced wine on its own – a single-grape red wine. And one of the grapes being used as a parent is the Leon Millot, the French Kuhlman hybrid. Interesting that the German research should include this French hybrid vine, which further underlines my returning interest in this family of vines. The future of red wine in England, if it has a future, could well lie with these vines.

Another grape to come from German research is the Dornfelder, a generous moderately early ripening vine which has shown great promise in East Anglian trials in 1986, a poor year. The single grape wine is fresh, light, clean and fruity, not unlike a young Beaujolais.

The Austrian Zweigeltrebe, a Pinot Noir cross, is another later ripening grape producing a massive crop of big bunches of big grapes, and a vine that looked to have considerable promise when first introduced, followed by Blauberger, another Austrian vine. Long term trials have proven disappointing, ripening being late and the must lacking in fruit, body and colour.

Having discussed the principles of blending grapes to achieve a superior end product, an undertaking that must be approached with great care, first ascertain whether the grapes in question are compatible in style and flavour. For example, it is useless trying to merge two grapes each of a totally different and overpowering character. Secondly, one must be very cautious when attempting to blend grapes from the Pinot family – Pinot Noir, for example – with grapes from another area – indeed, grapes of any ancient noble lineage with hybrid grapes, unless they have a common parent or a very similar style. Trial and error are the only guidelines to success here.

Having also run through the majority of the possible vine varieties, discarding the useless ones and describing the merits and limitations of the possibles, let us, after making one final point, now move onto the next step of making wine from these red grapes. We are moving onto unknown and exciting ground here. Red wine has recently been taken seriously by a handful of English growers and their customers, indeed the demand is such that they are planting more red wine grape vines. This is a significant and hard won achievement. With care, vine age and wine maturity, this is an exciting new opening.

Making Red Wine

To make red wine, the crushed grapes must undergo a period of fermentation on the pulp in order that the colour can be extracted from the skins to stain the wine red. With very few exceptions, black grapes have a clear pulp and if they are merely crushed and then pressed, as with white wine, the juice from red grapes would also be devoid of any colour. The depth of colour is decided by the length of time the red wine is allowed to remain fermenting on the skins. This should be no longer than 7–8 days after which the colour starts to be re-absorbed back into the must.

Red Wine Must Improvement to 93 Oechsle – 12.9% Alcohol

Sugar additions relate to a given volume of 100 litres of wine

°Oe	Kg sugar (1 Kg = 2.2 lb)
50	11.0
52	10.5
54	9.9
56	9.4
58	8.8
60	8.3
62	7.8
64	7.3
66	6.8
68	6.3
70	5.7
72	5.2
74	4.7
76	4.2
78	3.7
80	3.2
82	2.7

Ascertain the Oechsle of the must with a hydrometer. Find the oechsle on the chart, and the figure opposite under the sugar column denotes how much sugar should be added for each 100 litres of wine.

°Oe	Kg sugar
	(1 Kg = 2.2 lb)
84	2.2
86	1.7
88	1.2
90	0.7
92	0.2

Natural Fermentation

Many winemakers on the Continent are content to rely on the natural wine yeast cells on their grapes to ferment their wines. This system is traditional in many, many areas.

The outer surface of all grapes is covered by a waxy substance to which adheres a down or bloom. If grapes grown in wine areas of France and Germany are examined under a microscope, this surface is seen to be covered with microscopic fungi or yeast cells, each grape having as many as 100,000 true wine yeast cells and as many as 10 million wild yeast cells, plus thousands of bacteria cells, some malevolent, others beneficial.

In general the true wine yeast cells, being the strongest, take over when the wild yeast cells die when an alcohol content of about 5 per cent has been reached, and are also usually sufficiently tough to overcome any harmful bacteria present. It is maintained that the gradual accumulation of dead and dying wild and wine yeast cells adds definite nuances of flavour and bouquet not found in wines whose must was originally sterilized and then inoculated with a chosen activated wine yeast.

In England the situation is different. There are not vast areas of vineyards here that have been in existence for a thousand or more years, so there is no vast reservoir of true wine yeasts that will inhabit the skins of our grapes before harvest. There are wild yeasts in abundance and, of course, the bacteria cells, as has been confirmed by an intensive study made by a scientist at the Long Ashton Research Station near Bristol, so it is useless for the English grower to rely on nature. Remember wild yeasts have a low alcohol tolerance, so a wine allowed to ferment naturally will stick when 5 per cent of alcohol has been achieved.

A wine will not keep in a sound condition without a minimum alcohol content of about 10 per cent by volume, so it is essential that all wine musts be sterilized thoroughly with potassium metabisulphite (SO_2) at the rate of 5–20 g per 22 gallons (1 hectolitre) and fermentation induced by the introduction of a yeast starter.

Fermentation Containers

All fermentation vessels must be washed with scrupulous care and then sterilized before use. Glass, polyester, stainless steel and cement glass-lined containers are fairly straightforward to clean, but casks present more of a problem. It is obviously easier to choose a vessel of man-made material in which to ferment and store wine, indeed for white wines this is a necessity. But with red wine it is an attractive thought to ferment in wood and, indeed, contact with wood, oak in particular, does *so* much to soften and mellow a harsh young red wine. The ideal is a new oak cask each year; the few top Bordeaux chateaux adopt this practice and sell off their used casks after a single year's use to lesser chateaux, who are content to use one-year-old casks for their wines.

Old casks are too risky for precious young red wine, the one exception being newly emptied brandy casks: all other spirits would taint the flavour. Ex-beer or cider barrels are useless. Casks are no more expensive than any other vessel in fact, so if one can run a cooper to earth in London or Bristol, or in any city into whose docks wine is regularly imported, the cooper will often have a fair range in stock, or be able to make one or two or more, given time. Casks need tremendous care over cleaning and sterilizing, the usual method being steam sterilization followed by burning a sulphur-candle inside. Masses of boiling water is a substitute for the steam sterilization and, to prevent shrinkage when empty, always leave a cask full of water liberally dosed with SO_2.

A word of warning here; too small a cask offers too great a surface of the wine to the air via the slow porous action of the wood, and the greater ratio of wood to wine creates a tannic rough wine that could be undrinkable. Fifty gallons is really the smallest size to be safe in this respect. It is recommended that red wines are not stored in wood for the full 12-month fermentation/maturing period – six months is ample.

Crushing

The grapes should be milled or crushed as soon as possible after arrival in the winery. A hand-powered or motorized grape mill is used, preferably with a de-stalker – otherwise most of the stalks must be removed with a sterilized plastic rake head, thus avoiding the risk of making an over tannic wine.

The milled grapes are tipped straight into the container in which the pulp fermentation will take place. In a good year one will be dealing with fully-ripe grapes which present no problems, but in a poor year one may be faced with less than ripe grapes on sappy green stems, with a percentage, perhaps, of minute bullet-hard green berries, the result of a partial set. If all this undesirable material is left in for the pulp fermentation, the wine could end up irreparably tannic and bitter. A de-stemmer will extract all these unwanted elements most effectively.

The pulp ferment is conducted in a large vat, either of wood, glass, food-grade plastic or polyester. It has to have an open top so that the winemaker can inspect daily and make sure that the mass of pulp and skins is kept submerged beneath the surface. Their natural inclination is to collect on the surface as a 'cap' and, unless submerged, will become infected with airborne bacteria and contaminate the wine. Therefore, a minutely perforated wooden disk is used to keep this mass beneath the surface so that all the colour and flavour can easily be extracted by the action of the ferment. The top of the container is kept closely covered, preferably with a sulphite-soaked closely-woven cloth over which the lid is placed – re-dampen the cloth each day and check that the cap is still beneath the disk.

Do not fill the pulp-fermentation vessel more than 75 per cent full, or the activity of the initial violent fermentation will cause the new wine to overflow and much will be lost. Immediately the container is, therefore, 75 per cent full, add the appropriate amount of SO_2 at the ratio of 5 gms, or 1 oz, per hectolitre, or 22 gallons. This suppresses the wild yeasts and knocks out any potentially harmful bacteria. Pour in the necessary amount of wine yeast when the steeping vat is no more than a quarter full so that the fermentation begins from the base of the pulp; it will quickly spread to the rest of the vat.

In the meantime the gravity or density and the total acidity of the must has to be ascertained and corrected if necessary.

Adjusting the Gravity and Acidity
(See the chapter on white wine production)

Having arrived at a situation whereby we have ascertained the gravity or density of the must, and the acidity, after the 6–12 hour sterilization period, the amount of sugar to add can be worked out and added, and, finally, the yeast can be stirred well into the length and depth of the must.

Quickly re-cover the container, using a well-fitting lid which allows the gas to escape but denies air access, or, failing this, a damp blanket which has been soaked in SO_2 solution.

Temperature

It is essential that the pulp fermentation is conducted at a reasonable temperature. Too hot a temperature will result in a quick fast fermentation which leaves the wine lacking in colour and flavour, whereas with too cool a temperature the fermentation is in danger of stopping and sticking. It is recommended that red wine is fermented between 15°C and 20°C (60°F–70°F).

The very action of fermentation raises the must temperature. In England the likelihood of the temperature rising too high is slim, our autumn temperatures being fairly temperate. Should, however, the danger of either extreme present itself, the must can be cooled by pouring water over the vats as is practised in Champagne, or, should shock tactics be demanded, a polythene bag full of ice cubes can be suspended in the overheated vat, or remove 50% of the pulp until it cools down.

If the obverse be the case and the temperature of the must be too cool, then an immersion heater can be suspended in the must until such time as the temperature has risen to an acceptable level.

Certain questionable practices have crept into Burgundian winemaking. The age-old principles of a slow cool fermentation tend to be disregarded in favour of a short fast ferment, some houses resorting to subjecting one-fifth of the total must to a 'hot fermentation' at 34°C–35°C. This might run for eight days, fermenting out totally and then being returned to the remainder of the wine. Other establishments favour a 12-day, cooler ferment at 25°C–28°C, Romaneé Conti maintaining a traditional cool fermentation at a maximum of 23°C–25°C. Other speeding-up processes, shortcuts in wine production to hasten the wine from the vine to the customer's dinner table, including the pasteurization of young wine to render it stable for early bottling and sale, are abhorred by the more traditional houses. Such are the pressures of economics that these practices are made attractive to those of slightly less than impeccable principles, and obviously result in a lowering of the quality of some Burgundies. The wines are thus saleable much earlier, although they lack in colour, depth and elegance, and are also alarmingly short-lived compared to Burgundies made by the *methode ancienne*.

Variety Blending

Should a grower be making his red wine from more than one grape variety, there is a distinct chance that the ripening may not be concurrent. This presents no problems, however, as many of the most famous red

Bordeaux châteaux pick and process their 3–4 different grapes as they ripen, and blend sooner or later according to their own particular tradition. At Château Mouton Rothschild the ferment lasts ten days at a temperature of between 19°C–30°C, and the subsequent two weeks is spent on the skins drawing further colour and staying power. The *egalisage* or *assemblage* of the three grape varieties then follows immediately, it being the practice of the house to blend sooner rather than later. The wine is then transferred to new 225-litre (50-gallon) barriques or casks of Limousin oak, where it stays for 1½–2 years. The grape percentages in the Mouton blend are Cabernet Sauvignon 90 per cent, Cabernet Franc 5 per cent, Merlot 3–4 per cent and 1–2 per cent Petit Verdot.

Stalk stripping, or *egrappage*, is practised here and also at Château Lafite where the grape percentages are Cabernet Sauvignon 66 per cent with 32 per cent of Merlot and Cabernet Franc and 1–2 per cent Petit Verdot. At Lafite, in a year that has been too hot, the free-run wine, *vin de goutte,* might be too flabby and soft, and may need the addition of some *vin de première presse* and *vin de seconde presse,* pressed out in small wooden presses to provide backbone.

Château Lafite is stored for 2½–3 years in new hogsheads or barriques of Troncais oak from the Auvergne, which are only used once.

Château Lafite shows great finesse, fragrance, breed, softness and depth of flavour compared with the bigger harder fuller wine of Château Mouton Rothschild. Note the high percentage of Cabernet Sauvignon in Mouton.

At Château Margaux similar ancient traditional winemaking practices are followed, in common with Châteaux Lafite, Mouton, Latour and Haut Brion, whereas most other chateaux have changed to stainless-steel fermentation vats, quicker processing throughout and earlier sales – and certainly a shorter total bottle life. At Château Margaux the grapes are delivered into large stone troughs, and from there to enormous coopered oaken vats to ferment after crushing. New Limousin oak casks are made annually on the premises, and to visit the cellar where the wine of the previous vintage is quietly and coolly maturing slowly in hundreds of casks, is a staggering onslaught on the senses of sight and smell, the whole cellar being filled with a glorious heady musky bouquet of a young and yet already elegant wine, an unforgettable experience.

M. Georges Siloret, an eminent grower and author of a definitive work on viticulture and winemaking, owner of Château Guardet Le Franc Grace Dieu in St Emilion, makes his wine in three batches as the grapes ripen. Merlot is first and Cabernet Sauvignon is last, the vendage lasting about eight days. The wines are fermented on the pulp in large glass-lined concrete tanks, and then transferred to casks after blending.

The wine matures in bulk for 22 months before being bottled and is not sold until it is four-years-old.

At Château Franc Mayne on the other hand, also a St Emilion vineyard, M. Jacques Marckert puts all his grapes together from the start, including grapes from severely chlorosed vines and vines of 100 years old, and more, and though such vines yield a minute amount compared to a young vine, the quality and elegance these grapes give to his wine more than merits their continued existence. He never grubs up ancient vines until they die; some of the vines are so old that the stems are like old thorn trees, gnarled and split into two.

To sum up here, it would appear that different red grapes achieve different degrees of sweetness and other qualities each year, so that one has a better chance of creating a better-balanced wine and a consistency of style by conducting a few blending percentages and having comparative tastings with earlier vintages before blending. Thus any major aberrations can be adjusted by adding more or less of a given grape if need be. Therefore, the top Bordeaux châteaux practice of blending after the first ferment, or even after the second racking a month later, would seem to be advisable.

Pressing

The length of time the red wine remains on the skins and pulp should be determined by the cessation of the aerobic primary fermentation. Take a reading of the density each day, and as soon as it drops down to between 4° and 0°, usually within 7–8 days – at the outside – run the free-run juice off into containers via a tap at the base of the fermentation vat. Otherwise transfer all the pulp to the wine press.

Scrub both the wine press and all the other equipment to be used with hot water and washing soda, rinse well, then give a final rinse with an SO_2 solution. The free-run juice will run out of the press, and should you have a vast amount of red wine under production, the free-run juice can be kept apart as an élite wine, and the pressed-out red wine stored separately. Mix the free-run juice with the pressed juice later and fit a bored cork and an airlock to the containers and the red wine will begin its secondary fermentation.

A constant chore is frequently to check that the tanks, casks or jars are kept really full, otherwise the young wine is open to contamination by spoilage organisms. As the fermentation slowly continues and ceases, the wine lessens in volume. It is, therefore, necessary to have extra containers of lesser sizes into which to rack the wine as the volume decreases, and to top up all containers each week.

Oakies

To leave young red wine in used casks for the total of the fermentation and maturing period can result in the wine becoming impossibly woody, tannic and rough, therefore, unless one can offer the wine a new oak cask, restrict the time it rests in a cask to a mere two or three months. In the USA many winemakers, who have been dubbed 'oakies', slip mature oak chips into the red wine for the entirety of the secondary ferment and maturing period; this practice gives the wines the benefits of contact with oak without the risks. Put the oak chips into a fine muslin bag, add glass marbles or pebbles to hold the chips down on the bottom of the vat.

The secondary fermentation should be conducted at cellar temperature, between 10°C and 15°C (50°F–60°F) which ensures that progress will be slow and steady and enable the wine to have ample opportunity to mellow and subsequently mature.

It is recommended that red wine is racked every two months in order that it does not absorb a bitter flavour from the dead and dying yeast cells. Remember to top the wine right up to the cork, and when all possible signs of fermentation activity have ceased, solid corks or bungs can be fitted.

Malolactic Fermentation

More often than not a malolactic fermentation will occur naturally. Should the wine have been over-acid at harvest, then the malolactic ferment will more than likely put this problem right. Should the wine have been lacking in acid at harvest, then one should endeavour to prevent the malolactic ferment occurring by heavy sulphuring to stabilize the wine before it occurs.

There are two acids present in wine – tartaric and malic. When conditions within the wine demand, a malolactic ferment will take place. This can take place as early as during or at the end of the alcoholic fermentation, but is more usual in the following June. It requires, ideally, a temperature of between 17.5°C–20°C (65°F–70°F) to trigger it off and maintain and complete the process, so it is more usual for the malolactic fermentation to occur in June as the temperatures reach a level to encourage this natural phenomenon.

Grape must contains two acids – tartaric and malic. Tartaric is the acid particularly associated with grape juice. As grapes ripen, the tartaric acid does not alter greatly, but malic acid, high in unripe grapes, decreases sharply as the grapes ripen.

Thus, during the malolactic ferment, the malic acid is replaced by the milder lactic acid, causing a dramatic drop in the total acidity, resulting in a drop of one half of the acidity of the original malic acid. During this reaction, some CO_2 is formed and is given off.

Should the must be too acidic for a malolactic fermentation to take place, for example in the wines of a poor cool summer made with unripe grapes, then it may be necessary to lower the offending acidity slightly so that the malolactic ferment can move in and finish the job naturally. This will occur in fermented wines with a total acidity in excess of 11 g per ml.

To lower the acidity, add a dose of precipitated chalk, no greater than 1 gram per litre, and make sure that the wine container is no more than three-quarters full to cope with the vesuvial eruption that will occur. Precipitated chalk acts on the tartaric rather than the malic acid, and if too great a dose were to be added, one would eliminate the tartaric acid, which would result in a wine with no acid at all following the malic acid eradicating malolactic fermentation, which in turn would leave the wine dull, flabby and soft with no keeping powers at all.

Do not dose the wine with SO_2 before or during the malolactic fermentation, otherwise the process will be at best halted, or at worst smothered. But when this reaction has totally ceased, rack the wine and then dose with SO_2 to stabilize.

Clearing and Fining Red Wines

The easiest and most effective way of clearing a wine stubbornly refusing to fall star bright, is to expose it to the cold in mid-winter. An age-old custom is to roll the barrels outside, and subject the contents to several nights of considerable frosts. The results can be dramatic.

It is, however, rare that a wine presents any problem in clearing. Should the frost method fail, there are several natural and highly effective materials one can use, namely white of egg, isinglass, gelatine, blood, Bentonite and milk.

The minute particles in wine that cause a haze or cloudiness carry a negative charge and instead of slowly collecting and settling, they repulse one another as would the negative poles of two magnets. The fining substances already listed carry a positive or neutralizing charge, and they coagulate and flocculate within the wine and, as they sink as a fine web or veil through the wine, they collect all the haze particles and render the wine star bright.

White of egg is recommended for red wines. Use at the ratio of four egg whites per unit of 225 litres or forty five gallons, whisk gently with a little water and a pinch of salt, but do *not* beat to a fluffy consistency. Mix this with a little of the wine, and then pour it gently into the top of the wine vessel. If gelatine is to be used, take 2 grammes of unflavoured gelatine per 5 gallons of wine, moisten it, then mix with a little warm water and stand in a warm situation until it is clear. Lastly mix with a little wine and gently add to the bulk of the wine. Before clearing, the wine first becomes very cloudy, and the clearing can take several days. Gelatine can also be used for fining white wines.

Bentonite is effective, but has the drawback that it has a bleaching effect on red wines and, swelling as it does to many times its original volume within the wine, it settles into a deep deposit, and thus much wine is lost. Also, microscopic particles can remain in the wine, requiring a further fining with gelatine. Use Bentonite at a ratio of 5–10 grammes per 5 gallons. Rack the wine off the finings after 45 days.

Fining, if necessary, is usually undertaken just before filtering and bottling. One should avoid attempting to filter a wine unless it is clear and bright, or the filter pads will be continuously clogging and needing frequent replacement. Therefore, one can postpone fining a wine until the time arrives for bottling, by which time the majority of wines will have cleared themselves during the cold spells in the winter.

Maturing

The length of time given to a particular red wine for bulk maturation depends on two factors. The first, space, is largely dependent on the size of the winery and the availability of bulk containers. But, before making provision for prolonged bulk storage, a given wine must show enough promise of quality and finesse to merit taking up space in bulk for more than one year. A poor red wine will never advance beyond mediocrity, whereas a red wine of substance can take two or three, even as many as six years to reach the zenith of its potential, to soften in colour from a raw purple to the gentle hue of orange-brown Tudor bricks, and soften from a harsh astringent pithy flavour to a smooth mellow elegance with a perfect balance of softness and acidity. These changes can only be wrought with time and patience.

Take a situation in which a grower plants early-ripening black grapes in a superb situation, creates a wine with three carefully chosen and matched varieties, makes the wine under carefully controlled conditions using traditional methods, allows a more than adequate time for the wine to mature and ameliorate before bottling, and time laying away in bottle before drinking – at six to seven years old these wines can be outstanding.

With the Alsatian hybrids, a total of six years is none too short a time for the wine to approach its best – these wines have not enjoyed a good reputation to date because they are drunk at a year or at most two years old, and are at this stage sappy, raw and all over the place. Therefore, dear reader, I implore you, should you make red wine, to leave the wine in bulk in the cool for longer than usual, to leave it laying away in bottle for longer than usual, and your patience will be well rewarded.

Filtering

Most red wines will only require a coarse filtration before bottling if they have been well made, racked several times, and matured in bulk for eighteen months to two years. To subject red wine to the punishment of an EK or EKS filtration will rob it of a great deal of hard won colour and a certain degree of the depth of flavour. Ensure that the wine is totally stable and naturally cleared before bottling.

We find that by racking wines every three months, cask maturing for 6–12 months, white of egg fining at 15 months for 45 days, one can bottle at eighteen months straight from the tap without filtering at all. The wine is a deep dark colour, mellow, supple, with a superb balance and great length on the palate, masses of complex fruit flavours – a sophisticated and elegant wine.

15
The Small Vineyard

The emphasis has, perhaps, been biased so far towards the larger vineyard, therefore this chapter is devoted to discussing how a small vineyard might be established and function.

Some people plant a few vines in the corner of the vegetable garden, on a rough steep bank, others clear an area in their orchard, or in the corner of a field, or in their allotment. Such sites are perfectly viable, and are wholly capable of producing grapes for making house wine for the grower. Bear in mind that an outdoor vine is capable when mature of providing the grower with one or two bottles of wine each year and that, therefore, it pays to plant vines in multiples of five or six so that you are planting an annual yield of one, two, five, ten or twenty gallons, which simplifies the winemaking process. Vines grown on walls or fences can, when mature, produce a very considerable weight of grapes each year.

The size of the small vineyard is usually limited by the area available. Some people grow their vines along south-facing walls or fences; others in rows in the garden. The basic principles for planting and training apply, whether on a large or small scale, but remember that the vine is a sun lover, and needs day-long sun if it is to ripen its grapes efficiently. So choose the site with care, and provide the sunniest location possible.

When planning a garden mini-vineyard bear in mind that for efficient pollination it pays to plant the vines, if possible, in a block rather than in a long single row. Though vines are self-fertile, a swift pollination is more likely if there are several rows of vines adjacent to one another. Though a garden site is, in general, far better protected and warmer

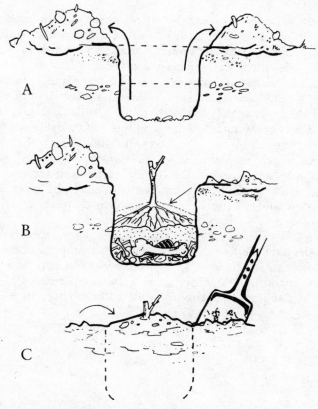

52 Planting individual vines in the garden or on a wall, or small garden vineyards, it pays handsomely to plant a vine with great care.

A shows a hole about 0.5 m × 0.5 m (1 ft 6 in × 1 ft 6 in), taking care to keep the friable top soil apart from the subsoil, if the latter is inferior in any way.
B shows a layer of rubble in the bottom for drainage, broken tiles, broken earthenware plant pots, old bones etc. Next put in a layer of old manure or well-rotted compost, followed by a mound of top soil onto which the vine is replanted with the roots fanned out. Cover the roots with the rest of the topsoil.
C fill in the hole with the subsoil, firming well with your boot as you fill. Leave no more than 5–8 cm (2–3 in) of the vine exposed to the air.

than an open field vineyard site, due to the close proximity of house walls and hedges, all of which trap heat; garden locations can be subject to tremendous through drafts; therefore, plant well away from such situations. Do not choose areas that are shaded by trees much of the day; try to choose open sunny sites, with free-draining soil and adequate protection from the east, west and north.

It is equally important that the vines chosen for the small vineyard are able to ripen; take advice on vines that are suited to your area, for we in Britain have more poor summers than good summers, and nothing is more disappointing than unripe grapes year after year.

In the garden situation, however, with some ingenuity the grower can overcome a cold wet autumn by enclosing his wine rows in clear polythene sheeting, which can be bought in rolls 2 m (6 ft) wide. This can be laid across the middle wire, and moored to the ground on either side of the vine rows by stones or logs. Thus miniature polythene tunnels are created, which keep the grapes warm and dry, and allow them to ripen in a cold wet autumn. Do remember to keep the ends open for ventilation – use netting across the ends to keep the birds and wasps out, but allow plenty of fresh air to keep fungal attack away. Maintain good spray cover.

Similarly, when vines are grown on walls or fences, it is an easy matter to hang a net over the vines, or even to put up a simple wooden structure to which one can attach polythene sheeting with battens, as a temporary measure to encourage ripening, or, indeed, as a permanent feature. Do remember to maintain adequate ventilation to prevent mildew and botrytis.

Training

The garden vineyard can be trained in the traditional Guyot way, with posts and wires. In general this is the best method as the vines are adequately supported during the entire growing season, and can easily withstand gales and cloud bursts. Some growers, however, not wishing to have rows of posts and wires in their gardens, opt for training their vines as individual bushes, and spur- or head-prune them each winter. This eliminates the need and expense of a strong post and wire trellis, each vine being supported by a bamboo or stake until the stem has thickened with age to be free-standing without any support. The vines can either be planted in a row or a block, the latter preferable in order to encourage good pollination, or even be planted at intervals along a flower border if there is no room for a separate plot. Another plan is to put up a wooden trellis between the flower garden and the vegetable area, and grow vines all over the trellis to screen one area from the other. Illustrated details of both methods will be discovered in the chapter on training vines.

There is a place in every garden for a few vines, for producing grapes for eating, grapes for winemaking, or for purely ornamental reasons.

Many vines develop glorious rich and contrasting autumnal colouring, turning yellow, gold, all shades of red, bronze and brown.

Mildew

In the garden there are likely to be more problems with mildew, and with birds and wasps, due to the proximity of many other gardens and, in consequence, a concentration of fruit growing. It is, however, not too demanding a task to maintain a regular spray programme on a garden scale, a small pump sprayer is perfectly adequate, and a small hand puffer is excellent for applying powdered sulphur.

Mildew and botrytis sprays can be bought in horticultural shops; you will need sulphur in some form or other, either used as a powder, or micronized so it can be applied as a spray – this chemical deals with oidium or powdery mildew. Downy mildew needs a copper or zinc spray, Bordeaux mixture or Zineb. For botrytis use Elvaron, Benlate, Bravo or Rovral, preferably in rotation in order that immune strains do not develop, and so that the grapes do not suffer too great a chemical build up, and, in consequence, affect the fermentation of the wine.

Consult the yellow pages for Agricultural and Horticultural chemical suppliers.

Birds and Netting

If a grower maintains a strawberry bed and, perhaps, a raspberry cage, he will have some netting to keep the birds off these crops. This netting can be used to protect the grapes from the birds. If your vines are trained in rows on a trellis, give then a final thorough summer pruning and if the net is of adequate size, drape it over the entire area, having first run wires or strong nylon cord from post top to post top in each direction, as a support system for the netting. Alternatively, run narrow rolls of netting up either side of each row, attached above the middle wire of the trellis with plant ties, and moor it to the ground with stones or logs. If wasps are a problem, buy netting of sufficiently fine mesh to keep them out (see appendix for suppliers).

Wall vines are much easier to net. Insert several nails or hooks along the wall above the vines, and run a wire tightly from one end to the other. Attach the netting to this wire, netting of sufficient size to reach beyond the vines at each side, and to be moored to the ground with stones or logs in front of the vines.

It is imperative to net garden vines, or the birds will strip the entire crop in one day, and well before the grapes are ripe enough to eat or to convert into wine. The wasps will similarly descend on semi-ripe grapes, and devour the whole crop in just a day or two. It may be a nuisance to have to buy a net and to take the trouble to net the vines, but if the net is a good one it will last indefinitely and so is an investment. If a grower takes the trouble to plant, maintain, prune, train, spray and care for vines for a whole year, it is a crime to allow some pest to eat the entire crop just for the sake of a net, and an hour or two to cover the vines.

Take care never to use the same sprayer for spraying the vines that has previously been used for spraying weeds. All growers should have two sprayers, each clearly marked FUNGICIDES and WEED CONTROL – it is impossible to completely clean plastic containers of chemicals, as the material absorbs a certain amount. Most weed killers are so lethal that the vapour alone can kill or distort such tender plants as vines, let alone spraying from the same equipment. Many modern insect sprays are highly poisonous if inhaled or if they touch the skin, so, again, be very careful for the sake of yourselves, your neighbours and your pets that you only use safe insect sprays such as pyrethrum or derris. You may have to spray your plants more often as pyrethrum and derris are contact sprays rather than residual sprays, and to catch the next hatching of any pest you may have to spray once a week for two or three weeks to eliminate subsequent generations. Vines have few insect enemies, other than wasps, but can sometimes be troubled by vine weevils, red spiders, and, under glass, the mealy bug or vine scale. For the latter a winter wash with tar oil is the answer, applied in late December or early January.

Cropping

Follow advice given in the chapter on training and pruning, remembering to cut back hard at the end of the first growing season, and begin to allow the vine to take shape in the second year. Do not allow the vine to bear any fruit until the third year, nor allow them to bear heavily until the fifth year.

The actual harvest date depends on many factors. First, if the vines are protected under polythene, then the harvest can be postponed until the grapes are fully ripe. Alternatively, should an outbreak of mildew or botrytis occur, then one's hand is forced and the grapes should be picked immediately. The refractometer is a little expensive for the garden or botrytis occur, then one's hand is forced and the grapes should be picked immediately. The refractometer is a little expensive for the garden vineyard, so to determine the sugar content squeeze sufficient grapes to fill a hydrometer trial glass with juice, and determine the reading with a hydrometer.

Grapes can be converted into wine without any additional sugar when the sugar tops 75–80 degrees oechsle; less than this, consult the table on p. 221 and add the appropriate amount of sugar to each gallon. An enclosed garden site very often affords greater heat concentration by day and is, therefore, likely to produce higher sugars in the grapes than those from an exposed open vineyard; wall vines and vines on fences ripen earlier and better than those in the open in the garden, as they enjoy the best of all outdoor locations.

In these troubled times, when everyone is trying to be more self-sufficient and to grow as much fruit and as many vegetables as possible, to devote a few yards to growing one's own wine, and raisins for cake making, is just another aspect of this drive towards a better household economy. The vine is no more demanding than raspberries or black-currants in terms of hardiness, training, pruning and general care; it is not a tender exotic sub-tropical weakling. The vine will survive greater winter frost than most plants, and *after* the first year when it does need care to establish itself, the vine will survive drought and most weather extremes without flinching. Care should be taken to avoid planting the vine in a wet situation, in an ill-drained hollow, because wet feet is the one condition that vines cannot tolerate.

16

Vines Under Glass

The fashion for growing vines under glass began in the eighteenth century at a time when a great many of the large houses and mansions in Britain were built surrounded by their glorious gardens and grounds. Whether the environs were of expansive park-like proportions, planned by Capability Brown, or Italianate, strictly formal with a maze of geometrically laid-out areas divided and adorned with neatly clipped hedges, stone balustrades and a wealth of marble statuary, most establishments had a considerable area devoted to the production of vegetables and fruit, including grapes. This period coincided with the importing of many tender and exotic plants from the foothills of the Himalayas and other points east by the intrepid early plant hunters.

These exotics required protection from the vagaries of the English climate and, therefore, houses of glass were planned and built to accommodate them. Many of these early glasshouses were extremely attractive, often built of classic Georgian proportions and features, some with stone rear and end walls with huge glass windows on the south front, housing orange, lemon and banana trees, tender ferns and flowering plants and shrubs.

Gradually the gardeners who tended these plants became highly skilled in understanding the needs of their charges, no less with the vines that were imported from the warmer areas of France and Germany – Chasselas, Muscat, Trollinger (Black Hamburg), Muscat Hamburg and so on. These skilled gardeners experimented with these early vines and by cross-pollination bred some new varieties which were named after the house, the lady of the house or the gardener himself. Three examples would be Madresfield Court, Lady Downe's seedling and Fosters' seedling. Thus the limited range of indoor vines was enlarged.

In the heyday of the vinery the building might well be divided into many different sections, each housing a different collection of vines, the success as much to do with the care lavished upon the vines as the preparation of the border and careful nutritional and health programme.

Vinery

Vines grow better if planted in a south-facing glasshouse, a house aligned east to west. This gives the vines sun access from dawn to dusk and, in consequence, a greater chance of ripening the grapes to perfection. The perfect house would have a stone or brick base, the windows opening fully if required to encourage massive fresh air circulation as a preventative against mildew and botrytis, and adequate roof ventilation.

Planting Outside or Inside

Vines can be planted inside a glasshouse if conditions and the structure permit or, alternatively, they can be planted outside and then introduced into the house via a hole near ground level.

Obviously if it is possible to excavate and put in a proper vine border inside the house, and the vine roots will be able to make their way in time under the foundations into soil outside the house, then this system is the best, for the grower has far more control over the nutrition, watering and well-being of the vine.

On the other hand, if the house be so set up, either with other plants or crops, or by virtue of its construction, that it is preferable to plant the vines outside, then, if it is at all possible to prepare the border outside into which the vines are to be planted along similar lines to the ideal indoor border, the vines will thrive.

The advantages of the vine planted inside are that an earlier start into the growth cycle is achieved due to the soil and atmosphere warming in spring before the outdoor border would do so. The root system planted outside is inclined to take up excessive moisture in late summer and early autumn. If, once the grapes approach ripeness, which is indicated by black grapes beginning to colour and white grapes beginning to turn from green to gold and becoming translucent, much rain should fall before the grapes are picked, the now set and thickened skins simply burst with the excess moisture. This can be avoided by leaning a sheet or sheets of corrugated iron against the outside of the glasshouse wall over the area occupied by the vine roots to shoot all rain beyond the root area as the grapes are ripening.

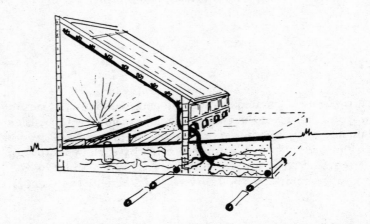

53 Method of planting a vine *outside* a glasshouse, in a border specially prepared, as shown below, and introducing the rod in through a hole in the glasshouse wall. Train from 1 to 10 or more rods up the roof, leaving 30–45 cm (12–18 in) between each rod. Spur prune in December.

Preparation of the Border

There is no way of better insuring success with indoor vines than a really thorough preparation of the border in which they are planted. Here again we can learn from the past by studying the way in which our forebears planted their glasshouse vines. Obviously in many cases the following advice would be neither practical nor even possible; to follow just one or two of the principles explained will, however, better the performance of a vine.

Months before planting, the grower should prepare his vine border compost. Build a heap of compost in layers using animal manure, vegetable waste, woodash, charcoal, soil and sand, if possible turning it upside down once or twice to mix it thoroughly. Aim at making enough to fill the whole border if you are planting the whole border with vines, or a part of the border if you are planting one or two vines.

Ideally the border should be totally excavated and all soil removed. Make sure the bottom of the trench is sloping downhill so that the lower end corresponds with the lower area outside. Lay clay land drains along the bottom of the border placing them in a slight trench, taking the further end out of the house and into a drainage pit that can be filled with stones.

Cover the whole of the bottom of the trench with broken tiles, bones, smashed brick pieces, placing this over a layer of grass turves, grass side down. This forms an excellent drainage system so the roots never become waterlogged, and all excess water escapes down the piping. Cover this with a layer of manure.

The next layer is the specially prepared vine border compost, liberally sprinkled with hoof and horn, bonemeal, with a little boron and magnesium sulphate. This medium should be thoroughly rotted, having a soil-like appearance and texture. Into this one plants the vines, sur-

54 Section through vine border (indoor or outdoor). (A) Fertile top soil, with added wood ash, charcoal, hoof and horn, bonemeal and general fertilizer. (B) Manure or compost (C) Layer of turves placed face down (D) Layer of rubble, with land drain at the bottom, to carry away excess moisture.

rounding the roots with a pocket of John Innes No. 3 soil. Firm the vines in with the foot really well so they are really solidly planted.

Certain training systems suit glasshouses in which a variety of plants are grown, in which case the vines are trained in such a way that they do not shade or draw the other plants. Should the house be solely devoted to vines, then the vines can be trained up the front and then on up the inside of the roof of the house. A system of wires must be installed to provide support for the vines at 30-cm (1-ft) intervals.

Planting

The one- or two-year-old indoor vine should be pruned down to two or three buds at planting, and if the roots are long these should be pruned back to 7 cm (3 in). This ensures that the roots do not suffer from dieback, but the cut root ends quickly sprout and make masses of tough new growth.

Support the vines as they grow by tying them in to the wires or to a bamboo. There are basically three locations offered to vines, the best being planted in the south-facing border, and after the initial formation of horizontal rods, canes are trained vertically from these at approximately 30 cm (1 ft) intervals up the south front and south-facing roof area. Secondly, in a lean-to house, vines can be grown up the back wall, freeing the front of the house for other crops. Lastly, some growers train a single or double rod up one end of the house and then run one or two rods along the roof apex of a glasshouse used for other plants.

Spraying

Due to the lack of constant fresh air-flow within a glasshouse, indoor vines are far more vulnerable to mildew and botrytis infection than the outdoor vine. Therefore, a regular and efficient spray programme is an essential deterrent.

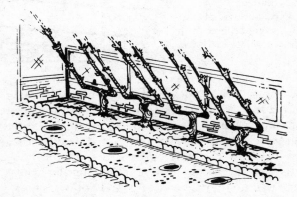

55 Showing vines planted *inside* a glasshouse: prepare the border as on p. 256 and plant the vines at 1.6 m or 5 ft intervals, training two rods up from each plant. Spur prune in December and keep up a good spraying programme. Note upright land drains in the floor for watering the roots and feeding with ox blood in spring.

Under glass the application of a fungicide, particularly sulphur, in a dry form, is very effective.

The procedure is to spray the vines with water from a hose, allow it almost to dry off, and then apply the powdered yellow sulphur mixed 2–1 with a dry copper or zinc fungicide (Bordeaux mixture/Zineb) and the powder will adhere to the leaves, rods and flowers and later to the grapes. To protect the vines and grapes in a house in which there are several vines, on a moderate to large scale, the spray programme recommended for outdoor vines would offer an excellent preventative programme. It may at first glance seem an onerous chore, but once the spray is mixed and the sprayer filled, it only takes a short while to spray the vines to protect them for another two or three weeks.

Finally, the powdering is fine for most of the fungicide applications, but the vines really do need a break with a good anti-botrytis chemical such as Benlate at budbreak, just before and immediately following flowering, and again as the grapes start to colour in autumn with Rovral.

A mid-December to mid-January (no later) spray with 5 per cent tar oil helps to clean the vines for the new year and kill any overwintering pest eggs that may be lurking in the bark crevices.

Spraying is as vitally important for vines in their first year as it is for mature cropping vines – for once mildew and botrytis are firmly established in a glasshouse, they are almost impossible to eradicate and are always liable to re-infect the vines year after year.

Training and Pruning

In the first year a vine will make anything from 6 in–6 ft or more according to the care or lack of care taken over the preparation of the border. The rods must be tied to some support as they grow, to keep them straight.

Indoor vines are pruned in mid- to late-December, to be sure that the vine is thoroughly dormant and that all the sap is out of the wood. The dormant period for an indoor vine is naturally much shorter than that of an outdoor vine and, should spring begin early, the sap can rise in late January or February and late pruning could cause the vine to bleed very heavily. Though it is claimed that bleeding does no harm, it is better if it can be avoided.

In the first December, from one-third to two-thirds of the shoots or rods are removed. Cut away all the green unripened rod, leaving a nut-brown pencil-thick rod. Should the vine have made but a few inches of growth, cut down the shoot to leave just two or three buds on the stub, and the vine will surely grow away strongly in the second year.

The rods you retain can then begin to be trained to the framework or design you have in mind for them. For this a trellis or system of wires must be installed, keeping the wires some 15–22 cm (6–9 in) away from the walls, or glass roof, to allow adequate air circulation between the vine and the roof or wall, thus trying to avoid mildew and botrytis infection.

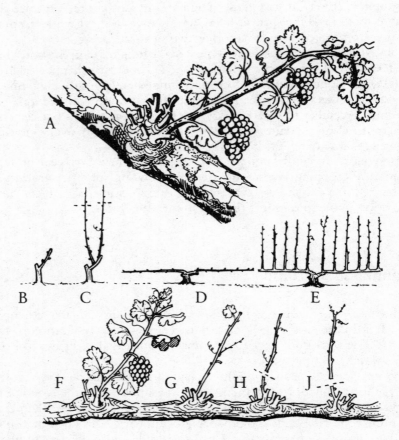

56 The indoor or glasshouse vine.   **A** shows a fruiting lateral giving some detail to the spur area from which growth springs anew each Spring.   **B** shows a newly planted indoor vine, two or three good buds being retained.   **C** growth at the end of the first season – two good rods.   **D** in January tie these two rods down onto a wire about 0.5 m (1 ft 6 in) above ground level.   **E** at the end of the second growing season vertical rods have been trained at 0.3 (1 ft) intervals. Remove side shoots, crop very lightly in the third year.   **F** detail of fruiting lateral with one bunch of grapes.   **G** fruiting lateral after leaf fall.   **H & J** show where to spur prune each fruiting lateral in December, leaving two buds on each spur.

The Second Year

The second season is devoted to establishing the framework of the vine and, if the border was really well made and filled with nourishing material, the vine will make massive rod growth, and be in a condition to fruit in the third year. Maintain a preventive spraying programme during the growing season, tie the rods onto the wirework as they grow, and pinch out all unwanted side shoots or laterals, leaving just a one-leaf stub. This prevents the bud in the leaf axil from growing away, the bud carrying the embryo rods and fruit in the following year. The one-bud stub is a safety valve, for if conditions dictate that the vine is showing extreme vigour, the bud on the stub will grow away, and the dormant embryo bud will remain so in readiness for the following year. Pinch out the growing tips once the rods have made sufficient length to fill the trellis.

No grapes should be allowed to develop in the first or second year – any flowers that form should be removed immediately.

Pruning for Fruit

Look at your vines very critically in December at pruning time. Only pencil-thick well-ripened rod is retained, all green unripe wood is cut away and all side shoots or laterals are cut back to leave just two buds at the base to form spurs. The main framework of long rods should not be closer than 30–45 cm (1–1½ ft) apart from one another, and try to keep them straight and parallel to maintain an attractive and professional appearance.

After pruning, spray the vines with a 5 per cent solution of tar oil, between mid-December and mid-January. In January or February spray with lime sulphur, and in March with copper – and at some time in the winter, wash and scrub down well the windows and woodwork of the glasshouse with a mild solution of chlorine to kill all mildew and botrytis spores and verdigris. Thus both the vines and the vinery are rendered clean and fit for the growing season ahead.

Lowering Rods

Well before budburst, and preferably just after pruning, untie all the vine rods from the wires and arch them right over until the tips touch soil level. At budburst, the rising sap would rush headlong to the highest end of each rod, charging these furthest buds with masses of sap and subsequent fruitfulness, wholly bypassing all the buds at the lower and middle stations of the rods. Therefore, the grower will have superb bunches at the top of the vine, and no grapes on the lower regions. By arching the rods in an inverted U back to the border, the rising sap will hit this rise and check, gorging the lower and middle buds with sap before continuing along the rods at a slow pace and activating all the buds in the right order as it advances.

Repeat this performance each and every year. Tie the rods up carefully after the furthest buds have burst.

Maintaining Border Fertility

Should the vine border have been made as outlined in this chapter, it is unlikely to need attention until the fourth year but, if the vines were simply planted into an existing border, then an annual nutrition plan will have to be followed. To do this, scrape away the top 15–30 cm (6 in–1 ft) of soil, and dress this lower area with hoof and horn, bonemeal, woodash and charcoal, lime, sulphate of potash and a layer of compost or manure before replacing the top soil. Many old vineries had land drains sunk into the soil in front of each vine stem, and soon after budburst diluted blood from the butcher was poured down the land drain, which also served as a watering hole. The above feeding suggestions are applicable for all indoor vines from the third or fourth year. Avoid using peat as it is too acid.

Indeed we are told that dead cats, even dead horses, were buried under mature vines, and the minerals were slowly released over the years to the ever-hungry vines. Indoor vines respond to frequent and generous feeding, and are very partial to rotted or burnt seaweed.

Controlling Fruit Output

In the third year, the first fruiting season, cropping must be restricted. Unchecked, the vine's instinct is to produce a vast number of bunches, quickly exhausting itself and sliding into a non-productive torpor.

Each spur will produce some two or three shoots, some without any bunches and some with embryo bunches. First remove the blind or bunchless shoots then, choosing the shoot with the biggest best-shaped bunch, remove the others, leaving just one shoot and one bunch of grapes on each spur to develop. Do not allow bunches to form closer than 30 cm (1 ft) from each other, to avoid the cardinal sin of over-cropping and, ideally, the spurs and their bunches should be situated on alternate sides of the main rods so that they do not shade one another and do not have to struggle for light and air.

Spraying with a Hose

From budburst to flowering it is advised that the whole vine is sprayed gently with a hose on all warm and sunny days, preferably in the morning. This practice must cease at flowering and not be resumed afterwards.

The floor and walls should also be dampened daily; this should continue throughout flowering and right through to the beginning of veraison, or the colouring of the grapes, when all watering ceases.

Mildew and Botrytis Spraying

Maintain the spraying and sulphur-dusting programme suggested earlier in this chapter. This, combined with good nutrition will ensure freedom from deficiency and behavioural problems such as coulure, millerandage and shanking and, of course, mildew and botrytis.

Flowering

In late May or early June the vines begin to flower. The old system of ensuring a good set was to take a hare's foot or a stoat's tail, and touch every flower in turn to ensure that every berry was pollinated. Then, some four weeks later, out would come the forked stick and the grape scissors, and about 70 per cent of the berries were cut out, so that none that remained touched one another. This resulted in a bunch of perfection, beautifully distributed large berries.

To save all the backbreaking thinning operation, give the house plenty of through draught when the vines are in flower, and on the third or fourth day go into the house at midday. Run every floret once through the hand, going from vine to vine so that the pollen from one vine is used on another. When all have been treated thus, spray the floor and border with a fine spray from a hose, close up most of the windows and close the door, and the increased humidity will complete the set or fertilization of the grape flowers. Repeat this performance the following day.

The joy of this simplified pollination is that *not* every single berry is set, and the berries do not subsequently require thinning.

Do not spray with fungicide during flowering, but resume immediately afterwards and continue until veraison, the stage at which the black grapes start to colour and the white grapes begin to turn translucent and from an acid green to a rich gold. Do not spray during this final ripening stage.

Stopping

The shoots or laterals that bear the grape bunches should be stopped, that is to have their growing tip pinched out four to six leaves beyond the bunch of grapes. The stopping of the fruiting laterals directs the growth and energy of the vine into grape rather than rod production. All side shoots that grow out from the leaf joints or leaf axils should be pinched out after one leaf and should they re-form, repeat the pinching again leaving one leaf and one bud as a safety valve.

Tie in the fruiting laterals to the wire framework, for the bunches of grapes become heavy as they colour and ripen and the weight might snap off the whole branch.

Watering

During the growing season the vine border must be thoroughly watered frequently and never allowed to dry out. Watering must be gradually reduced and then phased out as the grapes ripen. If the vines are watered heavily at this time, the grape skins which set at a certain size, will burst with the sudden rush of juice into the grape. Burst berries attract wasps, mildew and botrytis and, as a result deteriorate fast.

Wasps

Should wasps or bluebottles attack your ripening grapes, make some small netting bags out of discarded fine nylon stockings or tights, or from fine onion or vegetable bag netting discarded by the greengrocer.

Lavender is a great wasp deterrent. It is no bad plan to plant a few dwarf lavender bushes in the border, or even to hang bunches of lavender in amongst the bunches of grapes during the ripening period.

Grapes for the Table

The benefits of growing more than one variety of vine now become apparent as the grower has grapes ripening over four months or more. Under glass grapes will hang sound on the vine for many weeks, the earliest becoming edible in August in a hot summer, and the latest being gathered to decorate the Christmas table, beginning with Black Hamburg and finishing with Muscat of Alexandria, Canon Hall and Gros Colmar. Cut the grapes with a T piece of stem and present them on the table in a bed of vine leaves, or amongst other fruit in a fruit bowl.

Preserving Fresh Grapes

A method used for prolonging the life of cut ripe grapes which evolved in the era of the great gardens, was to make a framework with layers of racks set at 45° on which rows of bottles were laid, each filled with water. The grape bunches were cut within a 15-cm (6-in) length of lateral retained on the lower side of the bunch, this rod was pushed into the bottle of water, which kept the grapes in a fit state for many weeks. This apparatus would need to be kept in a dry, clean frost-free situation. Friends who have a great Victorian vinery have discovered a cache of these bottles in the back of their potting sheds.

17

Glasshouse Vine Varieties

In past centuries when life was different, a great many large houses had extensive vineries, giant glasshouses containing a wide collection of vine varieties. Often these glasshouses were divided into three – a cold house, a cool house and a hot or muscat house – enabling grapes of the three categories to be grown to perfection.

Cold-house grapes need no heat to ripen; cool-house grapes *may* need a little heat in early spring to encourage an earlier start into growth, and will need a little heat in September and October to finish them to perfection; hot-house grapes require a month or two of heat in spring and the same at the end of the season and considerable care and cosseting between times to encourage these later ripening grapes to ripen.

The exorbitant cost of all fuel today, the high cost of labour and the lack of time experienced by most people make the hot-house vine a creature of the past. This would be a greater tragedy than it is were there not some superb varieties amongst the cold and cool-house vines.

A vine that has had the border really well excavated and prepared, has been expertly planned, trained, pruned, fed and sprayed, can produce an abundance of quality grapes each year, and a real joy to the grower. Indoor vines are an excellent rainy-day chore, for there is always some job that can be done to further their well-being whatever the time of year.

A vine can occupy a house with other plants, providing the air can be kept buoyant and on the move in order to keep humidity and subsequent fungal attack at bay. Tomatoes and cucumbers are not ideal companions as they prefer a more humid atmosphere.

Cold-House Grape Vines

Black Hamburg (*Trollinger* in Germany)

Black Hamburg is the easiest vine to grow. It is a free-growing vine, is a generous cropper, the black grapes setting well and ripening early. In a hot year the grapes can ripen as early as mid-August, and, with care and luck, they will hang sound on the vine until Christmas. There are more Black Hamburg vines in Britain than any other indoor vine. They have tough dark-green leaves that discourage mildew, they set well with their own pollen, ripen well in a moderate cool summer, and produce large wedge-shaped bunches of firm round grapes which have a pleasant juicy flavour. The vine is not prone to shanking, coulure or off-seasons, and needs no heat, being the earliest to ripen under glass. It is highly recommended to the amateur grower.

Chasselas Rose Royale

This vine is also vigorous, a generous cropper, producing an abundance of bunches of glorious, rounded, pinky-gold grapes that will ripen under glass even in a cold sunless summer. The bunches are wide-shouldered and tapering, and a mature vine can produce bunches of massive proportions. The thin-skinned berries must be allowed to ripen fully and achieve a deep pink old-gold colour in order that the beautiful aromatic flavour can be fully developed. The Chasselas is, therefore, the ideal companion to the Black Hamburg, both, grown in a cold-house, being suitable for most areas in Britain.

Chasselas d'Or
(Also known as *Royal Muscadine* and *Chasselas de Fontainebleau*)

The Golden Chasselas is identical in all patterns of behaviour and adaptability to Chasselas Rosé, the latter being a clone of the Golden Chasselas, except that the grapes ripen to a pale yellowy gold. Chasselas vines are grown extensively in France and sold at the roadside to passers-by, particularly in Alsace. In Switzerland it is called Fendant, and in Germany Gutedal.

Cold- or Cool-House Grapes

Muscat Hamburg

This vine is not as simple to grow as the Black Hamburg and Chasselas vines. It tends to be reluctant to produce fruit, needs pollen from other vines to set a good crop, tending to set only a proportion of berries in each bunch, and is a few weeks later ripening than the aforementioned vine varieties.

The vine needs a careful balance of soil nutrients, requiring the usual bonemeal, hoof and horn, sulphate of potash and lime required by all indoor vines, but benefits greatly from the trace elements magnesium and boron, and also zinc applied as a spray in the form of Zineb. These elements bring the vine into the flowering situation in peak condition, encouraging a generous supply of flowers and a good fertilization. The situation can be further encouraged by hand pollinating each floret with pollen from another vine variety with a hare's foot or fine soft paintbrush.

The fully ripe grapes, which are oval in shape and a deep red maroon colour, are without doubt a finer, more delicious flavour than any other black grape, and so well worth their place in a vinery and the extra care they need to maintain a fruitful condition and full productivity. The grapes may need a little heat to complete ripening in northern counties or in ill-placed cold glasshouses, but will ripen to perfection by late September-early October in a good to average situation in southern and midland counties. This is the connoisseur's grape.

Muscat of Alexandria

A totally ripe grape of this variety is a classic grape of majestic elegant flavour. The vine is vigorous, is a generous cropper with an undeserved reputation of setting badly on its own pollen. Modern clones tend to avoid this fault, though to make sure of a good set, it is advisable to grow another variety in the same house. The bunches are of a classic wide-shouldered tapering shape, often of massive proportions, the oval muscat grapes ripen through green to a glorious golden-yellow colour, and must be left until fully ripe before harvesting.

Muscat of Alexandria is quite able to ripen its fruit without heat in all southern counties and in well placed sunny cold houses, but may need a little heat to finish ripening in less favourable areas. There is a great challenge in growing it to perfection.

Canon Hall Muscat

Known as the Guernsey grape, the Canon Hall is a clone of the Muscat
of Alexandria. It is known to be a difficult vine to maintain in a fruitful
condition and needs all the care that has to be lavished on the Muscat
Hamburg to maintain a state of fertility. The bunches and grapes are
larger and more luscious than Muscat of Alexandria and the grapes
ripen to a glorious old-gold colour, a delight to the eye. I am advised
by a descendant of several generations of Guernsey Canon Hall growers
that the secret to success with this vine is a liberal annual dressing of
seaweed and seaweed ash. To produce the latter, the grower collects
seaweed and dries it before burning it, carefully collecting the ash
afterwards. Probably the French fertilizer produced from calcified
seaweed would be a good substitute for those growers who live too far
from the sea to collect seaweed. Use Gros Colmar as pollinator.

Woodash and charcoal are very beneficial fertilizers and soil sweet-
eners, being rich in lime and in potash, and suit all indoor and outdoor
vines very well.

This vine will ripen in all southern counties with no heat, but will
need a little heat to finish off the ripening process in midland areas and
in less well placed exposed glasshouses.

Buckland Sweetwater

This vine can be difficult to establish, being a weak grower and having
little will to survive. It is, however, a very old vine and is the ancient
white English grape grown on house and cottage walls for centuries in
this country, and herein lies its appeal. It has none of the classic flavour
or elegance of any of the aforesaid grapes, tasting rather watery and
lacking in either sweetness or acidity, is rather bland, and has little to
commend it in comparison with better flavoured indoor grapes. It is
not, therefore, recommended to those wanting just one or two vines,
but would merit a place in a collection of indoor vines for its historical
connection. These grapes will ripen grown on a hot south-facing wall.

Madresfield Court

Madresfield Court requires heat to finish to perfection, bringing out the
delicate blue bloom on the tender juicy berries. The berries are muscat
flavoured, the bunches have good shoulders and taper, and can be very
large indeed. The berries set well with their own pollen, the vine is
fruitful though not very strong growing.

The aforegoing are the more common indoor vines, and in average
seasons in southern counties can ripen their grapes without heat. Muscat
Hamburg and Canon Hall Muscat are not vines for beginners, but set

a fascinating challenge to the more experienced grower to try and encourage consistent fruitfulness. With today's expenses and difficulties in mind this concludes the collection of grape vines one can recommend as suitable for all situations and locations.

Collectors' Vines

For the collector or indoor vine specialist, willing to devote much time and care to the vines, the following list covers the vines that are becoming rare today. It would be tragic if any should become extinct due to lack of interest.

Alicante
(Also known as *Black Alicante* and *Meredith's Alicante*)

A vigorous vine, that *will* ripen its grapes without heat, but likes heat to ripen to perfection. Alicante produces large oval black berries which set well, and hang sound on the vine over a long period.

Appley Towers

The grapes set well, and become large, oval and black with a glorious rich juicy flavour, definitely a vine to recommend most highly.

Gros Colmar

The value of this vine lies in the fact that Muscat Hamburg will flower, set and fruit admirably when grafted or inarched onto Gros Colmar. In its own right this vine is less attractive than others, the grapes tending to be rather tough and coarse and of a rough flavour, though handsome in appearance. It may need heat to ripen to completion.

Gros Maroc

A vigorous vine, ripening wood well, Gros Maroc flowers and sets a good crop of large oval deep-maroon black grapes which have a rich, sweet and juicy flavour. The bunches are well-shouldered and tapering and may need some heat to finish in autumn. The grey, rounded leaves are attractive and colour prettily in autumn.

Lady Downe's Seedling

To ripen fully this vine does need heat, producing oval sweet firm generously flavoured berries that develop a reddish black colour when approaching maturity.

Mrs Pearson

A strong grower, Mrs Pearson produces well-shouldered long tapering bunches of pale gold grapes with a pink flush. The grapes have a Muscat flavour and are firm, rich and succulent. The leaves have a feathery appearance. It is a slow, late ripener and may need heat.

Mrs Pince

This vine throws long cylindrical bunches that tend to divide at the tip, and will ripen the free-setting large oval dark-purple tough-skinned grapes without heat. The grapes are solid, sweet and rich with a definite Muscat flavour, grapes of very considerable quality and style.

Conclusions

If you can only grow *one* vine, choose Black Hamburg, for two vines choose Black Hamburg and Chasselas Rose, for three vines choose the two aforegoing plus Muscat of Alexandria, and for a fourth choose Muscat Hamburg to complete the collection.

Indoor Vines for the Far North of England and Scotland

For the grower living as far north as Lancashire and Yorkshire, the *Reichensteiner Schönburger* and *Dornfelder* would ripen happily in the average summer. Neither grape is as large as the recognized indoor varieties, but show adequate vigour and adapt readily to glasshouse cultivation, producing delicious gold and black grapes respectively.

Scottish growers should plant *Perle de Czaba, Siegerrebe* and *Leon Millot* in their cold glasshouses. These ultra-early-ripening varieties should ripen with ease in the growing season, and will provide a plentiful supply of delicious eating grapes. The Perle de Czaba ripens to a translucent opalescent white-gold, the Siegerrebe to a dark golden pink, and the Leon Millot to an intense black.

The German *Rotberger*, a Black Hamburg-Riesling cross, is a prolific vine producing masses of medium-sized black bunches of elegant flavoured grapes, early ripening under glass. It is a vine worthy of its noble parentage. The bunches are wedge-shaped, and the berries large and spherical, and the vine a worthy addition to any collection.

18

Ornamental Vines and Vines in Polythene Tunnels

Where just one or two vines are to be planted for decoration, then the choice of wine will depend upon certain features of the site or position. You might want to plant a vine as a cover for an ugly wall or fence, to swarm quickly over an unattractive garage, to furnish an open-work barrier between the pleasure garden and vegetable area, or as a beautiful and productive cover for a pergola for a covered walk.

The most effective way of setting off a decorative vine is with another of sharply contrasting colour; some vines develop very dramatic autumn colouring, maroons, yellow and gold, green with a red border and a yellow band between the green and red, browns and reds.

Following directions on planting and feeding covered in the relevant chapters, remembering to support the vines at all times as they grow to prevent wind damage.

Vitis Brant

This is, perhaps, the most common of the vines sold by nurserymen for this purpose. This Canadian hybrid is fairly strong-growing and produces many small bunches of black grapes by mid-October accompanied by the most beautiful autumn leaf colouring, the well-cut leaves turning red and gold round the edges. Some growers make a very decent wine from their Brant grapes, with a year or two bottle age not unlike a passable Beaujolais.

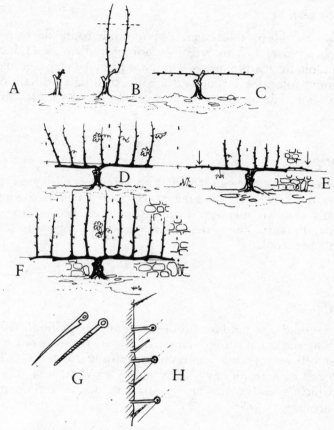

57 Training a wall vine. **A** Plant the vine in a specially prepared hole some 15–20 cm
(6–9 in) out from the wall. Prune to leave just two or three buds. **B** The vine at the
end of the first growing season. If it has grown very weakly, prune down hard again
to leave just two to three buds. If it has grown well, cut the top off each of the two
canes grown. **C** Tie these canes down onto a horizontal wire some 30–45 cm above
ground level. **D** The vine at the end of the second year before ... **E** and after
pruning, where one-third of the new canes are removed to cut back to mature pencil
thick cane. Tie the two end canes down onto the bottom wire (see arrows) if you
want the vine to occupy a greater area. **F** Our vine at the end of the third growing
season has nearly attained its full proportions, and has been allowed to carry a bunch
or two in the fourth season. It can crop moderately in the fifth and thereafter
fully. **G** Vine eyes. **H** Vine eyes in a wall with 15 cm clearance from the wall.

Vitis Cognettiae

This Japanese vine produces a mass of luxuriant round dark green leaves of a lovely texture, the vine is really vigorous and covers a fair area fast. Only suitable for warmer areas. Does not produce viable edible grapes. The autumn colour here is most dramatic, turning a brilliant orange to deep scarlet and finally to maroon before dropping with the first frost.

Vitis Purpurea

The downy finely-cut leaves, which range from a greyish pink to a dusky purple as they develop, make a magnificent show all the growing season, and would thus complement a garden or area devoted to grey- and silver-leaved plants. They are also an attractive contrast to other vines on a wall or pergola.

Dunkelfelder

A German-bred vine used for producing grapes with blood-red juice for intensifying the colour of red wines. Therefore the grower can produce wine as well as enjoying luxuriant beautifully cut leaves which turn through red to maroon fairly early in the growing season, a blaze of colour which is really arresting. Vigour is moderate, and the grapes are early-ripening.

Portuguese Blue

This vigorous vine produces a heavy crop of big bunches of black grapes on lovely nut-brown canes, the grapes make a wine of moderate appeal, but the leaves turn a beautiful colour of red with yellow bands which gives a wonderful show for many weeks.

Deckrot

This German colourizer grape produces a fair crop of grey-red grapes which make a good wine, but here again the glorious maroon-grey leaves are the real feature; they maintain this colour from budburst until autumn, with a lovely downy velvety quality.

Vines in Polythene Tunnels

It is claimed that the yield of grapes grown in plastic tunnels is four to five times greater than grapes grown in the open. Added to this considerable advantage one can plant far later-ripening varieties, and harvest fully ripe healthy grapes each and every year, and can thus be sure of a regular annual output.

One grower in particular who has pioneered tunnel-grown vines in south Devon is Colonel George Nangle. He has evolved over the years, by trial and error, a system of spacing, training, spraying and ventilation that gives optimum results. (Address: Redhills, Stokenham, Nr Kingsbridge.)

It is advised that only two rows of vines are grown in each 20 m (60 ft) × 4 m (14 ft) wide tunnel, each row sited well away from the sides of the tunnel to allow adequate air flow between the polythene sheeting and the vines in order to discourage fungal problems. Apparently the tunnel should be half into the prevailing wind so that the least form of resistance is presented to the force of the wind.

The ends should be open to allow full air flow during the growing season. Netlon makes a stiffish windbreak mesh which is splendid for fixing to the side and top panels of each end, and to the door panel, which should be made able to roll up or across to allow full ventilation if necessary. It is a good idea to run a sheet of polythene across each end at ground level to a height of 30 cm (1 ft); this keeps draughts out in spring when the vines are bursting bud, and when one might have semi-tender plants such as courgettes, aubergines, peppers or lettuces, just establishing themselves, down the centre of the house.

House Life

It pays to buy a well-made strong house structure, so that it has a long troublefree life. A cheap house will collapse in four or five years, whereas a tough framework will outlive many skins, each of which has a life of three or at most four summers before becoming brittle and breaking up. Buy a copy of *The Grower*, and write off to all the firms advertising polytunnels for a list of their models and prices, and compare the data to find the house best suited to your pocket and the area you plan to cover. Polytunnels are made in 60′, 100′ and 120′ lengths.

Vines for Tunnels

Why grow varieties of vines in tunnels that can be equally well ripened in the open? Why not grow later-ripening varieties of immense quality from which really superior, elegant wines may be made? For white wine I would recommend Riesling and Scheurebe or, if you prefer a classic French wine such as Chablis or white Burgundy, then grow Chardonnay. If red Burgundy is your scene, then the Pinot Noir is the vine, or should you wish to grow a wine as near red Bordeaux as possible, then plant 75 per cent Cabernet Sauvignon, 20 per cent Merlot and 5 per cent Petit Verdot. All these vines will ripen grapes with ease south of a line from Ipswich – Cambridge, Worcester, Hereford to Bristol; further north than this imaginary line try Scheurebe, Auxerrois, Rotberger, Pinot Noir, and perhaps Gewurztraminer. Another field is table grape production of course; here one would recommend Chasselas Rosé and d'Or, Muscat Hamburg, Black Hamburg and Rotberger.

Training and Pruning

It is recommended that the vines are planted 1.30 m apart, and that three rods are grown up from each vine to form permanent arms which are in due course spur pruned. In this way the grower obtains the highest yield from the vines and the area, remembering to renew the permanent rods every few years. Stop the rods some 2 ft before they reach the apex, and *keep* this area free of growth.

Stop each fruiting lateral four leaves beyond the last bunch, and pinch out all sub-laterals that grow from the leaf axils thereafter, leaving a stub of one leaf and one bud as a safety valve.

Spraying

Maintain a skeleton spraying programme only, for in a tunnel there is no rain to wash off the chemicals; spray in April, June and July with sulphur, Zineb and Rovral to maintain adequate spray cover. Wood ripening is, however, usually quite excellent, so there is little likelihood of overwintering fungal problems, though a good tar oil wash at 5 per cent is recommended in mid-December.

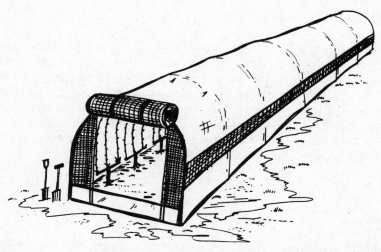

58 A 20 m (60 ft) polytunnel with windbreak mesh ends, both side and centre panels, and mesh ventilation let in right along the entire length of the sides. Note the vines, planted four foot apart, each with three permanent spur-pruned rods.

Ground Preparation and Feeding

Prepare the ground before planting and putting up the tunnel as advised for the outdoor vineyard site, also feed the vines in similar fashion. Bear in mind that the vines do not have full access to moisture until their roots have penetrated out underneath the buried skin of the tunnel, so it is advisable to obtain two lengths of perforated self-watering hose, and in warm and hot weather turn the hose on for an hour or two every few days to give the ground a good soaking. Stop watering once the grapes reach veraison, when they begin to turn gold or red. It is recommended that the vines are grown 2 years in the open before being covered.

Ground Care

Keep the earth weed-free in the tunnels. The centre area can of course be rotovated through, and nasty weeds such as docks or thistles dug out or spot weeded with Roundup. You may need to use a hoe between the outside skin and the vines, hence the need to keep a 1 m–1.30 m alley for ease of operation here.

Ground Crops

Once the ground is fairly weed-free within the tunnels, one can grow courgettes, green peppers and aubergines, lettuce, carrots and strawberries, etc. right along the centre of each house. I find that to have a second crop in the house is an *excellent* plan, as it makes one pay daily visits to look after and harvest the plants, which in turn enables one to tend the vines frequently and, thus, if any fungal problem should occur, it can be caught early and duly stamped on before it has time to spread and cause widespread trouble.

Warnings

It is impossible to lay sufficient emphasis on the importance of ventilation and airflow through polytunnels. It is imperative to keep the ends open, with or without a windbreak mesh, and to keep all growth well away from the top of the house, so that there is a 1.30 m wide span totally free of vine for free air flow. In any structure the roof apex is always the area where there is least air movement, heat rises and is at its greatest in this area, and therefore mildew etc. is more likely to occur here.

One or two firms make polytunnels with an integral windbreak mesh panel right along the entire length of each side. Such skins are of course more expensive, but would be very suitable for vines.

One point worth mentioning: a 20 metre (60 ft) tunnel becomes breathlessly hot in warm let alone hot weather, so it follows that a house three times larger will become really stifling, perhaps not the ideal environment for anyone with asthma, bronchial problems or an uncertain heart. It is advisable that one works and does the daily chores in a tunnel in the early morning, or in the evening after the heat of the day has subsided.

Also remember that if you spray your weeds with herbicide, the vapour will not be blown away as it would in the open air, and could well be *very harmful* to the operator, and also to vines and any other plants. Likewise, fungicides could well effect the operator adversely, so perhaps a Martin's breathing mask would be advisable, and keep all skin surfaces covered with protective clothing. *Always spray in the cool of the morning or evening, never in the heat of the day.*

19
Vine, Wine and Grape Recipes

Grapes when dried become sultanas and raisins. Naturally where grapes are grown commercially for this purpose certain varieties have proved themselves outstanding for dried-fruit production. Muscatelle grapes are grown for conversion into raisins, and seedless Sultana grapes, the small green grapes that are in the shops in July in Britain, for sultanas.

The rich Muscatelle grape would not ripen in the open in Britain, but, given good glasshouse conditions it could well do so. The true Sultana grape likewise would not ripen here out of doors, but there are two substitutes that will ripen, namely the American Himrod seedless and the Austrian Ramdas grapes, both white and both seedless. Alternatively, the richly flavoured early-ripening Siegerrebe grape must be an ideal candidate; they ripen in September, which would indicate that the grower would have a chance of drying the grapes naturally in the sun if we enjoy an Indian summer in October. The alternative is to dry them, gently covered to keep wasps and dust away, in a warm dry room, turning them frequently, and putting them out in the sun on every dry hot day. How much more satisfying to make cakes with home-grown fruit, especially since the price of raisins and sultanas has rocketed recently.

Stuffed vine leaves, known as Dolmas, are absolutely delicious. They are eaten in Greece and Turkey, and indeed in most Mediterranean countries, each district having its own particular traditional and favourite fillings and sauces. Therefore, rather than adhering to one or two specific recipes, be adventurous and try different fillings.

How to Can Vine Leaves

Vine leaves should be picked in late May or early June when they are tender. This time may vary in different climates.

Wash the leaves very well, stack them over each other about 30 deep, the stems together side by side in a row. Fold over once or twice and tie with string. Bring to the boil 2 quarts of water and $\frac{1}{2}$ cup of salt. Drop the bundles of leaves into this boiling water and take them out again one by one. Let them cool a little, then put them in sterilized jars tightly packed, pour the boiling water over them and cover immediately. Each pint of leaves will serve 10–12 people.

Vine Leaves in Olive Oil

Gather your vine leaves as advised in the first recipe, wash them well, and again bundle up 30 or so, tying them up with string. Pack them into washed and sterilized jars, and fill the jar with olive oil. Cover and screw down immediately. Kilner jars are recommended.

Frozen Vine Leaves

Put a large saucepan of water containing 1 teaspoon of salt on to boil. Wash the vine leaves well using medium-sized leaves that are young and fresh. Tie several into a bundle by their stems, and dip them for 25–30 seconds into the boiling water. Lay them out to cool, and pack them into proper deep freeze tubs or ex-ice cream plastic boxes, with a sheet of greaseproof paper between each leaf. When the box is full press the lid down and place in the deep freeze. Thaw well before attempting to separate.

Derevi Sarma (1)

1 cup of boiled long-grain brown rice
1 cup chopped onions
$\frac{1}{2}$ cup finely chopped parsley

juice of 1 lemon
salt and pepper to taste
$\frac{1}{4}$ cup currants or sultanas

$\frac{1}{4}$ cup chopped dill
1 cup olive oil

$\frac{1}{2}$ cup pine nuts (optional)
about 50 vine leaves

Squeeze chopped onions with your hands to make the onion soft, add the rest of the ingredients and mix well. If vine leaves are fresh, soak them in boiling water for a few minutes, if canned wash them in hot water and cut off the stems. Spread a leaf on a small plate, wrong side up with the stem towards you. Put a teaspoon of the filling near the stem end and, with your hands, fold over the sides and then roll the leaf up like a cigarette. Place some leaves in the bottom of the pan to prevent burning, arranging stuffed leaves side by side in a pan and in 2 or 3 layers, according to the size of the pan. Place a plate over the top to keep them in place, add 2 cups of water, cover and cook slowly for $1\frac{1}{2}$ hours, preferably baking them in the oven. After they are cooked, do not remove plate until Sarmas are cool, in order to prevent discolouring. *Serve cold.* Sprinkle with olive oil to make them shine and garnish with lemon slices.

Derevi Sarma (2)

1 cup brown rice
3 cups chopped onion
1 cup olive oil
3 cups boiling water
2 tsp crushed dry dill or fresh
    chopped dill
$\frac{1}{4}$ tsp cinnamon (optional)

2 tsp salt
$\frac{1}{2}$ tsp chopped mint
1 tsp paprika
$\frac{1}{2}$ tsp pepper
$\frac{1}{2}$ tsp allspice
1 large lemon
vine leaves

Fry onions in olive oil in a big pan until they are light brown. Add rice, previously boiled for 30 mins, and salt, and mix well. Add hot water, cover, and boil for a few minutes until all the water has been absorbed. Take the pan off the stove, wait 5 minutes and then add the rest of the ingredients, and mix together. Allow to cool. Follow same directions for rolling the leaves and cooking as in the first Sarma recipe above.

Grape Vine Leaf Canapés

Stuff vine leaves with:
rice
pine nuts
finely chopped onion

lemon juice
salt and pepper to taste
dried mint

Prepare as for Sarma, but fold leaves over filling to make little packages (like Chinese egg rolls); cook with water, herbs, *or* on bed of chicken. Brush with olive oil when cold, and serve, garnished, as cocktail canapés.

Derevi Dolma

1 lb minced beef
2 onions, chopped fine
¼ cup brown rice
vine leaves
1 small can tomatoes

chopped parsley and mint
garlic
salt and pepper to taste
stock

Cut stems from leaves, and, if fresh, soak in boiling water. Wash rice and boil for 30 mins, then add to the meat. Add parsley, mint, salt and pepper and blend together with the chopped onion and tomatoes. Arrange a small amount on each vine leaf and roll. Cover the bottom of a baking dish with vine leaves, and pack the vine-leaf rolls round tightly, cover with a plate, fill to the level of the plate with stock, home-made preferably, adding some lemon juice to the stock. Put the lid on and bake for 1 hour. Serve with yoghurt.

Dolma Mixture

Basic Dolma stuffing to serve 4–6
1 lb minced beef
¼ lb brown rice, boiled and soft
2 chopped onions

¼ cup tomato sauce
salt and pepper to taste
chopped parsley

Mix all these ingredients together well by hand in a bowl. If there is more stuffing than is needed, shape into balls and cook with Dolma. Whatever vegetable is used add some stock and tomato sauce over Dolma to cook. Add more later if necessary. Vegetables commonly used for Dolmas are tomatoes, green peppers, courgettes, cabbage and vine leaves.

Dolmades

1 medium aubergine
4 tbs olive oil
1 medium chopped onion
2 tbs lemon juice
1½ tsp oregano
1 clove garlic
1 tsp salt

fresh ground pepper
1 lb long-grain brown rice, cooked
1 lb peeled tomatoes
¼ tsp basil
vine leaves
a pinch of dill

Peel aubergine and chop finely. Heat olive oil in a large pan and add onion, aubergine, lemon juice, oregano, dill and garlic, finely chopped. Stir until oil is evenly distributed over aubergine. Season with salt and pepper and add ½ pt or so of hot water. Allow mixture to simmer for an hour, until aubergine is very tender and the water nearly gone. (If it cooks away before the aubergine is ready add more.)

When mixture is thick and very soft turn off heat and stir in the rice; season to taste.

Wash the vine leaves in hot water, place filling in centre and then wrap the leaf around the filling, folding over the sides.

Chop up the tomatoes into a thick sauce, seasoning with basil, salt and pepper. Arrange Dolmades in an oiled baking dish and pour the tomato sauce over them. Cover, and bake in the oven for 30 mins at 350°F, Gas Mark 4.

Serves 6.

Potatoes in Wine

4 large *mealy* potatoes
3 tbs butter
8 tiny white onions

salt and pepper
1 bay leaf
½ bottle dry white wine

Floury brown-skinned potatoes are necessary, waxy ones will ruin the dish. Melt butter in a large skillet. Peel onions and slice into thirds and sauté in butter for a few minutes. Peel potatoes and cut them into ¼-in thick slices. Put them in the skillet with salt, pepper and bay leaf. Pour dry white wine over until they are just covered. Cover pan and cook gently for at least 1 hour. Check that the wine is covering potatoes and add more if necessary, move the potatoes around so that they cook evenly. When they are cooked, carefully remove the potatoes and onion into a serving dish, bring the sauce to a rapid boil and pour over the potatoes and onions. Serve very hot.

Serves 4–6.

White Wine Sauce

½ pint chicken stock
½ pint dry white wine
6 dried mushrooms
3 tbs butter
3 tbs flour

2 tbs cream
1 egg yolk
salt and pepper
grated lemon peel
1 garlic clove

Mix wine and stock in a saucepan, add the mushrooms, cover tightly and simmer for 30 minutes. Strain through muslin and discard mushrooms. Melt the butter in a heavy saucepan, when it bubbles add the flour and cook for 1–2 mins, stirring often. Slowly add hot stock, stirring with a whisk. After the sauce has thickened, continue to stir over a low heat for a further 10 mins. Beat the egg yolk into the cream, and stir into the sauce. Season to taste with freshly ground pepper and salt, adding a small pinch of freshly grated lemon peel.

Herb and Wine Sauce

1 pint chicken stock
¼ pint dry white wine
¼ tsp dried dill
¼ tsp dried rosemary
grated lemon peel

3 tbs flour
3 tbs butter
pinch of tarragon
garlic juice

Make the chicken stock, boiling it in a small saucepan until it has reduced to just over ½ pint. Add the herbs and wine and simmer a further 5 mins. Melt the butter in a heavy saucepan adding the flour and stirring frequently. Slowly add the stock stirring this in with a whisk, season with a little grated lemon juice and the juice of 1 garlic clove. Simmer for a further 5–10 mins.

Stir frequently and let the sauce simmer for a further 10–15 mins. Serve hot with soufflés, crêpes and vegetables.

Aubergine and Wine Pasta Sauce

6 tbs olive oil
3 cloves garlic
2 green peppers
1 medium aubergine

3–4 capers
12 oz tomato purée
¾–1 pint dry white wine
1 tsp oregano

2–3 oz black olives, sliced
½ lb chopped peeled tomatoes

½ tsp basil
salt and pepper to taste

Heat the olive oil in a large heavy pan, mince the garlic adding this to the oil, and put on mild heat. Peel and chop the aubergine, and slice the green peppers, removing the seeds. Add the tomatoes, olives, peppers, aubergines and capers to the oil, stirring well until all the vegetables are well coated with the oil. Add the rest of the ingredients and, after stirring well, cover the pan. Lower the heat and allow to simmer for 1 hour, stirring from time to time to prevent burning. If it becomes too thick, add more wine.

Tomato and Wine Sauce for Pasta

Red wine
¼ green pepper
½ chopped onion
1 lb tomatoes
2 cloves finely chopped garlic

2 tbs olive oil
bay leaf, parsley
salt and pepper
oregano
basil

Heat the olive oil, and sauté the garlic and onions. Put green pepper and tomatoes into the blender and blend at high speed for 1 min. Pour the liquid into the pan with the olive oil etc., adding the parsley, oregano, bay leaf, basil, salt and lots of freshly ground black pepper. Simmer for 30 mins, or more if possible, stirring a few times, and if it looks too dry add some water. Add some red wine, and serve hot over freshly cooked pasta with grated parmesan cheese.
Serves 3.

Grape Pie

7 cups stemmed black grapes
3 tbs cornflour
1½ cups sugar

grated rind of 1 orange
¼ tsp salt
pastry to fit a 9-in dish

Wash grapes, skin pulp and keep skins. Heat the grape pulp to boiling and rub through a coarse sieve to remove pipe. Mix cornflour, orange rind, sugar and salt and add the grape pulp, cooking until it thickens, stirring all the time. Add the grape skins and cool.

Make a pastry case, pour in the filling, and lattice the top with strips of pastry. Cook in a very hot oven, 450°F, Gas Mark 8, for 10 minutes, lower heat to 350°F, Gas Mark 4 and cook for a further 25 mins. Serve with fresh cream.

Grape Lime Sorbet

1 cup grape juice
juice of 2 small limes or lemons
2 cups water
1 cup sugar

After turning the refrigerator down to its coldest, boil the water and sugar for 5 mins and cool. Pour in the fruit juices, mix, and pour into ice tray and semi-freeze. Pour out of tray into a chilled bowl, beat until fluffy and light in colour. Pour back into the ice-tray and freeze until firm.
Serves 6.

Appendices

1 Weather Recording

Many winegrowers keep certain weather records, mainly daily rainfall and minimum-maximum temperature figures; some also record humidity, and perhaps a few record wind speeds.

Such records become more interesting, indeed highly significant, when compared with records of other years, and of course with those of other growers, more particularly when allied to important dates such as varietal budburst, flowering, fruit set and harvest, together with accurate sugar and acidity readings.

This task is easier when one has a proper weather box, known as a Stephenson screen, an air ministry roof of one's own, in which certain instruments may be kept, together with a recording book and pencil in a polybag to keep them dry.

A min-max thermometer kept inside will record shade temperatures, all the more interesting if you keep identical thermometers outside, one on the vineyard floor in full sun, and others at 30 cm, 60 cm, 90 cm and 1.30 m above ground level in the sun, and you will quickly appreciate the very considerable heat absorption and higher temperatures at ground level – more apparent if you have a cultivated earth floor to your vineyard.

Keep a keen look out at house sales for an instrument for measuring sunshine hours. These have a slowly rotating drum covered in graph paper on which a needle draws a trace, the sensitive mechanism recording sharply when the sun actually shines. This instrument stands on a south-facing window ledge that enjoys uninterrupted light from dawn to dusk.

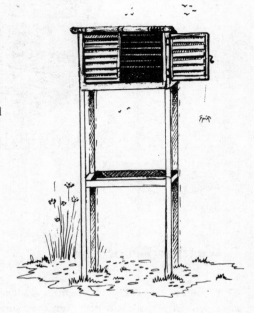

59 A Stephenson screen in which temperature, barometric pressure and humidity recording instruments are housed.

A rain gauge must stand clear of any object that might prevent a correct reading; it could be fixed with a bracket to the top of the weather box, so that it projects well above the roof line.

It is interesting to take temperature recordings from, perhaps, below, in the middle of and above your vineyard area, so that you can check if the temperature within the vineyard is greater than the temperature outside, to discover, in fact, if you have achieved a micro-climate within the plot. Naturally this will not become evident until the vines are fully leaved and have begun to absorb and hold heat between and underneath the rows.

Day Degrees

It is interesting to extend your min-max recordings to encompass an understanding of heat units or day degrees. Individual sites may be assessed for the accumulation of day degrees they accrue *above the base line of 10°C (50°F)*. In England significant day degrees begin in May and end in October. The calculations are worked out on a monthly, and then a yearly basis, after you have your min-max figures to hand for the current month and, finally, for the year as a whole.

Calculate your average min-max temperatures for the month by adding up first all the minimum temperatures, and then dividing the resulting figure by the number of days of that month. Repeat the process with the maximum temperatures. Let us assume for the calculation that the ...

average minimum is 11
average maximum is 21

$$\frac{11+21}{2} = \frac{32}{2} = 16$$

$16 - 10 = 6$ (we subtract 10 here as 10 is the base temp. of calculation)
$6 \times 31 = 186$ (31 is the days of the month, use 30 if it is a 30 day month)

The monthly totals from May to October inclusive are then added together; on the Continent the summation of day degrees is over 1000, but we can probably expect little more than 800 in an average summer.

2 Vine Prunings

To many growers the ever-increasing litter of prunings they leave in their wake as they methodically prune row after row of vines presents a disposal problem. Many have adopted the simple system used on the Continent of incinerating the prunings in an old oil drum or metal dustbin, which has been punched with many large holes, and transported in a metal wheel barrow, as they work down the rows. This is an excellent idea as far as it goes, the benefits being threefold:

a) the prunings are dealt with at the same time as the pruning operation, and although it obviously retards the time taken during the pruning as the discarded wood must be cut to fit into the incinerator, at least this prevents the grower having to trudge up and down the rows again to collect up the prunings later;

b) the wood ash, rich in potash and also containing lime, can be dressed directly back into the vineyard where it will do good;

c) lastly, the hot, glowing incinerator is a welcome companion for warming frozen hands during the winter pruning when conditions more often than not freeze the growers to the bone in an hour or two.

This practice has great merit in that it saves valuable man-hours and effort.

The alternative is to collect the prunings with a pitchfork and dump them in enormous heaps at one end of the vineyard, and burn them in due course.

Fire Kindling

May I suggest an alternative or two that I met in France that represent a saving in another form of energy. In St Emilion, a fascinating little walled medieval hilltop town to the north of the Dordogne river, encompassed within the great Bordeaux winefield, I was invited to join a lunch party at a nearby château by the owner, the party being a feast for six men who had celebrated their friendship since schooldays in like manner every year.

Before the six-course meal began, the great open fire was lit with small bundles of vine prunings, and then large tied bundles of full-length prunings were thrown on, again and again, while we enjoyed our first course of local shrimps, prawns and oysters and the second course of local pork pâté. When the heaps of glowing vine charcoal had reached the desired size, they were gently raked flat to form a six-inch deep bed some three feet in length by two feet wide. Over these glowing embers was placed on iron grid, and onto this were placed enormous beef steaks – without exaggeration, an inch thick, fifteen inches long by nine inches wide. These steaks were cooked for a few minutes on each side and were then presented to the guests accompanied by a tossed fresh salad.

I will not bore you with the description of the remaining courses, nor of the succession of great wines from this château, one from each of the previous 12 or 15 vintages, nor of my visit to the cellar, or the wealth of winegrowing lore the owner explained to me; this is another story. The real reason for this little cameo is to put across the merit of vine prunings as kindling and as fuel. In these days when we all are trying to find methods of alternative heating, to convert your cuttings into small bundles for kindling relieves the need for chopping sticks or buying firelighters, and if you have a large or open fireplace, long cuttings tied into bundles and put on the fire from time to time create a heap of glowing charcoal which greatly increases the heat output into the room. Vine prunings do not spit.

Noticing the high price of bundles of firelighting sticks in the local ironmongers, this is obviously a good outlet, and as there is rarely labour or time to prepare the 'bundles' oneself, they could be sold to someone locally who is already involved in this business, which would both resolve the labour problem in collecting the cuttings and bring in, perhaps, a little reserve to offset costs.

Charcoal

The word charcoal has a clue to the next suggested re-use of cuttings. Vine cuttings and willow twigs make the highest quality artist's drawing charcoal. To convert vine cane to charcoal instead of ash, it must be burnt slowly and robbed of the presence of air. Ideally the rods should be tied up into neat tight bundles, tightly packed into a large cone-shaped heap, so shaped that it can be covered with earth and finally turf, leaving a small channel in at the bottom with some paper as kindling material. Obviously, the prunings must not be fresh off the vine or they will not burn and conversely they must not be totally dried out and dead or they will be too brittle and burn too fast.

As addicts of Arthur Ransome's *Swallows and Amazons* will no doubt remember, charcoal burners must tend their fires to make sure that all places where the flames and smoke begin to break out are recovered with earth, so that the heat is contained and the fire continues to simmer on slowly until all the cuttings have been converted into charcoal, when the fire will slowly cool down and go out of its own accord. Remember to leave a hole at the top to allow the smoke to escape and the fire to draw.

Charcoal is a recommended fuel for igniting Aga cookers, to use on barbecue grills – why not try and find a sale at shops that sell barbecue kits to campers and the back garden or patio barbecue sets? – as well as a drawing medium for the artistic fraternity via local art shops.

This re-use of cuttings brings us back to the problem we solved at the beginning of this chapter. Should we consider the re-use of prunings, we will be back in a situation whereby we have to return after pruning to collect the prunings.

I have evolved a method that reduces the time involved in the collection of cuttings by three-quarters. When you are pruning, cut the wood roughly into pairs of rods by cutting through the old wood between every other lateral, and throw these, in heaps, into the next row to the one in which you are working, which in practice means that these heaps form in every fourth row. When you have finished pruning, take some strings, and lay a string flat across the ground above each heap, and lift the heap up and onto the string, and tie the bundle up tightly; it can thus be carried easily out of the vineyard. I find the wood from four to five vines from four rows across is quite enough for each bundle. Thus the prunings are semi-painlessly collected and removed from the vineyard rows.

Banking and Ditching

Should one wish to sheer up a weak bank, the earth should be dug away to reveal the angle of fall you want. Take sufficient bundles of cuttings, tightly bound with polythene baler band, and build them up two deep in front of the bank, ramming the bundles tightly against the bank with stakes driven in well in front of the bundles. Shovel the earth you removed when straightening the bank gently through the vine pruning bundles – it will gradually filter through with the interaction of sun and rain and in time grass seeds will germinate within and the bank will consolidate itself. This method is used in Italy for holding banks and is regarded as a semi-permanent practice.

From medieval times until relatively recently, wet fields were drained by digging out a fairly deep trench system, laying tightly tied bundles or 'faggots' of birch twigs in the bottom and replacing the soil firmly. This method may appear to be a temporary measure, but would last for generations, the damp airless conditions keeping the twigs from drying out and disintegrating. It would, therefore, follow that one could use vine pruning bundles in the same way for field drainage. This method has been used with birch twigs in Devon for centuries; surface and percolating subsoil water on hitting the line of submerged cuttings, taking the place of clay land drains, runs along and down the air gaps between the twigs and so away. Ideally a site should be drained before being planted if the site should be damp and hold water in wet weather. Use the natural fall of the land as obviously water is not going to flow uphill or along the level, and mark out a herring-bone system which collects all the offending water.

If you discover after the vineyard has been planted that you have a damp area, then a simple system can be put in to take this water away. For example, my vineyard is situated from 200 ft–250 ft above sea level on a hillside that rises to 800 ft behind. In wet winters the excavated green lane above my vineyard collects water in the middle section. Therefore, I plan to run a ditch along the upperside of the green lane, line it with vine prunings, and take a T junction from the lowest area in the middle of the run where most water collects and extend the leg of the T right down through middle of the vineyard and out at the bottom.

Replace all the earth back over the prunings so that there is no outward indication of the drain being there. Alternatively, if you have masses of stone you do not want, fill the trench with tightly-rammed stone which can be covered with earth and turf. This makes an excellent drainage system.

Use a plough to take out a deep square furrow for your drain or drains, and if the drain needs to go under a fence, this will have to be hand dug, and resume with a tractor on the far side.

Another ancient method was to use large flat stones and line the four sides of the drain like a box, the top stones of course overlapping the side supports so that the top could not subside. The point is to try to use whatever material you have available, and vine prunings are free for the asking.

3 Biological Care of Vines

Wasps

Wasps are repelled by the smell of lavender and will not cross a lavender bed. Sow several packets of a miniature lavender, raise the seedlings, and plant one out under each vine, particularly under varieties, such as Siegerrebe, which are plagued by wasps. Lavender also repels moths from plants.

Hyssop

Apparently grape yield is increased if hyssop is planted nearby.

Nasturtium and Tagetes minuta

Nasturtium will repel whitefly in the glasshouse, and *Tagetes minuta* (French marigold) is also an excellent deterrent for white and greenfly and other pests in the glasshouse.

Garlic

Planted under trees will keep them free of insect invasion, i.e. Peach Leaf Curl, and keep roses free of greenfly.

Elm and Mulberry

Grape vines trained on elm and mulberry trees bear especially good grapes.

Cypress Spurge

Has a very bad effect on vines, causing them to be sterile.

Ants

Will not cross a bed of spearmint, *Mentha spica,* so, if your vineyard or house is plagued by ants, mint may help you to be rid of this pest.

4 Wine Storage in Casks

Few growers use new casks, so some hints on caring for used casks may be of some value. Never allow a cask to dry out, so keep all casks full of clean water when not in use. Oak is preferable to chestnut for fermenting and storing wine, and really a cask of approximately 50 gallons is the smallest size to recommend, because, with smaller casks, there is an increasingly larger area of wine exposed to the wood and the risk of spoilage is magnified.

White wines, due to their more delicate constitution and balance of bouquet and flavour, are naturally more vulnerable to such spoilage, whereas red wines can positively gain from a short storage in wood.

Cleaning Casks

Sound clean casks that have been maintained full of clear sweet water are emptied, and rinsed with cold water before use. Should the cask smell *woody,* wash out the cask with 10 litres of boiling water per hectolitre of volume some two or three times, then rinse with cold water, followed, finally, by a rinse with lees and cold water. Should the cask smell *musty,* pour in 10 gm of calcium chloride together with 20 gm of sulphuric acid and 3 litres of boiling water. After 2 hours, empty the cask and rinse well with a 10 per cent solution of hydrogen peroxide. Empty the cask and finish with a rinse of water.

A *stagnant* smell may be combated with a wash of 10 litres of boiling water to which calcium chloride is added. After two hours, empty and rinse with a 10 per cent solution of sodium hydroxide, followed by a final rinse with water.

A *vinegar* aroma may be combated by filling the cask with cold water and leaving for two whole days. After emptying, add 120 gm of sodium hydroxide to 5 litres of boiling water and leave to stand a further 12 hours, shaking the cask every two hours to make sure every inch of wood is treated with this solution. Next rinse the cask well with cold water and give a final rinse with water.

Should the cask have an *undefined bad* smell, steam the cask interior under pressure for three minutes, following this treatment with a cold-water rinse. After emptying, light a sulphur candle or stick and burn some 2–3 gm per hectolitre of cask volume, and use immediately. Should the cask not be needed until later, dry it out, repeat the sulphur burning, and bung it up tight until needed.

5 Buying-in Grapes from the Continent

Some form of legislation should be employed against the, as yet, small percentage, perhaps 5 per cent, of English winegrowers who annually import wine grapes from Germany and Italy, and elsewhere.

Quite apart from the feelings of the vast majority of producers of *English* wine (denoting wine made in this country from grapes grown in this country) that to buy in foreign grapes might imply that the growers involved perhaps planted non-viable sites, or planted their sites with the wrong vine(s) for that site, we must all be totally satisfied that the wine from imported grapes is kept absolutely apart from any home-grown product, and NOT used to stretch a grower's wine in a poor year.

We must also insist that the wine label of wines from imported grapes must make it obviously clear to the buyer that the contents are made from imported grapes or grape juice. The term *British wine* or *British-made wine* is to 99 per cent of the public wine made from *British* grapes. Few people realize that a wine has to bear the word *English* to be made from home-grown grapes. Wine from imported grapes or juice can be called 'British wine', and carries the added bonus of a lower duty structure.

Thus it follows that it is wrong for an English grower who might produce from one to four or even six different wines from homegrown grapes, to label the wine he makes from imported fruit with an identical label to those used on his own wines, with, perhaps, his house or vineyard featured on the label. The only difference between the two products here is the wording 'made from grapes from ECC countries', or 'British wine' or 'British-made wine' in small print along the bottom of the label.

Three points therefore arise here; first the word *British* should never have been allowed to be used for wines made from imported raw materials – this fault is of many years' standing; and secondly some form of control must be levied on winegrowers who use imported grapes or grape juice to prevent any possibility of stretching the home-grown product with Continental grape juice; and thirdly the label must clearly and boldly identify the country of origin of the grapes.

These remarks are not intended to condemn making wine from

imported grapes; indeed it is no bad thing to put one's expensive winemaking equipment to greater use, and to have a better throughput of wine in a lean year, wine that can possibly be sold relatively cheaply due to the lower cost and lower duty. But we must strive to keep the identity and character of English-grown wine true to type – the frightening fact is that if one grower adulterates his wine and is duly discovered, then the reputation and credibility of all producers of English wine will suffer irreparable damage.

6 Vineyards Open to the Public

Write to the vineyard owner and ask for dates of open days or if you may join a conducted party. Do not turn up unannounced, as growers are very busy people. All usually set aside certain days for visitors.

Notes for Intending Visitors

Facilities Available:

V	Visitors Welcome
CP	Coach Parties
CP/BA	Coach Parties by Appointment
OD	Open Days
VA	Visitors by Appointment
WTF	Wine Tasting Free
WTC	Wine Tasting Charged
VS	Sales from Vineyard/Shop
S	Snacks available
M	Meals available

List of English Vineyards Open to the public

Avon

AVONWOOD (1 acre) Dr J.D. Minors, Seawalls Road, Sneyd Park, Bristol, Avon. Bristol (0272) 686635   VA. VS.

Berkshire

ASCOT (3 acres) Col A.R. Robertson, Ascot Farm, Winkfield Road, Ascot, Berks. Ascot (0990) 23563   V. CP. WTF. VS. M.

THE HOLT (1½ acres) Brigadier W.G.R. Turner, CBE, Woolton Hill,

Newbury, Berks. Highclere (0635) 253680   VA.

JOYOUS GARDE (2½ acres) D. T. Dulake, Crazies Hill, Wargrave, Berks
Tel: 073 522 2102   VA. OD. WTF. VS.

THAMES VALLEY (17 acres) J. S. E. Leighton, Stanlake Park, Twyford,
Berks. Twyford (0734) 340176   CP/BA. VA.

Buckinghamshire

WICKENDEN (4 acres) R. H. Lock, Wickenden, Cliveden Road, Taplow,
Bucks. Maidenhead (0628) 29455   CP/BA. VA. WTC. VS. S.

Cambridgeshire

CHILFORD HUNDRED VINEYARD (18 acres) S. Alper, Chilford Hall,
Balsham Road, Linton, Nr. Cambridge. (0223) 892641
                         CP/BA. OD. VA. WTC. M. VS.

THE ISLE OF ELY (2½ acres) Messrs. Reeve-Goring, Twentypence Road,
Wilburton, Cambridgeshire. Ely (0353) 4960   V. VA. VS.

Devon

HIGHFIELD (1 acre) Ian & Jennifer Fraser, Long Drag, Tiverton, Devon.
(0884) 256362   V. VA. OD. VS. WTF. M.

LODDISWELL (4 acres) R. H. Sampson, Lilwell, Loddiswell, Kingsbridge, Devon. Kingsbridge (0548) 550221
                         V. CP. OD. VA. WTC. VS.

WHITMOORE HOUSE (2 acres) Richard and Ann Trussell, Ashill, Cul-
lompton, Devon, EX15 3NP (0884) 40145
                         VA. WTF. CP/BA. VS. M.

WHITSTONE (1½ acres) George and Laura Barclay, Bovey Tracey, Nr.
Newton Abbot, South Devon. (0626) 832280   OD. VA. WTF. VS.

YEARLSTONE (2 acres) Gillian Pearkes, Yearlstone Vineyard, Bickleigh,
Tiverton, Devon   VA. OD. VS. WTF.

Essex

NEVARDS (1 acre) W. Hudson, Boxted, Colchester, Essex. Boxted (0206
230) 306   VA.

Gloucestershire

ST ANNE'S (2 acres) A. V. & B. R. Edwards, Wain House, Oxenhall, Newent, Gloucester. Gorsley (098 982) 313   CP/BA. WTF. V. VS.

TAPESTRY WINES (3 acres) The Vineyard, Wells Farm, Apperley, Gloucester. (045 278) 435   V. CP. VS.

THREE CHOIRS (20 acres) T. W. Day, Rhyle House, Welsh House Lane, Newent, Gloucester. Dymock (053 185) 223 or 555
V. CP/BA. OD. VA. WTF. VS. S.

Hampshire

ALDERMOOR VINEYARDS (5 acres) M. F. & W. A. Baerselman, Aldermoors, Picket Hill, Ringwood, Hants. Ringwood (04254) 2912
V. VA. CP. WTF.

BEAULIEU (6 acres) The Hon. Ralph Montagu, John Montagu Buildings, Beaulieu, Nr. Brockenhurst, Hants. Beaulieu (0590) 612345
VA. CP. VS.

BROADLEY (1 acre) D. H. Brown, Broadley Farm, Mead End, Sway, Hants. (0590) 682310   V. BA.

HOLLY BUSH (4 acres) C. & E. Landells, Holly Bush Farm, Brockenhurst, Hants. Lymington (0590) 23054   V. CP.

LYMINGTON (6 acres) C. W. & M. M. R. Sentance, Wainsford Road, Pennington, Lymington, Hants. Lymington (0590) 72112
V. WTC. VS.

MEON VALLEY (8 acres) C. J. Hartley, Hillgrove, Swanmore, Southampton SO3 2PZ (0489) 877435   VA. CP. OD. VS. WTF.

Herefordshire

BROADFIELD (10 acres) Mr & Mrs K. R. H. James, Broadfield Court Estate, Bodenham, Herefordshire. Bodenham (056 884) 483 or 275
CP/BA. OD. VA. WTC. VS. S.

CROFT CASTLE ($\frac{1}{2}$ acre) The Hon. Mrs F. Uhlman, Croft Castle (National Trust) Nr. Leominister, Herefordshire. Yarpole (056 885) 246
V. CP. VS.

Hertfordshire

FRITHSDEN ($2\frac{1}{2}$ acres) Peter Latchford, Frithsden, Nr Hemel Hempstead, Herts. Hemel Hempstead (0442) 57902   CP/BA. WTF. VA. VS.

Isle of Wight

ADGESTONE (9 acres) K. C. Barlow (and others), Upper Road, Adgestone, Sandown, Isle of Wight. Isle of Wight (0983) 402503
VA. WTF. VS.

BARTON MANOR (5½ acres) Mr & Mrs A. H. Goddard, Whippingham, East Cowes, Isle of Wight. Isle of Wight (0983) 292835
CP. OD. WTC. VS. S.

CRANMORE (12 acres) V. J. Hui, Solent Road, Cranmore, Nr Yarmouth, Isle of Wight. (0983) 761414
VA. WTC.

HAMSTEAD (4 acres) T. J. Munt, Hamstead Vineyard, Yarmouth, Isle of Wight. (0983) 760463
VA. OD. VS. WTC.

MORTON MANOR (1¾ acres) J. A. J. Trzebski, Morton Manor Vineyard, Brading, Isle of Wight. (0983) 406168
V. V/BA. WTC. CP/BA. M. S. VS.

Kent

BARDINGLEY (2 acres) H. S. & B. Turner, Babylon Lane, Hawkenbury, Staplehurst, Kent. Staplehurst (0580) 892264
V. VS. WTC.

BIDDENDEN (18 acres) R. A. Barnes, Little Whatmans, Biddenden, Ashford, Kent. Biddenden (0580) 291726
V. CP. WTF. VS. S.

CHIDDINGSTONE (6½ acres) J. M. & D. Quirk, Vexour Farm, Chiddingstone, Edenbridge, Kent. (0892) 870277
VA. OD.

CONGHURST (½ acre), Mrs B. Bridgewater, Conghurst Oast, Conghurst Lane, Hawkhurst, Kent. Hawkhurst (05805) 2634
WTF. VA. VS.

ELHAM VALLEY (3 acres) Mrs J. V. Allen & Mr P. W. Warden, Breach, Barham, Kent. Canterbury (0227) 831266
VA. WTC. VS. OD.

HARBLEDOWN & CHAUCER VINEYARDS (2 acres) A. G. Fisher & L. C. W. Rea, Isabel Mead Farm, Harbledown, Canterbury, Kent CT2 9AJ (0227 463913)
WTC. V.

HARBOURNE (2½ acres) L. S. Williams. Vineyard: High Halden, Nr Tenterden, Kent. Winery & Wine Shop: Wittersham, Nr Tenterden, Kent. Wittersham (07977) 420
V. VA. VS. WTF.

IGHTHAM (3 acres) J. M. B. & K. R. Corfe, Ivy Hatch, Nr Sevenoaks, Kent. Sevenoaks (0732) 810348
VA.

LAMBERHURST (55 acres) K. McAlpine, Ridge Farm, Lamberhurst, Nr Tunbridge Wells, Kent. Lamberhurst (0892) 890844 & 890448
CP/BA. V. OD. CP. WTF. VS. S. M.

LEEDS CASTLE (2¾ acres) Leeds Castle Foundation, Leeds Castle, Maidstone, Kent. Maidstone (0622) 65400   CP. OD. VA. S. VS.

PENSHURST (12 acres) D. E. Westphal, Grove Road, Penshurst, Kent. Penshurst (0892) 870255   CP/BA. WTF. V. VS. OD. MS.

ST NICHOLAS OF ASH (2 acres) J. G. Wilkinson, Moat Lane, Ash, Canterbury, Kent CT3 3DG (0304) 812670 CP/BA. WTF. V. VS. S.

STAPLE (7 acres) W. T. Ash, Church Farm, Staple, Canterbury, Kent. Ash (0304) 812571   CP/BA. V. VA. WTC. OD. VS.

TENTERDEN (12 acres) W. Garner & D. Todd, Spots Farm, Small Hythe, Tenterden, Kent. (05806) 3033   V. CP. WTF. VS. M.

THREE CORNERS (1½ acres) Lt-Col C. S. Galbraith, Beacon Lane, Woodnesborough, Kent. (0304) 812025   VA.

Norfolk

ELMHAM PARK (7 acres) R. S. Don, Elmham House, Dereham, Norfolk. Elmham (036 281) 571 or 363   CP. VA. WTF.

HEYWOOD (2 acres) R. C. Aikman, Heywood, Holly Farm, The Heywood, Diss, Norfolk. Diss (0379) 2461 and 01-340 9635 OD. VA.

LEXHAM HALL (8 acres) W. R. B. Foster and Partners, Lexham Hall, Nr Litcham, King's Lynn, Norfolk. Fakenham (0328) 701288
CP/BA. OD. VA. WTF. VS.

PULHAM (6 acres) P. W. Cook, Mill Lane, Pulham Market, Diss, Norfolk. Pulham Market (037 976) 342 and 672 CP. VA. WTC. VS.

Nottinghamshire

EGLANTINE (3⅓ acres) A. M. & V. Skuriat, Ash Lane, Costock, Nr Loughborough, Leicester. East Leake (050 982) 2386
VA. OD. WTF. VS.

Oxfordshire

BOTHY VINEYARD (3 acres) R. & D. B. Fisher, The Bothy, Bothy Cottage, Frilford Heath, Abingdon, Oxon. (0491) 681484
VA. VS. WTF.

CHILTERN VALLEY (3 acres) D. J. Ealand, Old Luxters Farm, Hambleden, Nr Henley, Oxon. (049163) 330   VA. OD. WTF.

Somerset

BRYMPTON D'EVERCY (1 acre), Charles E. B. Clive-Ponsonby-Fane, Yeovil, Somerset. (093 586) 2528 V. CP. VS. S.

CASTLE CARY (4 acres) Mr & Mrs P. C. Woosnam Mills, Honeywick House, Castle Cary, Somerset. Castle Cary (0963) 50323 V. VS. WTF.

CHEDDAR VALLEY (3 acres) N. A. & P. K. McDonald, Stoneleys, Hillside, Axbridge, Somerset. (0934) 732280 CP/BA. WTF. V. VS.

COXLEY (4 acres) W. Austin, Church Farm, Coxley, Nr Wells, Somerset. Wells (0749) 73854 CP. OD. WTF. V. VS. S/M.

H.R.H. VINEYARD (8 acres) Nigel Hector, Alastair Reid, Derek Hector, The Willows, Curload, Stoke St Gregory, Taunton, Somerset. (0823 69) 418 V. VS.

PILTON MANOR ($6\frac{1}{2}$ acres) J. M. Dowling, Pilton Manor, Shepton Mallett, Somerset. Pilton (074 989) 325
CP. OD. WTF. V. VA. VS. WTC. M/S.

SPRING FARM (12 acres) Mr & Mrs T. Rees, Moorlynch, Bridgwater, Somerset. (0458) 210393 CP/BA. V. WTF. VS. S.

STAPLECOMBE (4 acres) M. M. Cursham, Burlands Farm, Staplegrove, Taunton, Somerset. Kingston St Mary (082 345) 217 VA. WTF.

WHATLEY (4 acres) M. J. E. Witt, Old Rectory, Whatley, Nr Frome, Somerset. Nunney (037384) 467 V. CP. VS. WTC. S.

WOOTTON (6 acres) C. L. B. Gillespie, North Wootton, Shepton Mallet, Somerset. Pilton (074 989) 359 V. CP. VS.

WRAXALL ($5\frac{1}{2}$ acres) A. S. Holmes and Partners, Shepton Mallett, Somerset. Ditcheat (074 986) 486 and 331 V. VA. CP/BA. WTC. VS.

Suffolk

BRANDESTON PRIORY ($6\frac{1}{2}$ acres) H. P. B. Dow, The Priory, Brandeston, Woodbridge, Suffolk. Earl Soham (072 882) 462 V. WTF. CP. VS.

BROADWATER ($3\frac{1}{2}$ acres) A. W. & S. F. Stocker, Broadwater, Framlingham, Suffolk. Framlingham (0728) 723645 CP. VA. V. WTF. VS.

BRUISYARD (10 acres) Mr & Mrs I. H. Berwick, Church Road, Bruisyard, Saxmundham, Suffolk. Badingham (072 875) 281
CP/BA. WTF. V. VS.

CHICKERING (2½ acres) P. H. Day, Chickering Hall, Hoxne, Eye, Suffolk. Hoxne (037 975) 227   VA.

WILLOW GRANGE (1 acre), W. A. Sibley, Street Farm, Crowfield, Nr Ipswich, Suffolk. 879 234   CP/BA. WTC. VA. OD. VS.

Sussex

BERWICK GLEBE (2 acres) Jane Broster & Doreen Birks, Frensham Cottage, Berwick, Nr Polgate, Sussex. Alfriston (0323) 870361
VA. VS. WTC.

BOOKERS (5 acres) J. M. & R. V. Pratt, Foxhole Lane, Bolney, Sussex. Bolney (044482) 575   VA. VS.

BREAKY BOTTOM (4 acres) Peter Hall, Northease, Lewes, Sussex. Lewes (0273) 476427   V. WTF. CP. VA. VS. M.

CARR TAYLOR (21 acres) David and Linda Carr Taylor, Westfield, Hastings, East Sussex TN35 4SG. Hastings (0424) 752501
V. CP/BA. WTF. VA. VS. S/M.

CHILSDOWN (10½ acres) The Old Station House, Singleton, Chichester, West Sussex. Singleton (0243 63) 398   V. CP/BA. OD. VS. WTF.

DITCHLING (5 acres) Claycroft, Beacon Road, Ditchling, Hassocks, Sussex. Hassocks (079 18) 2634   V. VS. WTF

DOWNERS (7 acres) Commander & Mrs E. G. Downer, Downers, Clappers Lane, Fulking, Henfield. Sussex BN5 9NH. Poynings (079 156) 484
V. VS. WTF. VA. S.

ENGLISH WINE CENTRE (1 acre) Christopher & Lucy Ann, Drusillas Corner, Alfriston, East Sussex. Alfriston (0323) 870532
CP. V. M. S. OD. VA. VS. WTF.

FIVE CHIMNEYS (5 acres) W. Russell, Hadlow Down, Uckfield, East Sussex. Buxted (082 581) 3159/2541   VA. OD.

FLEXERNE (5 acres) Peter & Brenda Smith, Fletching Common, Newick, East Sussex. Newick (082 572) 2548   VA.

HOOKSWAY (3 acres) S. R. Moore, c/o Lares, Bepton Road, Midhurst, Sussex. Midhurst (073 081) 3317   VA. VS. WTF.

LEEFORD (25 acres) J. P. Sax, Leeford Vineyard, Battle, East Sussex. (04246) 3183   WTF. VA. VS.

LURGASHALL (Winery only) Virginia & Jerome Schooler, Windfallwood, Lurgashall, Nr Petworth, West Sussex GU28 9HA (0428 78) 292 or 654   CP/BA. WTF. VA. VS.

LYMINSTER (1½ acres) J. & V. Rankin, Lyminster Road, Nr Arundel, West Sussex. Arundel (0903) 882587 and 883393   V. VA. WTF. VS.

NUTBOURNE MANOR (14 acres) J. J. Sanger, Nutbourne Manor, Nr Pulborough, Sussex. (07983) 3554   OD. V. VS. WTC.

ROCK LODGE (4 acres) Norman Cowderoy, Scaynes Hill, West Sussex. (044 486) 224   V. CP. WTC. VS. S.

ST GEORGE'S (20 acres) Gay Biddlecombe, Waldron, Heathfield, East Sussex. (043 53) 2156   M/S. V. VA. CP. WTF. OD. VS.

SEYMOURS (2 acres) Mr & Mrs H. McMullen, Forest Road, Horsham, Sussex. Horsham (0403) 52397   CP/BA. VA. OD. VS. WTF.

STEYNING (3 acres) Joyce Elsden, Nash Hotel, Ashurst Road, Steyning, West Sussex BN4 3AA (0903) 814988   CP/BA. VA. VS. WTC. S.

SWIFTSDEN HOUSE (3½ acres) William & Moira Gammell, Swiftsden House, Hurst Green, East Sussex. (058086) 287   VA. VS. WTF.

Wiltshire

CHALKHILL (6½ acres) D. Mann, Knowle Farm, Bowerchalke, Salisbury, Wilts. Salisbury (0722) 780451   VA. WTF.

ELMS CROSS (3 acres) A. R. Shaw, Elms Cross, Bradford-on-Avon, Wilts. Bradford-on-Avon (022 16) 6917   V. VS.

FONTHILL (6 acres) C. P. M. Craig-McFeeley & J. F. Edginton, The Old Rectory, Fonthill Gifford, Tisbury, Wilts. Tisbury (0747) 870231/89365
VA. VS. WTF.

SHERSTON EARL (3 acres) Norman Sellers, Sherston, Malmesbury, Wilts. (0666) 840716   V. VS. WTF.

STITCHCOMBE (5 acres) N. Thompson, Stitchcombe, Nr Marlborough, Wilts. Marlborough (0672) 52297   V. CP. OD. VA. VS. S.

TYTHERLEY (1¼ acres) J. R. M. Donald, Mallards, Norman Court, West Tytherley, Salisbury, Wilts. (0794) 40644   VA. VS. WTC.

Worcestershire

ASTLEY (4½ acres) R. M. Bache, The Crunels, Astley, Stourport-on-Seven, Worcs. Stourport (02993) 2907   CP. VA. VS.

Wales

Glamorgan

CROFFTA (3 acres) J. L. M. Bevan, Groes-Faen, Pontyclun, Glamorgan
CF7 8NE (0443) 223876   VA. VS. WTC.

Gwent

TINTERN PARVA (4 acres) Martin & Gay Rogers, Parva Farm, Tintern,
Nr Chepstow, Gwent. Tintern (029 18) 636   CP. VS. V. WTF.

Channel Islands

LA MARE (6 acres) R. H. and A. M. Blayney, St Mary, Jersey, Channel
Islands. (0534) 81491   CP/BA. V. WTC. VS. M (Light)

7 Sources of Supply for the Vineyard and Winery

Vines – Imported Grafts
Winegrowers Equipment and Supplies (Mr Derek Pritchard), Ordesa,
dept V. B., Wootton Courtenay, Nr Minehead, Somerset will advise and
import all the classic German varieties and also all the wide range of
vinifera crosses from the most highly respected vine nurseries in
Germany and Luxembourg. Highly recommended.

*Madeleine Angevine grafted onto SO4 Rootstock, also rare élite vine
varieties* from Gillian Pearkes, The National Vine Centre, Yearlstone
Vineyard, Bickleigh, Tiverton, Devon.
We send all our Madeleine Angevine prunings to the continent in
December for grafting onto SO4 rootstock at a top vine nursery; these
are returned to us for distribution from March each year. We also raise
rooted cuttings of a few of the élite performance hybrid varieties which
are not available as grafted stock, also rarities. Please send a stamped
self-addressed envelope for all details.

Posts and Stakes

Consult your yellow pages directory for local forestry products, compare
prices and quality with your nearest Fountain Forestry agent, also
Jacksons Fencing, Mrs Edwards, Jacksons Fencing, Stowling Common,
Nr Ashford, Kent. Jacksons are also the English agents for the Swiss
nylon vineyard trellis system, posts, clips and monofilament.

Winegrowers Equipment and Supplies (see above) also import individual
vine supports in steel, rachets, clips, chains and hooks, also stainless
steel wire.

Chemical Spray Materials for Vines

Consult your local agricultural merchants. Should you draw a blank, then contact your nearest vineyard to find out where they obtain their spray materials.

Rain Gauges and Thermometers

Chave and Jackson Ltd, 6 & 7, Broad Street, Hereford.
S. Brannan & Sons Ltd, Cleator Moor, Cumbria (also record book).
Casella (London) Ltd, Regent House, Brittannia Walk, London N11.

Felco Swiss Secateurs

Winegrowers Equipment and Supplies (see above).
Burton McCall Ltd, Samuel Street, Leicester LE1 1RU (free servicing).

Kestrel Bird Scarer

The Country Garden, Binns Close, Coventry.

Fertilizers

Local agricultural merchants.

Knapsack Sprayers

Solo Power Equipment Ltd, Brierley Hill, Staffordshire.
Cooper-Pegler. Both available from agricultural merchants.

Self-propelled, Trailed or Mounted Sprayers

Solo, Cooper-Pegler or Hardi – from local agricultural merchants.

Bamboos

The Bamboo People, Cerne Abbas, Dorchester, Dorset.
Fred Aldous Ltd, 37 Lever Street, Manchester, M60 1UX.

Pocket Refractometer

Winegrowers Equipment and Supplies (see overleaf).

Protective Polythene Vine Sleeves

Dunelm Packaging Co Ltd, The Furnace, Mayford Centre, Smarts Heath Road, Woking, Surrey.

Vineyard Tractors and Equipment

Consult your local agricultural merchants; firms making tractors and equipment for vineyards are Yanmar, Kubota, Iseki and others – also rotavators, fertilizer spreaders, link boxes, trailers and hedgecutters, etc.

Windbreaks

Paraweb, Fyffes Munro Horticultural Supplies Ltd, Forstal Road, Aylesford, Maidstone, Kent ... also MONOFIL plastic trellis filament.

Windbreak Trees

Buy a copy of the *Farmers Weekly,* near the back are firms advertising trees for farmers; we recommend Italian alder, and possibly *Leylandii.*

Vineyard Netting

Netlon Ltd, Kelly Street, Blackburn, Lancashire BB2 4PJ.

Rotavators (for the smaller vineyard)

We recommend *Honda* having found this make to be trouble free, starts first pull and very robust.

Wine Vats and Tanks

Winegrowers Equipment and Supplies (Derek Pritchard), Ordesa, Wootton Courtenay, Nr Minehead, Somerset.
H. Erben Ltd, Hadleigh, Ipswich, Suffolk.
Centriplant, Gooserye House, New Road, Gomshall, Guildford, Surrey.

Winepresses and Berry Mills

Italian Centre Screw Basket Presses, rachet or hydraulic, from half hundredweight up to $\frac{1}{4}$ ton capacity; hand driven and electric mills, Tim Pearkes, Yearlstone Vineyard, Bickleigh, Tiverton, Devon.

Stainless steel water pressure model, stainless crusher-destemmer, Winegrowers Equipment and Supplies, see overleaf.

Vaslin rotary wine press Biddenden Vineyard, Biddenden, nr Ashford, Kent.

Howard Rotapress H. Erben Ltd, Hadleigh, Ipswich, Suffolk.

Wine Press Liner Cloth

Firmin & Co Ltd, Handford Road, Ipswich, Suffolk.

Wine Filters

Winegrowers Equipment and Supplies (small) see above.
Seitz, Enzinger Noll (GB) Ltd, 6 Monkspath Business Park, Shirley, Solihull, W. Midlands.
Sartorious Ltd, 18 Avenue Road, Belmont, Sutton, Surrey.

Corkers, Bottling Heads

Tim Pearkes, Yearlstone Vineyard, see p. 308.
Winegrowers Equipment and Supplies, see p. 308.
Seitz, Enzinger Noll (GB) Ltd, see p. 308.

Capsuling and Labelling Machines

Winegrowers Equipment and Supplies, see p. 308.

Winemaking Services

Three Choirs Vineyard, Rhyle House, Welsh House Lane, Newent, Gloucestershire.
Lamberhurst Vineyards, Lamberhurst, Tunbridge Wells, Kent.

Wine Pumps

Winegrowers Equipment and Supplies, see p. 308.
Watson Marlow Pumps Ltd, Falmouth, Cornwall.

Wine Analysis

Dr Christopher S. Hunter, Dept of Science & Technology, Bristol University, Bristol.
Professor Gerry Fowles, Dept of Science & Technology, Reading University, Reading, Berkshire.

Laboratory Wine Testing Equipment and Chemicals

David Cowderoy, Rock Lodge Vineyard, Scaynes Hill, Haywards Heath, West Sussex.

Wine Yeasts

Siha Active German Yeast, H. E. Lunken, D. M. R. Supply, tel. 035 98 697.
Novo Yeasts & Enzymes, Ubichem Ltd, 281 Hithermoor Road, Stanwell Moor, Staines, Middlesex TW19 6AZ.

Wine Bottles

Rawlings & Son (Bristol) Ltd, Cecil Road, Kingswood, Bristol.
The London Bottle Co., Glenthone House, Glenthorne Road, London W6.

Wine Corks

(Branding, waxing and SO2 treatment)
J. Perkins & Son (London) Ltd, Algarve House, 1 Joan Street, The Cut, London SE1 8DA.
Rankin Brothers & Sons, 139 Bermondsey Street, London SE1 3UR.

Wine Capsules

Metal Closures Ltd, Bromford Lane, West Bromwich, B70 7HY.

Vineyard Associations

The English Vineyards Association:
Commander Geoffrey Bond, 38 West Park, London SE9 4RH. 01-857 0452.
South West Vineyards Association:
Miss Gillian Pearkes, Yearlstone Vineyard, Bickleigh, Tiverton, Devon.
East Anglian Wine Growers Association:
Mrs Berwick, Bruisyard Wines Ltd, Bruisyard, Saxmundham, Suffolk.
Weald and Downland Vineyards Association:
Dr Ivan Williams, Harefield, Stream Lane, Hawkhurst, Kent.
Central Southern Vine Growers Association:
Mr Cliff Sentance, Lymington Vineyard, Wainsford Road, Pennington, Lymington, Hampshire SO4 8OB.

The National Vine Centre

The largest collection of vine varieties in Britain; vines from France, Germany, Luxembourg, USA, Canada, Austria, Switzerland, etc.

Ancient classic varieties, and all the most promising modern varieties from the European viticultural stations maintained in a working vineyard.

Send an SAE to Gillian Pearkes, Yearlstone Vineyard, Bickleigh, Tiverton, Devon for dates of the two or three annual Open Days and also directions.

8 Wine Law

Anyone who has some ground may grow vines in Britain, and make wine solely for home consumption without permission to do so, and without a licence from the Customs and Excise Office.

But if wine is made to be sold, then a licence must be obtained before so doing. Therefore, if you have planted a vineyard of sufficient size to be obvious to everyone that it is too large for a private enterprise, and is obviously of commercial proportions, then it is politic to make an appointment with your local Customs and Excise Officer, and inform him of your action and your intent. In this way he learns of your purpose to make and sell wine in due course from you, the grower, and not what are more than likely to be distorted views from other people, or from the press or television.

If possible invite your Customs Officer to see your vineyard and winery before your first harvest, and ask his advice on all the up-to-date requirements and rulings with which you will be obliged to comply before he will grant you a licence to sell wine. He has all the necessary information and you will be well advised to go about all the necessary procedure which will save time for all concerned in acquiring a wholesale licence, which will allow you to sell wine by the case, to be consumed off the premises.

You will be required to identify the building(s) in which the wine is made and stored by fixing to the exterior door of your winery or wineries the following wording, Winery FR1, (FR1 denoting Fermentation Room 1). The cellar(s) must also be identified as follows, Cellar 1, Cellar 2, Cellar 3 and so on, and all the jars, casks, vats, vessels and tanks must be identified by numbers thus, FV1, FV2, and so on (Fermentation Vessel 1, 2 and 3), and if you should ferment and later store your wine in separate vessels the latter are identified SV1, SV2 (Storage Vessel 1, 2), and so on. If you opt to ferment and store your wine in the same vessels then they are marked FSV1, FSV2, (Fermentation and Storage Vessel 1, 2), and so on *ad infinitum*. The volume of each container is also marked, in litres, on the outside.

This marking is done clearly in white paint, so that both the grower and the Customs Officer can register exactly the amount, in litres, of any wine(s) made each year. Later when the wine(s) are sold, they are entered in a ledger so that the grower and the Customs Officer has a complete record of every litre of wine from its beginning to the point at which it finally leaves the premises.

Duty at the current rate is then paid monthly on the amount of wine that has left the premises in the month previous to the declaration. It is vital to keep a really tight and accurate account of every bottle that is sold, for if one forgets to enter just one or two purchases, one will never remember where one went wrong, and the wine sold will never tally with initial volumes.

Once registered, by law the grower is allowed to make and retain, duty free, 200 gallons of wine for his own consumption each year, and is also allowed 10 per cent of the remainder of his wine duty free. Naturally the grower will need samples of wine to take around to prospective buyers, to give trade and private wine tastings in an effort to build up a clientele both within the trade (hoteliers, restaurateurs, publicans, wine-bar owners and so on), and, hopefully, to build up a good section of private custom. This wine is termed trade samples, and has to come out of the grower's allowance.

If you wish to sell your wine retail, you will require a retail licence from your local Justices of the Peace. An application is made for a hearing at the next sitting at the Magistrates Court and you will have to attend, with or without your solicitor for moral support, to state your case.

This licence will enable you to have a two-price structure whereby you can sell your wine by the bottle as well as by the case, again for consumption off the premises.

Yet another licence must be obtained from the local Justices if you plan to sell wine by the bottle and glass on the premises, known as an on-licence, and is obviously far more difficult to come by – many provisions and conditions must be met by the grower at this stage in order to satisfy the rating and health conditions. Remember to renew your licence(s) annually by the correct date, for, once lapsed, they may not be so easy to reinstate.

The Trading Standards Board will want to see your wine label to see it it complies with the set regulations regarding size of lettering, correct wording and description, that it states the exact volume of the contents, the alcohol content of the wine, the name and address of the supplier, and the year of vintage. The label must indicate that the wine is English

White (or Red) Table Wine, that it is the produce of the United Kingdom. The Board will also check the name of your wine, which could be named after your house, village, town or district. They will also insist that you use only Euromarked bottles, bottles stamped with an E on the side of the base, together with the volume of the bottle, which must be 75 cl from 1 May 1989. The E indicates that the bottles are of a pre-tested exact size.

The Wine Standards Board will send you a form on which they require you to inform them of the amount of sugar you have added to your wine or wines of the current year (see below).

Quality of the Must

Wine may not be made for sale unless the initial oechsle or gravity of the must is 45° or above; fair enough, the must would more than likely be unbearably acid and totally unbalanced at such a low natural sugar assimilation. This base reading will be raised to 50 oe by 1990.

Since 1980 no winemaker has been allowed to effect an acid reduction by watering the must or wine, or stretching the must with sugar syrup for this purpose. Therefore it applies that the initial surgaring or chaptalization of a grape juice must not exceed 15 per cent, and this must be achieved by dry sugar addition prior to fermentation. Thus the increase in potential alcohol content may be up to 3.5° for white wines, and 4.0° for red wines, this on the understanding that the initial alcohol content is 5° (40 oe).

Fresh grape must, or semi-finished or, even, finished wine may be subject to de-acidification, but may not have acid added, other than by the addition to the initial low-acid must of a proportion of high acid must, for example Chardonnay or Pinot.

Name of the Grape on the Label

A wine label may carry the name of the grape variety if the wine is made solely from the juice of the given vine variety. It may contain must or juice of another variety or varieties up to 15 per cent of the whole, and may still be named by the name of the original grape variety.

Should the addition of the juice of another grape variety or varieties exceed 15 per cent, then all grape names should be listed, the major grape first, followed by the minor grape(s) in order of precedence, i.e. Pinot Noir, Auxerrois and Pinot Gris, the percentages here could be for example 60 per cent, 30 per cent and 10 per cent respectively.

It is not necessary that grape varieties be mentioned if the wine has its identity in its name; this is sufficient, be it a single grape wine or a blend. Wines may be described as dry, medium dry, medium, medium sweet or sweet, dry white, sweet white, etc.; from 1 May 1989 the wine label must state the alcohol content of the wine, accurate to within 0.5%.

9 Useful Equivalent Measurements

2.47 (c $2\frac{1}{2}$) acres	=	1 hectare (ha)
1 hectare	=	1000 square metres
3.28 feet	=	1 metre
1 gallon	=	4.5 litres
$1\frac{3}{4}$ pints	=	1 litre
$26\frac{2}{3}$ fluid ounces	=	75 centilitres (cl)
22 gallons	=	1 hectolitre = 100 litres
50 gallons	=	225 litres
1 ton	=	1016 kilograms (Kg) = 1.016 Tonnes (T)
22 pounds	=	10 kilograms
1 pound	=	540 grams (g)
1 ton per acre	=	2.5 tonnes per hectare
300 gallons per acre	=	34 hectolitres per hectare

An excellent booklet on useful facts and figures called *Metrication on the Farm* by Donald Hardy, published by the Ford Motor Company is available from Woodhead Faulkner Ltd, 7 Rose Crescent, Cambridge CBD 3LL.

10 Top Grafting Over to Another Variety of Vine

Should a grower be reluctantly forced to the conclusion that his vineyard is partially or totally planted with a wholly useless vine variety, he is faced with the horrific decision to grub all the useless vines and replant with a more reliable variety. This involves a great deal of effort and expense, besides having an area that produces no grapes for three or four years. There is an alternative.

It is possible to top graft a new reliable vine variety onto the established growing leg or stem. This grafting may be achieved in a number of ways, some of which are illustrated in the sketches.

The great advantage in grafting over to the new variety is that the vines can still be lightly cropped on the original variety during the year the grafting takes place; *if* the weather is good, and the grafting operation is successful the new vine variety will be bearing fruit in the year following the grafting.

With vines in the open, the grafting is best done in April or May, immediately prior to budburst. This operation will only be successful if the weather is really hot for two or three weeks subsequently, so keep

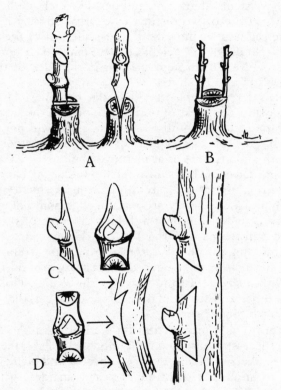

60 *Vine grafting*. A grower sometimes finds himself with mature vines of varieties he may wish to discontinue because of certain undesirable features. These vines will either have to be removed, or one could top graft them over to a better and more profitable variety. **A** A cleft graft with a one or two bud scion being grafted into a young stock. **B** Two cuttings grafted into an older stock (smaller scale). This method is used in February, March and April. **C & D** Two methods of bud grafting, operated during August. The Yemagraft evolved in Spain, and is executed in August at ground level, using well-ripened buds into two-year old stocks. Heap the soil over the graft and, if successful, cut the stock down 5 in above the graft in the following year.

an eye on the weather charts, and when a high pressure area develops over the Azores, accompanied by a south-westerly air flow – with no nasty low pressure areas lurking to the west of England in the Atlantic – and the weathermen promise a good spell of warm weather, this is the time to begin.

You will need a good budding knife, and a fine sharpening stone plus a clean damp rag, so the knife may be kept really brilliantly clean and razor sharp. You will also need several rolls of black insulating tape as used for electrical repairs. Cut the wood from the variety to be used for the grafting, the scion, on the day the grafting is to be done.

Look at the systems of grafting and decide which method you aim to follow. Grafts fall into two distinct categories, those where a 1-3-bud length of the scion is let into a slit across the top of the stock, which has been cut right down to a height of 30–45 cm (1–1½ ft), or alternatively a single bud is inserted through a T cut in the bark of the stock. For outdoor work I favour the latter.

With top grafts it is essential that the cambium layer, the layer immediately below the bark, of both the scion and the stock are in total contact with one another. Without this the graft will not take place. It is also vital that the cut edges or sides of the scion and stock are touching all their length and are are cut at identical angles.

When preparing single buds for insertion under the bark of the stock, cut the bud from the scion, carefully cutting a shield shape of bark around the bud, trim it neatly around the edge and make sure that the sliver of bark is paper thin. Cut a T into the bark of the stock, insert the bud, and pull the flaps of the T cut back into place *over* the sliver of bark surrounding the bud. Wrap insulating tape around the incision, both above and below, next wrap a little straw around the graft, and cover this with a sleeve of thin clear polythene film. Hold the film on tightly with tape, and lastly make a little cut near the bud to avoid condensation forming within.

Open air grafting is practised in Italy and the south of France, and will only be successful here in a really hot spell of weather, though the T bud is more likely to take being less exposed, and being easier to keep warm. Bear in mind that this time of year coincides with the greatest surge of growth and energy in the vine, so the stock will be swelling in girth and, thus, will quickly find the tight binding acting like a tourniquet; the binding may have to be changed before the union has taken place between the two varieties. If so, do this very carefully so any lesion that may have already taken place will not be spoilt.

11 Viticultural Courses for New Growers

These will take place at Yearlstone Vineyard, Bickleigh, Tiverton, Devon and are run by Gillian Pearkes, Nuffield Scholar on Viticulture and Oenology. Please send a self-addressed envelope for full details of the seminars for the current year.

This course is designed to give both those who are contemplating planting a vineyard and those who have already done so a complete grounding in all aspects of site preparation, planting, training and pruning the vine, care, maintenance and health of the vines and vineyard from planting to the first harvest. The setting up of a winery, the harvest and the marketing of the wine will be covered in detail. Participants will each be issued with a folder, and notes on each day – it is strongly recommended that students also take copious notes of their own so that all the ground we cover each day can be re-read for future reference.

Full Course: A Series of Five Seminars

1 MARCH Planning and planting a vineyard

How to choose a site, improve and plan the planting site; deciding on planting density, choice of vines and rootstocks, step-by-step planting, erection of trellis. Discussion on pruning of 1, 2, 3, and 4 year old vines, different methods of training, followed by demonstration of planting and pruning in the vineyard in the afternoon. We then return to the lecture hall to recap on the ground covered during the day.

2 MAY Viticulture – maintenance, nutrition, and health in the vine

Spring work in the vineyard, cultivation and herbicides; planning a balanced nutrition programme and a preventative spraying programme, the importance of soil balance, potash, the trace elements for maximum fertility and yield; in the vineyard a demonstration of disbudding to leave each vine with a fully viable but not overloaded crop.

3 JUNE OR JULY Flowering and pollination – summer pruning

Bringing the vine to flowering in optimum condition, importance of micro-climate at this time; discussion on laying down of fruit buds for next year's crop; and on varietal behaviour in optimum and adverse weather conditions at this time. Summer pruning will be demonstrated and explained in the Vineyard, also the continuing spraying programme.

Planning a winery, or making arrangements for your wine to be made for you. Netting – protection from birds and wasps.

4 SEPTEMBER – Preparing for harvest

A realistic look at the yield of popular and new vine varieties, early and late ripening vines, the importance of a vine demonstrating consistent habit of flowering, setting, viable yield, adequate sugar assimilation and wood ripening, and making a quality marketable product. Preparing the winery and equipment for harvest, picking and transporting the grapes, and demonstration of equipment and processes involved. Discussion on marketing techniques and opening to the public.

5 OCTOBER – Harvest and wine making

Students can spend a day at Yearlstone during the harvest, participating in the picking, transporting, milling, pressing and containerization of the new wine. The grape juice must be tested for sugar and acid, adjusted if necessary, and finally yeasted and fermented. This day will give new growers a good grounding on how to prepare for and manage their own harvest, whether on a private or commercial scale. Both white and red wines are made at Yearlstone, each demanding a totally different production process.

An alarming proportion of vineyards in England have been planted without any advice on the site, preparation of that site and discussion on the choice of vine for that particular site, and as a result many very expensive mistakes have been made, several proving to be total failures, and others proving unable to produce a return on the outlay, let alone a profit. Typical examples of plant in haste, repent at leisure. Certain of these vineyards have yet to produce a grape, which is disastrous.

This course is designed to prevent failure, and to show the way in which a vineyard can be really successful, whether run on an amateur or commercial scale. The emphasis will be on showing that growing and making wine is a simple natural process, providing the grower keeps mildew and other ills away, and the wine growing year is an enjoyable commitment, the end result proving to be an attractive even exotic reward for one's labours. The sight of that first crop ripening on the vines is a tremendous experience.

12 Further Reading

Viticulture
General Viticulture, A. J. Winkler – University of California Press.
Oxted Viticultural Reports, R. Barrington-Brock. Available from Jackmans of Woking.
Viticulture, F. Berrysmith – New Zealand. Available from Whitcoulls, NZ Bookshop, Royal Opera Arcade, Pall Mall, London, SW1 4UY.
Grape Growing and Winemaking, David Jackson and Danny Schuster, Alister Taylor Publishing Ltd, The Old Post Office, Martinborough, New Zealand.

Winemaking

Scientific Winemaking made easy, J. R. Mitchell, LRIC, FIFST., Argus Specialist Publications Ltd, No. 1 Golden Square, London W1R 3AB.
Winemaking and Brewing, F. W. Beech and A. Pollard – Amateur Winemaker, South Street, Andover, 1970.
Applied Wine Chemistry and Technology, A. Massel, Heidelberg Publishers, 1969.
The Science and Technique of Wine, Lionel Franklin – Patrick Stephens, 1974.

Phylloxera

The Great Wine Blight, George Ordish – Sidgwick & Jackson.
A fascinating study of the life-cycle and devastation of the phylloxera in the European winefields at the close of the 19th and in the early 20th centuries.

History of Winegrowing in England

A Tradition of English Wine, Hugh Barty-King – Oxford Illustrated Press, 1977. A wonderful in-depth treatise on the long history of winegrowing in England.

Indoor Vines

Grapes Under Glass, H. Parsons – W. H. & L. Collingridge, 1955.

Directory of English Commercial Vineyards

The New English Vineyard, Joanna Smith – Sidgwick and Jackson, 1979.

Wines of the World

Wine – Teach Yourself Books, Robin Don, M.W. – Hodder and Stoughton, 1977. An *excellent* introduction to wine.
The World Atlas of Wine, Hugh Johnson – Mitchell Beazley, 1971.

Chemicals in the Vineyard

List of Approved Products and their uses for Farmers and Growers (published annually). Ministry of Agriculture, Fisheries and Food, HMSO. Bookshops.
Directory of Garden Chemicals, British Agrochemicals Association, Alembic House, 93 Albert Embankment, London SE1 7TU.

Useful ADAS Publications

Windbreaks ref H621, 1979.
Artificial Windbreaks and their supports ref 2076, 1979.
Grapes for Wine ref 322 Tony Heath, 1980.
Soils and Manures for Fruit ref 107, 1979.

Vine Identification

A Practical Ampelography, Pierre Galet, translated and adapted by Lucie T. Morton – Cornell University Press, 1979.

13 Update on Botrytis

Much valid research has been done on botrytis recently on the Continent and also in the United States.

Botrytis overwinters in the vineyard on the vines and also in shrivelled mummified bunches in the form of hard black sclerotia of $\frac{1}{4}$ inch in diameter. In spring the warmer weather, rains and wind can spread these spores.

The spores require nutrients and dew, fog or rain for germination and growth. The preferred nutrient is the skin of the grapes, which only have to be wet for 2 hours for the spores to germinate. A period as short as 15 minutes with no available moisture can halt germination. Botrytis is more readily able to gain control where the berries have been damaged by wind, insects or birds, and is particularly attracted to the thin skinned varieties.

At 50°F some 30 hours of moisture are required for germination, at 72°F 15 hours of moisture is all that is needed, whereas at 85°F 35 hours of moisture are necessary, but botrytis will even grow slowly at 34°F – a daunting prospect. At 72°F with water botrytis can infect and destroy a berry, and begin to produce more spores for the infection of neighbouring berries in a mere three days.

If high temperatures occur after infection, the botrytis may dry up, but if the wet weather returns the fungus is alive and will grow once more.

It has been discovered that to increase air circulation around the fruit clusters by leaf removal enables them to dry out more quickly after rain if done from approximately two weeks after berry set, particularly from the centre of the vine hedge.

Wetting agents

It has been discovered that the use of spray spreaders or stickers, wetting agents, causes an alteration in the function of the protective layer of plant wax, thus rendering the berries more vulnerable to attack by botrytis. Many modern fungicides contain a wetting agent, so to add more is asking for trouble here.

Rotation of spray chemicals

Chemicals used to control botrytis include Benlate, Bravo, Elvaron, Ronilan and Rovral. Resistance against Benlate is very quickly built up, so this product should only be used once every one or two years. Resistance to Ronilan and Rovral has also been reported, therefore the only way to maintain a prevention control is to ring the changes with all these products, using each one no more than once a year for the three or four spray applications against botrytis.

These three or four applications against botrytis are recommended to take place at the following times, (1) immediately before blossoming, (2) immediately after berry set, maybe (3) at veraison if the weather demands or if the first signs of botrytis are detected at this time, and (4) 21 days prior to the expected date of harvest of each variety. Only apply Elvaron before flowering since if applied on grapes it can be detected in a finished wine, and always keep Rovral for the final pre-harvest spray since it does give the best protection of all products, and this is the time of greatest risk. If however an outbreak occurs in August, then Rovral is the best means of immediate and total control. But remember that after 18 consecutive sprays of Rovral, control with this product is lost forever; Rovral is far too valuable an aid to allow this to happen.

Research in France has shown that better control is attained by applying the fungicides in wet spells when the fungus is actively growing, and is thus more susceptible to control. A low dose of copper in the final pre-harvest spray, 4 oz/100 litres, mixed in with sulphur, Zineb and Rovral, does much to prevent late botrytis by hardening the grape stem and grape skin somewhat, and thus goes far in ensuring 100 per cent clean grapes.

To conclude, it is obviously sensible to plant varieties with a high mildew and botrytis resistance, to ensure a good air flow through the vineyard, leaf removal at least from the eastern side of the vine hedge to expose the bunches to the sun and air from mid to late August, and to formulate and adhere to a strict programme of spray prevention. A final note: when removing leaves, take them from the grape band only, no higher, and other than in heatwave conditions take them from the centre of the grape-band rather than from the outside, for rain and wind can damage exposed grapes. Once damaged, botrytis and grey rot quickly gain hold, and wasps begin to decimate the crop.

Index

ю.А.
1971.

Second Nature

ANDREI NAVROZOV

Second Nature

FORTY-SIX POEMS

BY

BORIS PASTERNAK

PETER OWEN · LONDON

ISBN 0 7206 0751 5

Extracts from T. S. Eliot's 'The Metaphysical Poets'
in *Selected Essays* (originally published in 1921)
are reprinted by permission of Faber and Faber Limited.

PETER OWEN PUBLISHERS
73 Kenway Road London SW5 ORE

First published in Great Britain 1990
Introduction, Notes and this translation
© Andrei Navrozov 1990

Photoset by Rowland Phototypesetting Limited
Bury St Edmunds Suffolk

Printed in Great Britain by St Edmundsbury Press Limited
Bury St Edmunds Suffolk

Contents

INTRODUCTION

Transporting the Elements

To the memory of Alexander Bisk
'Sein Bild: ich weih's.' (Rilke)

A visitor to modern Athens, if he is inclined to contemplation, will be startled by a Greek word emblazoned on lorries, vans, and often on tiny estate cars, whose owners make a living by hauling the cargoes of industry and the belongings of men from place to place as they have done since the beginning of history. The word is *Metaphorai*. It is less likely that a Greek-speaking resident of the city should be quite as affected by the presence of an idea so profound in surroundings so mundane. Nor is it any easier to imagine an English-speaking denizen of New York dumbstruck at the sight of the word *Transport* on the side of a moving truck, even if he became convinced that inside it were priceless artefacts bound for Sotheby's sale-rooms.

My aim, in offering these versions of Pasternak's poems, is to bring the Russian poet to the English-speaking world. Reduced to its Latin roots, 'translation' mirrors the Greek for 'metaphor', and the original working title of this collection, which I began working on some twelve years ago, was 'Transport of Elements'. The elements I had in mind were Pasternak's, but also, in their broader and deeper meaning, those of Russian verse, for only an iota of sense separates *stikhi*, derived from the Greek word for their orderly stance, and the great elemental *stikhii* of Aristotle. With the passing of years, the present title has evolved, capturing I believe the essential simplicity inherent in the work of a translator. I shall return to this subject later, addressing for the time being the essential difficulties of the task, present side by side with that simplicity.

When Horace transposed Aeolian song to the everlasting 'Italian mode', when Chopin transcribed simple village tunes in his polonaises and mazurkas, the spiritual cargo they were transporting can be said to have consisted of raw material. My cargo, by contrast, consists of a single meticulously crafted, priceless and unique cultural object which, if it is to be understood and appreciated by its recipients, must arrive whole, in one piece, ideally with the supporting stylobate of its cultural history still intact. This last is called a biography, and a suitable life of Pasternak remains to be written.

The literary reputation of Boris Pasternak in the West resembles a novel based on the life of an imaginary artist, a hypothetical figure along the lines of Adrian Leverkühn, the composer hero of Thomas Mann's *Doctor Faustus*. However much the English reader learns about the man, his work, like Leverkühn's music, remains a mystery. To be sure, the work is discussed, criticized, explained. Yet it does not exist. Is this, to use a phrase beloved of our critics, a problem of translation? I would rather present it as a problem of life or love – which, to a Christian or a poet, are the only elements worth thinking about in the first place.

I should like to begin with a truism, uttered with the confidence of St Paul's familiar words to the Corinthians which echo in Whitsuntide through the churches of Cambridge outside my window. A poet should never describe what he cannot love. Let us regard this breezy truism as a most solemn truth. Indeed, whatever the semantic implications of 'transport', it must be agreed at the outset that its emotional connotations are nothing if not sincere.

There are forty-six poems in this book. Not fifty, or a round hundred. Not *The Complete Poems of Boris Pasternak*, not *The Complete Early Poems*, nor even *Complete Poems: 1912–1932*. As she looked, in 1933, at what was then – and unbeknown to her would remain – the poet's final harvest, Marina Tsvetayeva exclaimed with prescient finality: 'Half a thousand pages'.

From these, I have chosen a mere handful. But in life as in love, is there really such a thing as choice?

When I was a child, I knew those five hundred pages by heart. The task of selection was neither frustrating nor gratifying, since T.S. Eliot's 'question of some nicety' to 'decide how much must be read of any particular poet' was never meant for children. When I became a man, I knew I had to do only what I could, and as much of it as I could.

The infatuation of a nine-year-old resolved an even more important problem of translation. As a child, I found in Pasternak a beauty which lay in something other than the 'meaning' of his poems. I use the word in its most unsophisticated sense: I simply did not understand many of the words. It was only later that I discovered a contemporary critic, Nikolai Aseev, who wrote that in his friend's verse 'the element of intonation predominates and is the *raison d'être* of the whole poem'. I do not think this is true today, and neither did Pasternak, but I certainly would have agreed with Aseev intuitively at the age of nine. When my vocabulary matured, encompassing the full 'meaning' of Pasternak's verse, my original, child's feeling did not shrink. The content of love filled the form and became an object.

In an article on translation, R. A. Brower has written:

> We translate the less familiar by putting the more familiar in its place, and when the right occasion comes along, we are prepared to use the once forgotten gesture or word 'like a native'. Much of our learning of our own language takes place through similar processes. The child points to a farmer in a hayfield and says – as I once heard a child say – 'Man haying' and the parent, who speaks the foreign language of the adult world, *dutifully corrects and translates*, 'The man is haying'. [My italics – A.N.]

Applied to Pasternak, in this case, such a learning process would entail the perpetual translation of his poetry into Russian, which is precisely what my love of him as a child has prevented me from doing as a man. Conceived *in puris naturalibus*, this love never needed correction and remains blind to duty.

I am not exaggerating the temptation to translate Pasternak into Russian. It is great, and few resist it completely. Still fewer are those who have resisted it for reasons other than ordinary contempt, intellectual idleness, or spiritual inadequacy, all of which a poet encounters in his critics. Here is one contemporary, discussing, in 1928, Pasternak's 'limitations':

> If we add to them a deficiency of taste – which was innate in him, though maybe later it became a matter of principle – we shall understand why he has had to go through a long struggle to free the language of his verse from various kinds of weeds all equally evident in it: near-meaningless un-Russian turns of speech, dubious stresses, incorrect cases and wrongly abbreviated endings. [Examples from *My Sister Life* and *Themes & Variations* follow – A.N.] This outrageous example is characteristic because it shows not only a lack of taste but also a deficiency of thought, that is, insufficient realization of how words should be used; and this is something from which Pasternak will never quite escape, nor can any more lately acquired knowledge of the language cure him of it. Indeed, such knowledge will always remain somewhat inert, pointless, founded more on a reading of dictionaries than on a deepening of linguistic awareness.

The author, a Russian émigré named Wladimir Weidle, became, thirty years later, a verbose admirer of 'mature' Pasternak and did not take the opportunity to revise his view of the 'early' work in his introduction to the most complete collection of the poet's writings published outside of Russia. How the Weidles of the world become the executors of spiritual estates which its Pasternaks leave behind is a mystery not unique to the Russian emigration, but I had better reflect on that elsewhere.

Vicious or ecstatic, contemporary Russian critics agree that the poetic world of Pasternak is as autonomous as it is unique: although created in language, it is outside language. Khlebnikov once called him 'the youthful German of Russian speech', and to Tsvetayeva's ears his speech was at once the gurgling of a baby ('and this baby is the world') and the wordless joy of an even younger earth ('created *before* Adam'): 'Pasternak doesn't speak, hasn't time to finish speaking.' But Khlebnikov and Tsvetayeva were themselves poets of genius, and their impressions are not representative. We need to turn to the best of the average, a critic or two with nothing more than a good ear between them. They concur. In 1922 Ilya Ehrenburg wrote:

> It's hard work talking to Pasternak. His speech is a combination of tongue-twisting, a desperate straining to drag out a needed word from within, and a stormy cascade of unexpected comparisons, complex associations and frank confessions in what is evidently a foreign language. He would be unintelligible were not all this chaos illumined by the singleness and clarity of his voice.

In 1924 Yuri Tynyanov quoted the penultimate stanza of 'Poetry' (p. 59), concluding much to the same effect: 'This is almost an instance of "meaningless soundspeech", and yet it is inexorably logical; it is a kind of phantom imitation of syntax, and yet the syntax here is impeccable.' Another critic, writing in 1927, summed up: 'Pasternak writes unintelligibly because he wants to write unintelligibly.'

This, then, is the difference between Pasternak and the child in the hayfield. The child of three one may 'correct and translate' into the language that is his by education. To do this to a poet of twenty-three, in a language that is so utterly his by birth, is to make a mockery of the breezy truism whose acceptance as a most solemn truth I require of myself and my reader.

'Like the original poet,' wrote Renato Poggioli, 'the translator is a Narcissus who chooses to contemplate his own likeness not in the spring of nature but in the pool of art.' Let us try to recapture that moment of contemplation. Obviously, among the first things to come to mind is the question of what its end result would be like. Where would the world of Pasternak 'fit' in the universe of English prosody? Turn to Pasternak's 'Definition of Poetry' (p. 28). Is there room for his star in our pond?

Here is T. S. Eliot, Pasternak's contemporary, writing in 1921:

> The poets of the seventeenth century, the successors of the dramatists of the sixteenth, possessed a mechanism of sensibility which could devour any kind of experience. . . . In the seventeenth century a dissociation of sensibility set in, from which we have never recovered; and this dissociation, as is natural, was aggravated by the influence of the two most powerful poets of the century, Milton and Dryden. Each of these men performed certain poetic functions so magnificently well that the magnitude of the effect concealed the absence of others. The language went on and in some respects improved. . . . But while the language became more refined, the feeling became more crude.

He proceeds very carefully from here, yet is courageous enough to speculate

> . . . whether it is not a misfortune that two of the greatest masters of diction in our language, Milton and Dryden, triumph with a dazzling disregard of the soul. If we continued to produce Miltons and Drydens it might not so much matter, but as things are it is a pity that English poetry has remained so incomplete. Those who object to the 'artificiality' of Milton and Dryden sometimes tell us to 'look into our hearts and write'. But that is not looking deep enough. . . . One must look into the cerebral cortex, the nervous system, and the digestive tracts.

Half a century later, these words are grist to the undergraduate mill, yet the poet, himself at a crossroads by 1921, was speaking of a real misfortune, a tragic, and not merely noteworthy, fact of literary history that affects every writer. Turn to 'The Riddle' (p. 58):

> Drank like birds. Drew until vision would cease.
> Stars take years to reach the stomach through sighs.

The cerebral cortex, the nervous sytem, even the ever-so-unpoetic 'stomach' (in Russian, literally, 'food tract'), perceived by contemporaries as a 'Futurist' excess: they are all here. Could a Russian poet be the missing link in the evolution of sensibility whose collapse in the wake of the seventeenth century so troubled his Anglo–American contemporary?

My point here is not to prove that Pasternak is a direct descendant of Donne, Vaughan, Herbert and Marvell. There is no doubt that an indirect connection, easily documented by the minutiae of his Germanic spiritual genealogy (Shakespeare and Goethe, Swinburne and Rilke), woven into the auto-biographical fabric of *Safe Conduct* and obvious in the poems, is there, however ambivalent the poet's attitude to the terminology of 'Romanticism'. The point is that we may well ask, with Eliot, 'what would have been the fate of the "metaphysical" poets had the current of poetry descended in a direct line from them, as it descended in a direct line to them? They would not, certainly, be classified as metaphysical'. So here is where these versions of Pasternak 'fit': into what might have been the mainstream of English poetry.

Eliot begins his now-famous essay with the now-famous nine lines from Donne's 'A Valediction: Of Weeping'. Turn to the poems of 'The Rupture' cycle (pp. 45–9) or 'Waving a fragrant anther . . .' (p. 25). The 'telescoping' of images, Eliot's now-famous term for the moments of 'metaphysical' revelation, seems to have been invented with Pasternak in mind.

Zanyatya filosofiyei is the name of one of the 'chapters' in *My Sister Life*. Needless to say, I render this as 'Studies in Metaphysics', not only because it describes more precisely what Pasternak studied at Marburg than the vague 'Philosophy'. In the light of everything said thus far, the risk of limiting the sense of the Russian word is justified. This, of course, is just an example of how the second Narcissus interprets his nature. The first Narcissus is always there to validate his poetic licence.

Perhaps I had better leave to others the critical exercises whereby the baroque synthesis of experience may be related to Pasternak's lyric technique. A recognition of the kinship between what was and what might have been is sufficient for my purposes. The English Pasternak must strive to possess the emotional temperature of Donne and the syntactic boldness of Milton, his uniquely Russian and uniquely contemporary qualities safeguarding the originality of the whole. But there is one aspect of this kinship which, again with Eliot's help, must be examined further.

The poems of Pasternak show at once that their author has interests: in philosophy, in music, in botany. These interests shape the poet's vast, difficult, unpredictable vocabulary, as Eliot thought they might:

> The possible interests of a poet are unlimited; the more intelligent he is the better; the more intelligent he is the more likely that he will have interests; our only condition is that he turn them into poetry, and not merely meditate on them poetically. . . . It is not a permanent necessity that poets should be interested in philosophy, or in any other subject. We can only say that it appears likely that the poets in our civilisation, as it exists at present, must be *difficult*. Our civilisation comprehends great variety and complexity. . . . The poet must become more and more comprehensive, more allusive, more indirect, in order to force, to dislocate if necessary, language into its meaning.

The English counterpart of Pasternak's Russian reader must bear this in mind. Turn to the second stanza of 'A Sultry Night' (p. 34) and a whole encyclopedia of baroque pathology seems to shed its blurry pages at our touch. 'Waving a fragrant anther . . .' (p. 25) seems to have sprung from the colour spreads of *Newcomb's Flower Guide*: 'Let the wind, *inspiring spirea*. . . .' In Russian: *po távolge véyushchiy*. Russians read John 3: 8, *Spiritus ubi vult spirat*, as *Dukh véyet, gde khóchet*, and yet it is a rare translator who has not dutifully corrected and translated these words along these lines: 'Let the wind, which blows over the meadowsweet. . . .' True, in English, John 3: 8 reads: 'The wind bloweth where it listeth.' But even if we assume, which I personally do with great difficulty, that the scriptural reference – rather than, say, Smirnitsky's *Russian–English Dictionary* – has motivated their choice, the result is not English poetry but, indeed, a verbatim quotation from *Newcomb's*, acceptable only to the spiritual heirs of Wordsworth. Thus the 'interests' of a poet are relevant only if they result in poetry.

I have written that the English Pasternak must strive to possess the emotional temperature of Donne and the syntactic boldness of Milton. Another way of saying it, as Schumann said of Chopin, is that great means are needed for great meanings. On the other hand, a contemporary critic said of Chopin's Études: 'Those who have distorted fingers may set them right by playing these.' The question here is no longer one of who is right about Pasternak, Wladimir Weidle or Marina Tsvetayeva; but rather of whether, even if one accepts the contention that there is room for Pasternak in English prosody, there exists today a critical milieu capable of treating the very idea of 'transport' with the sincerity it requires.

Of all the 'modern' poets to write in English, strangely enough, the one closest to Pasternak in temperament and attitude is Emily Dickinson, another possible 'missing link' that Eliot failed to take into account in 1921. I have published my translation of a selection of Dickinson's poems into Russian, and my love for her is second only to the one I describe here. In this connection, I propose the following experiment. Read the following lines:

> I mean to rule the earth,
> And he the sky –
> We really know our worth,
> The sun and I!

The experiment works only if one does not know *The Mikado* by heart, since this is sung by Yum-Yum in Act II. The talent of W. S. Gilbert is undeniable, and this excuses the confusion of many literary men whom I have convinced that the lines are Dickinson's. Indeed, when such things are taken out of context, their outlines begin to blur, and we can find Edward Lear in *King Lear* and Marshak in Pasternak.

Yet the curse of Lear, Edward, is sure to follow me as it has followed many an English poet who has had the misfortune of living in the twentieth century. Lydia Pasternak-Slater, who herself translated a few of her brother's poems into English with some success, felt compelled to point out, in a letter to *The New York Times* shortly after his death, that 'Pasternak, like Mayakovsky, the most revolutionary of Russian poets, has never in his life written a single line of unrhythmic poetry, and this is not because of a pedantic adherence to obsolete classical rules, but because an instinctive feeling for rhythm and harmony were inborn qualities of his genius, and he simply could not write differently'.

As for Pasternak's and Mayakovsky's rhyme, itself a kind of triumphal arch through which all Russian poetry inevitably progresses, there Pasternak in English passes the point of no return. Three full centuries of Eliot's 'dissociation of sensibility' weigh one down. Rhyme is no longer, to be sure, universally despised as a kind of correctional institution for the English soul; it is more like an old mine, abandoned as unprofitable long ago and now remembered only by the nostalgic townsfolk and the odd curious visitor from abroad who wants to trace his family's roots to their humble beginnings during a summer holiday. The 'progressive' critical community regards it as a sad anachronism blighting the landscape: willing as its members are to tolerate the occasional enthusiast, they are not about to welcome the conversion of this redundant enterprise into a going concern. Yet rhyme is not only the spirit of Pasternak, it is his letter.

In Russian as in English and other European languages, rhyme is above all an act of will. There is no more gross misrepresentation of the nature of rhyme than one by my fellow émigré Vladimir Nabokov who listed, in an article on his translation of Pushkin's *Eugene Onegin*, the 'six characteristics' by which 'Russian poetry is affected'. I trust that just one of these will suffice:

1. The number of rhymes, both masculine and feminine (i.e. single and double), is incomparably greater than in English and leads to the cult of the rare and the rich. As in French, the *consonne d'appui* is obligatory in masculine rhymes and aesthetically valued in feminine ones. This is far removed from the English rhyme, Echo's poor relation, a genteel pauper whose attempts to shine result merely in doggerel garishness. For if in Russian and French, the feminine rhyme is a glamorous lady friend, her English counterpart is either an old maid or a drunken hussy from Limerick.

This is so, of course, only if one has the ear of an accountant. Indeed, is there such a thing as 'rhyme' detached from the poet and dangling its *consonne d'appui* in no particular context? Sure enough, Nabokov is terrified that the curse of Lear, Edward, may be upon him. But what on earth is he counting? The Russian alphabet has thirty-two letters, the English twenty-six. What of it?

The assonance 'honest fingers'/'amethyst remembrance' is a rhyme in the hands of Emily Dickinson because she has faith – as do I, her reader – that the juxtaposition of these sounds mirrors the emotion which she finds herself facing:

> I woke – and chid my honest fingers,
> The Gem was gone –
> And now, an Amethyst remembrance
> Is all I own.

Would her faith have been shaken by Nabokov's grim gener-
alities about the nature of rhyme, or by the plain fact that, in
and of itself, 'fingers'/'remembrance' is not an 'acceptable'
rhyme by anyone else's standards? I shall return to Nabokov as
translator, to defend him as well as to ponder his wayward-
ness. For now, let us simply ask the question of who is more
likely to gain favour in Pieria, the 'glamorous lady', obsessed
with form in her 'cult of the rare and the rich', or the 'old
maid', writing with Dickinson's honest fingers. The faith in
the possibilities of one's language, including rhyme, is still
what Leonardo called the guide and the gate.

Here is a brief digression, with a moral. Rainer Maria Rilke
was Pasternak's Virgil, who, by his admission, led him to
poetry. Pasternak met Rilke as a child and corresponded with
him in later life. He knew German and understood Rilke better
than the authors of voluminous critical studies ever could.
And yes, he tried translating Rilke into Russian. He failed. It
does not matter why, he just did.

There once lived a man named Ludwig Lewisohn who
published, in 1946 in America, *Thirty-One Poems by Rainer
Maria Rilke, in English Versions*. He had the audacity to
announce, in his brief introduction to the 47-page book, that
poems 'cannot be split into meaning and form; they have, like
life itself, in Goethe's words, neither "shell nor kernel"'. He
went on to criticize American translators of Rilke for not
understanding this. Needless to say, the only Rilke that exists
in English to this day is Lewisohn's. Needless to say, he has
been universally forgotten, though not by me.

There once lived a man named Alexander Bisk who published, in 1919 in Russia, his *Selections from Rainer Maria Rilke*
and reprinted his versions in Paris in 1957, not long before his
death as an obscure émigré, in a hotel fire. The book was
dedicated to his son, the distinguished French poet Alain
Bosquet, who himself had published by then a collection of
French translations of Emily Dickinson. As it happened,
Pasternak read Bisk's translations after they first appeared,

many years earlier, and wrote to Bisk to acknowledge his genius. I do not know French and cannot judge Bosquet's translations of Dickinson, but there is no doubt that the only Rilke that exists in Russian to this day is his father's. Bisk succeeded where Pasternak had failed.

In 1960 a long article in an influential émigré periodical vilified both the son and the father. Entitled 'On the Untranslatable', it savaged Bosquet for 'conveying the rhythm of the thought, not of the word' and Bisk for daring to 'compete with the author'. The verbose polyglot and tone-deaf pedant philosophizing about the 'Untranslatable' was none other than Wladimir Weidle.

Needless to say, Alexander Bisk has been universally forgotten. No, not by me. One simple, diffident truth from his introduction to the poems abides with me always:

> I translated only what enchanted me: there was no question of translating one poem after another. Any attempt to convey 'The Complete Works' of a poet, or even one complete volume of verse, is doomed to failure. . . . To translate a poem one must fall in love with it, learn to live with it, penetrate its musical essence – this is particularly important with Rilke – and only then try to say something of the kind in one's own tongue.

Bisk and Lewisohn were born translators of Rilke, translators in Tsvetayeva's sense of the word:

> Today I should like Rilke to speak – through me. In everyday language this is called translation. (How much better the Germans put it – *nachdichten*: Following in the poet's footsteps, to lay again the path he has already laid. Let *nach* mean follow, but *dichten* always has a new meaning. *Nachdichten* – laying anew a path, all traces of which are instantaneously grown over.) But 'translate' has another meaning: to translate not only *into* (into Russian, for example) but also *to* (to the opposite bank of the river). I shall translate Rilke into Russian and he, in time, will translate me to the other world.

To them, the 'Untranslatable' was something dwarfed by the 'Untranslated'. Their faith in the possibilities of their respective languages, including rhyme, overcame the resistance of the original. It triumphed over everything but the world and made them martyrs of its indifference. They too shall gain favour in Pieria.

My concern with the critical milieu is not the private obsession of a young writer. It is peculiar to the condition of a man without a country.

After 1917, the writers of Russia lost the absolute right to remind the world of their existence, forced as they were into spiritual, or geographic, exile and separated from the natural means by which reputations – 'the quintessence of all misconceptions that collect around a new name', in Rilke's phrase – are made. Deprived of that right, those too young to have won recognition before 1917 acquired it in the West only by accident, and almost always posthumously. Even in the case of Pasternak, who had acquired not mere reputation but fame – sufficient for Stalin to use him as the representative of 'Soviet' culture in the 1930s – the history of his appreciation in the West is punctuated, apart from émigré writings, by no more than two or three serious studies (notably 'The Poetry of Boris Pasternak' in the July 1944 number of Cyril Connolly's *Horizon*), until the *Zhivago* scandal made him a political celebrity second to none. Similarly, it is only when these writers were discovered to have anticipated some of the directions within the mainstream of twentieth-century literature in the West that their names began to be exhumed from oblivion: Zamyatin and Orwell, Bely and Joyce, Evreinov and Beckett, Vvedensky and Ionesco are a few obvious instances. Vladimir Nabokov is a case in point. Although saved from émigré oblivion in the mid-1950s by the scandal of 'immoral' *Lolita*, he was fair game to academic critics for decades, though not at all because *Lolita*, by the standards he had set as V. Sirin, was a commercial travesty. No, the professors of American universities criticized their Cornell confrère's command of his native tongue.

In February 1966 Nabokov published a 'Reply to My Critics' in *Encounter*. The reviews, which he summarizes, of his four-volume translation of *Onegin* are so preposterous that he swears he 'shall be accused of having invented' them. Within its own frame of reference, the 'Reply' is a polemical masterpiece, making mincemeat, in particular, of Edmund Wilson's 'pompous aplomb and peevish ignorance', and only in its last paragraphs does one get a glimpse of Nabokov besieged:

> Finally – Mr Wilson is horrified by my 'instinct to take digs at great reputations'. Well, it cannot be helped; Mr Wilson must accept my instinct, and wait for the next crash. I refuse to be guided and controlled by a communion of established views and academic traditions, as he wants me to be. What right has he to prevent me from finding mediocre and over-rated people like Balzac, Dostoyevsky, Sainte-Beuve, or Stendhal, that pet of all those who like their French plain . . . [and] why should I be forbidden to consider that Tchaikovsky's hideous and insulting libretto is not saved by a music whose cloying banalities have pursued me ever since I was a curly-haired boy in a velvet box?

Vladimir Nabokov was a Russian writer, and an American writer devoted to the study of Russian – of Russia, of Pushkin – who questioned his knowledge of Russian – of Russia, of Pushkin – committed, *ipso facto*, a critical crime. Yet the American academic community, with barely a Russian grammar between them, was openly on the side of the criminal:

> A still more luckless gentleman (in the *Los Angeles Times*) is so incensed by the pride and prejudice of my commentary that he virtually chokes on his wrath and after enticingly entitling his article 'Nabokov Fails as a Translator' has to break it off abruptly without having made one single reference to the translation itself.

Characteristically, the reviews Nabokov cites as 'sympathetic' were without exception published in Britain, where true intellectual freedom of the press has always been somewhat larger and academic communion somewhat less masonic. In America, the situation has in fact deteriorated since Nabokov's day: in 1977 the national congress of Slavists marking the thirtieth anniversary of the American Association of Slavic Studies heard 317 papers on diverse subjects, nine of which were delivered by Russian-born participants, most with misbegotten academic credentials.

No, if Vladimir Nabokov failed as a translator, it was not because he did not know Russian, or English for that matter, as well as Edmund Wilson. If Pasternak was not born to translate anyone, Nabokov at any rate was not born to translate Pushkin. The first Narcissus is but a namesake of the second.

In one of his lighter moments an American academic poet and critic, whose 'pompous aplomb and peevish ignorance' ordinarily resemble Wilson's, once compared translation, in its quotidian sense of the written equivalent of simultaneous interpretation, with a game of tennis. Translating a poem, he allowed, 'seems to be a different sort of game entirely, in which one is required to get the ball into the right box on the other side of the court, even though the area across the net may be laid out differently'. In tennis, of course, both sides of the court are identical, but that is not what makes the banal simile wrong. If we choose to enlarge that simile, we may say that the layout of 'the other side' can complicate the game without rendering it qualitatively different. It is what the game is played with, rather than on, that matters, because, however complicated the configurations of the court, the tennis-ball is certain to behave in specific ways under certain conditions known to players of certain skill. By contrast, players using a live squirrel instead of a rubber ball would be playing a game that is qualitatively, not quantitatively, different from tennis. Here is a familiar passage:

> 'Do you know languages? What's the French for fiddle-de-dee?'

'Fiddle-de-dee's not English,' Alice replied gravely.

'Who ever said it was?' said the Red Queen.

Alice thought she saw a way out of the difficulty, this time.

'If you'll tell me what language "fiddle-de-dee" is, I'll tell you the French for it!' she exclaimed triumphantly.

But the Red Queen drew herself up rather stiffly and said 'Queens never make bargains.'

The relationship between the quantitative and the qualitative may be likened to a general knowledge of French and the specific knowledge of what 'fiddle-de-dee' is in French. Alice may have all of Larousse in her head, but she is in a quandary all the same: she is powerless to translate the phrase because she is unable to think in the qualitative mode. Her creative impotence as a translator is what makes her assert, with the confidence of a Weidle, that 'Fiddle-de-dee's not English.' This may be harsh on the girl. But translators all over the world have had to relive Alice's consternation when they set out to visit Wonderland for themselves. As they discovered, or should have discovered, a phrase could indeed be found, say in Russian, to make the Russian Alice deny its Russianness and in so doing cover up her inability to translate it into French.

The faithful translator sees possibility in impossibility. Unfortunately the reverse is equally true. While the creative freedom offered him by 'fiddle-de-dee' is virtually unlimited, an apparently simple phrase like 'replied gravely' forces him, in fact, into a strait-jacket of anxious literalism. If nuance is what he is after, he may well begin to feel intimidated by everything easy.

The continuum of a living language is never smooth, and at any given time some parts of it are discernible more and some less, forever flowing and forming new shores of familiarity, new shoals of aloofness. Take Pushkin's *Onegin*. Nabokov, in a 1955 article in *Partisan Review*, defined his aim categorically: 'The person who desires to turn a literary masterpiece into another language, has only one duty to perform, and this is to reproduce with absolute exactitude the whole text, and nothing but the text.' Written over a century and a half ago, *Onegin* cannot be translated into another language 'with absolute exactitude' any more than 'replied gravely' can be. The language of *Onegin*, like that of the English phrase, is dissolved in language. Nabokov's standard of exactitude would require the respective contents of Murray's and Dahl's to be appended to the translation like a giant footnote. Nabokov had the good taste not to play the qualitative 'game' with *Onegin*, for he knew that the chance for that had been missed in England a century ago, when Pushkin's utterance was still a living, reverberating echo of Byron. What he did not sense was that his quantitative 'game' would not attract an English audience to Pushkin: exegesis is not a spectator sport.

Once the language of a work has dissolved in language, its translations are bound to be temporal: so, for instance, the works of the ancients are notorious for the obsolescence of their translations. In his essay 'Seven Agamemnons', R. A. Brower gives a diachronic account of Aeschylus in English:

> When a writer sets out to translate – say, the *Agamemnon* – what happens? Much, naturally, that we can never hope to analyse. But what we can see quite clearly is that he makes the poetry of the past into the poetry of his particular present. . . . The average reader of a translation in English wants to find the kind of experience which has become identified with 'poetry' in his reading of English literature. The translator who wishes to be read must in some degree satisfy this want.

Eliot, as sensitive as Nabokov ever was to the wiles of the 'paraphrasts', would have agreed: 'Greek poetry', he wrote in 'Euripides and Professor Murray' in 1920, 'will never have the slightest vitalising effect upon English poetry if it can only appear masquerading as a vulgar debasement of the eminently personal idiom of Swinburne.' The point is that, in translation, what has been dissolved in language must always masquerade. If, like Nabokov, the writer spurns the mask, the reader is justified in buying a dictionary instead of his book. If, like several other translators of Pushkin, he wears it, the reader cannot be blamed for preferring Byron.

'The gifted translator', again in Poggioli's phrase, 'is an alchemist who changes a piece of gold into another piece of gold.' To reduce a poem to its elements is plainly not enough: one must bring about their transubstantiation.

In one of the poems from 'The Rupture' cycle (pp. 45–9) the reader will come across the verb 'wed' in the imperative, conveying the Russian *posyagní!* As today's Edmund Wilsons will be quick to point out, there is little 'exactitude' here, as the word means 'infringe' or 'encroach'. I shall save them the trouble.

The ancient Russian noun *poság* means 'wedlock' and can be traced back to the Sanskrit *sajati* – he attaches. The Russian bride *posyagáyet*, grips the wedding towel and follows the groom, 'goes to marry', *idet zámuzh*. *Prisyága*, oath, is similar, since one swears by what one touches, and indeed 'stake' is one of the meanings of 'wed' in English, from Old High German *wetton*, to wager. All this of course lies beneath the surface of the word: my version imposes etymology on the reader no more than does the original. Pasternak, in a letter to Tsvetayeva, once described a lyrical poem as 'the etymology of feeling'.

Here is another example. The last two stanzas of 'For My Enemies' (p. 51), I shall no doubt be told, are especially far from 'exactitude'. Yet like the original they are steeped in Shakespeare, puzzling the discerning reader in Moscow in 1923 as they do again in London in 1989.

Perhaps I should allow Poggioli to make the point again, in what is doubtless the most gallant defence of the art by a critic:

It may well be an error to believe that the translator has nothing to offer but an empty vessel which he fills with a liquor he could not distil by himself. One should play, at least tentatively, with the contrary hypothesis; one should even suppose, using a related, if opposite, image, that the translator himself is a living vessel saturated with a formless fluid or sparkling spirit, which he cannot hold any longer in check; that when the spirit is about to fizzle, or the liquid to overflow, he pours it into the most suitable of all containers available to him, although he neither owns the container nor has he moulded it with his own hands. Were this true, one could even claim that translating is like pouring new wine into an old bottle; and that if the wine fails to burst the bottle, it is only because the new wine required the old bottle as the only form or frame within which it could rest.

Here Poggioli reveals his source:

> To accept such a hypothesis one must believe, with the protagonist of *Doctor Zhivago*, the recent novel by the great Russian poet Boris Pasternak – who by the way is also a great translator of Shakespeare – that art is not 'an object or aspect of form, but rather a mysterious and hidden component of content'. According to such a view, the translator is a literary artist looking outside himself for the form suited to the experience he wishes to express.

In short, the 'mysterious and hidden' must never be made apparent and revealed. The poet's apocryphon is separate from his apocalypse. The translator's talent should keep him from confusing the two, and his skill heal the surgical scars left by the incisions of intuition.

Clearly the word *zhizn'* does not mean the same as the word 'life'. 'This *zh*', my father once wrote, 'is something raw, like the black sour bread in the village, burning, scalding, vital, dark, intense, and then the long *i*, in plaint and pity, bursts into the ending *izn'* like a fount, but in it the *z-z-z* is a fierce spray, like milk hitting the pail, and the palatalized *n'* is a soft nothing, the sound a baby makes when it strains to say something but knows no words.'

In 1964, when we still lived in Moscow, John Updike

stumbled upon my father's translation of Prishvin's *Nature's Diary* and later recalled its 'slightly ragged type' and 'drawings in the innocent Soviet style' as part of the English prose, 'now limpidly transparent and now almost gruff, a foxy prose glistening with alert specifics'. He was right to see it that way, for context is everything. Thus Rilke described his first moments in Moscow: 'Tired as I was, I set out, after a short rest, to see the town. . . . This spectacle, so extraordinary for me, shook me to the depths of my soul. For the first time in my life I was overcome by an indescribable emotion, as if I had found my native land.' It does not matter what Rilke had seen, the Iverskaya shrine across from the Grand Hotel where he was staying or an iridescent puddle in a cobbled street.

It does not matter what the Russian word means. In the context of an English version of a Russian poem, the English word may be *made* to 'mean' what the Russian word 'means', and sometimes more. When Pasternak uses a word, it may speak to the English reader in the context of every poem, of a whole cycle, of the entire book. It may bounce off his biography and skid through the lives of his contemporaries, whatever their language.

Philological nostalgia of the Nabokov variety is very common indeed. It is not always chauvinistic. At a symposium on translation at the University of Texas twenty years ago, Jean Paris confessed that

The secrets of English will always defeat us. The phonetic complexity of this language, its power to reproduce thousands of natural sounds – the roaring of the waves, the howling of the wind, the dripping of the rain – make it a perfect instrument for suggestion. Compare, for instance, *profond* and 'profound': while the French adjective is purely nominative, the English one seems to possess in itself the quality it indicates: profundity is the very substance of the word, we can almost hear a voice sinking into its depths. It is this splendid music of diphthongs of which we, the French, are dreadfully deprived. . . . Thus, in English discourse, the words seem to be counterpoints, they extend in great

complexes of echoes and correspondences, which suggest
behind the logical sense an obscure world where dreams can
travel indefinitely.

What is M. Paris leading up to? 'But of course, you
Americans, you 'ave Poe.'

Yet the French Symbolists who discovered Poe were not
merely envious: they had faith in their language, and they
overtook him. However highly one thinks of Poe, the following rebuttal by Kenneth Rexroth encourages such faith:

> Communion is as important to the poet translator as com-
> munication. I was taught the 'correct pronunciation of
> Latin', but I have never been able to take it seriously. On the
> other hand, who has ever forgotten the first time, on the
> streets of modern Rome, that he looked down at his feet and
> saw SPQR on a manhole cover? Sympathy can carry you
> very far if you have talent to go with it. Hart Crane never
> learned to speak French and at the time he wrote his triptych
> poem *Voyages* he could not read it at all. . . . Yet *Voyages* is
> by far the best transmission of Rimbaud into English that
> exists – the purest distillation of the boyish hallucinations of
> *Bateau Ivre*.
> Sympathy, or at least projection, can carry you far. All
> sensible men to whom English is native are distressed at the
> French enthusiasm for M. Poe, the author of *Jamais Plus*.
> Nobody in France seems to be able to learn, ever, that his
> verse is dreadful doggerel and his ratiocinative fiction
> absurd and his aesthetics the standard lucubrations that go
> over in Young Ladies' Study Circles and on the Chaun-
> tauqua Circuit. The reason is, of course, that the French
> translate their whole culture into Poe before they even start
> to read him.

By contrast, Aldous Huxley had no time for communion
when he discussed Poe in his *Vulgarity in Literature*. People
lacking in faith are often possessed of wit, and Huxley is no
exception:

The paramour of Goethe's king rhymed perfectly with the name of his kingdom; and when Laforgue wrote of that 'roi de Thulé, Immaculé' his *rime riche* was entirely above suspicion. Poe's rich rhymes, on the contrary, are seldom above suspicion. That dank tarn of Auber is only very dubiously a fit poetical companion for the tenth month, and though Mount Yaanek is, *ex hypothesi*, a volcano, the rhyme with volcanic is, frankly, impossible. On other occasions Poe's proper names rhyme not only well enough, but actually, in the particular context, much too well. Dead D'Elormie, in 'The Bridal Ballad', is prosodically in order, because Poe had brought his ancestors over with the Conqueror (as he also imported the ancestors of that Guy de Vere who wept his tears over Lenore) for the express purpose of providing a richly musical-magical rhyme to 'bore me' and 'before me'. Dead D'Elormie is first cousin to Edward Lear's aged Uncle Arly, sitting on a heap of Barley – ludicrous; but also (unlike dear Uncle Arly) horribly vulgar, because of the too musical lusciousness of his invented name and his display, in all tragical seriousness, of an obviously faked Norman pedigree. Dead D'Elormie is a poetical disaster.

There, the curse of Lear, Edward, has done its ugly work once again. Poe's immolation in the name of his superhuman faith in the English language – or, as he called it, originality – seems 'horribly vulgar' to his jaded compatriot a century later. But martyrdom is not a refined spectacle, and the philistine always finds it vulgar. Horribly vulgar.

Apart from the critical milieu in a general sense, there exists a smaller academic community whose opinions may well inhibit the fledgling impulse of originality. Idle philosophizing is addictive, but nowhere is this addiction more conspicuous than among the 'professional' literary theorists, for whom translation is the lotus of choice.

In recent years, the internecine warfare of the lotophagi has been conducted on the sofas of Structuralism, effectively dividing the community into two, a bad sign for the neophyte who wishes to cling to a vision of pluralism in culture. The radical 'Right', separated from the radical 'Left' by the vitreous expanse of a Giacometti table, espouses a kind of schoolmasterish fascism, most recently exhibited in an article by Peter Jones, 'Winged Words', in the January 1988 number of *Encounter*. Scornful of what he calls the 'social worker' theory of literature, with its insistence on a 'structurally correct analysis', he writes:

> If I knew what a 'structurally correct analysis' was, I should argue that it depends critically on faithfulness to the text. At least I can think of no useful purpose that could be served by such an analysis if it did not matter whether *arma virumque cano* was translated 'Arms and the man I sing' or ''Course it's a bleeding penalty, ref'.

The rebuttal, in the February 1989 number of *Encounter*, came in the form of 'Who Will Translate the Translators?' by Roy Harris, complete with obligatory references to Derrida and Saussure. The 'Left', in literature as in politics, is always intellectually better prepared, and it is difficult not to agree with Harris when he identifies the argument of his opponent as a nostalgic yearning for the halcyon days of old when the train of thought was always on time:

> This is accompanied by a contemptuous dismissal of doubts on that score as due to a misguided ' ''social worker'' theory of literature'. For Jones, all such attempts to undermine the fifth form's confidence in their Classics lessons are clearly subversive. 'There is nothing new to be said about translation,' he asserts categorically. So back to your grammar books, Smith minor.

Should Smith minor be inclined to protest, Jones deploys the ever powerful pedagogic strategy of ridicule. Smith minor will be invited to stand up and say whether he supposes that *arma virumque cano* might perhaps be rendered as ''Course it's a bleeding penalty, ref'. The class duly laughs, Smith minor is made to look a fool, and order is restored. Translation from the Classics can now proceed as before, soundly anchored to the certitude that chaps like Lewis and Short jolly well knew their Latin after all.

In general, it is difficult for a reader of Harris's article not to embrace his point of view without reservation: it is subtle, like being converted to communism by reading Shelley. What is seductive here is his optimism.

> Poor translations are the fault of incompetent translators, not a consequence of the inherent unviability of the translational enterprise. After all, if languages *were* structurally isomorphic, then any dullard would presumably be able to translate Racine into such English verse as Alexander Pope might have envied. . . . The clever translator is someone who manages to make inadequate equipment look as if it is doing the job: an artist who specializes in verbal *trompe l'oeil* by accommodating 'what the original says' to constraints imposed by what a different language *has* to say, and by making the accommodation sound like what a gifted writer in the latter language plausibly *might* have said if expressing 'the same thought'.

Yet optimism and faith, like pessimism and truth, are clean different things, and this realization ought to keep the neophyte out of the clutches of the radicals. Their discussion, he ought to remember, remains formalist so long as neither stakes his all on an original contribution to world culture, conceived, as such contributions invariably are, in the heat of reckless idealism. The honeycombs of sandstone outside my window, with their white-on-black dactyls of *Visitors Are Not Allowed to Walk on the Grass of the College*, have grown too cold for such orgies of feeling, as Pasternak once put it.

It becomes clear that this book is addressed to poets and, by extension, to their readers: to those capable of creation or of participating in creation. It is they, not professional critics of poetry and translation, who will ultimately decide whether or not to accept the consignment I have attempted to deliver over the barriers of language and history.

My uncle, a 'distinguished' Moscow poet and 'influential' Soviet littérateur, but privately a deeply reticent man with a unique sense of humour, had an unfortunate experience early in his career. A reviewer ridiculed his Russian. 'First they criticize your Russian,' my uncle recalled, 'and then your telephone is disconnected.' To avert the escalation of official hostilities, he confronted the reviewer in the corridor of the Writers' Club and, banging the head of his nemesis against a convenient wall, whispered to him: 'Do not ever criticize my Russian.' Mysteriously, it worked.

In the West such a course of action is not advisable, if only because literary life is less centralized. Yet there are certain similarities: genuine poets, cradled by the smaller publishers, niched by the leafier suburbs, here as in Russia, are not the poets one hears most about. To them, and to their readers, this book is addressed. But what of the others, those in the public eye?

'Zhonya,' Pasternak used to confide in his sister, 'what can I do? I cannot just kill them all!' Josephine Pasternak laughs every time she tells the story. The late N. N. Vilmont, an old friend of the Pasternaks, wrote in his memoirs: 'While a man of genius is alive, it is difficult to believe in his genius. . . . The recognition is made especially difficult by the inalienable quality of genius – unevenness, even imperfection – readily discernible in the Creator of the Universe. . . . Which is why, in my own life, I find it difficult to believe in Him.' It is my aim in this book to bring Pasternak's voice to life in English for the first time. If I have succeeded, I shall also, inevitably, revive the voices of those who did not believe in his genius while he was alive. In short, I expect to hear in English ('His English is questionable . . . Pasternak does not say that . . .') what he heard in Russian ('You cannot say this in Russian. . . . He is no Blok . . .'). My failure is integral to his success.

To those in the public eye who may choose to deride this equation as the height of arrogance, I put a question: What *do* they think Pasternak should sound like? A few years ago I was asked by *The Times* to review *The Electrification of the Soviet Union* by Craig Raine, a libretto for an opera ostensibly based on the poet's life and work. I can only describe its vulgarity as shocking, and I explained why.

In 1934, all independent publishing in Russia was abolished and the Union of Soviet Writers was convened in Moscow. To add proletarian colour, workers in their work clothes welcomed their new union brethren, among whom was Boris Pasternak. As a young woman bearing a sledge-hammer walked in, Pasternak jumped up and wrested the proletarian symbol from her, thinking it was too heavy. It was, and history records with embarrassment that the poet dropped it.

By then, Pasternak had already created the verse and the prose by which Russian culture is to be measured for millennia to come and of which his later, Nobel Prize-winning *Zhivago* period is but an echo. Gentleman or male chauvinist, in his personal life Pasternak clung to the standards of his milieu. Likewise, his poetry and prose exist as a logical continuation – or culmination – of the Russian literary tradition. . . . The libretto, like Mr Raine's earlier books, stands athwart that tradition.

The Last Summer, Pasternak's vaguely autobiographical novella on which Mr Raine's libretto is based, is a miracle of poetic prose whose salient feature is its near-cryptic subtlety. For his effort, Mr Raine 'hit on the notion of an octosyllabic line' which is 'both shapely and colloquial'. Indeed, his hero tells a woman that her 'slow nipples gather closely in the cold' (he goes on to list her other enchantments), to which she replies, 'My breasts aren't bad.'

On the whole, the exchange would be jarring in a *Dreigroschenoper*. In an opera about Pasternak, it's idiotic.

Earlier I mentioned John Updike. In fairness, it should be noted that when we read his novels in Moscow we found ourselves face to face with that very same sordid vulgarity I now find in Craig Raine's representations of Russian sensibility. Updike and Raine are incidental, of course, but their artifice is a valid example of the difficulty, if not the impossibility, of glimpsing the Russian civilization into which Pasternak had been born, many decades after it ceased to exist, and relating it to the present-day civilizations, East and West, with any degree of genuineness.

The saddest heritage of the present day, and the highest barrier in the way of my transport, is emotional nihilism. Our language, in the hands of its most public users, has become so sceptical of sentiment that the simplest emotional complexity is at once perceived as affected or contrived. Since poetry is the invention of feeling, it can hardly dare to make itself public in so chilling a climate. Can anyone imagine, in these mean days, one 'published poet' writing to another 'published poet', as Tsvetayeva wrote to Pasternak in 1926, a letter beginning:

> Boris:
> My severance from life becomes more and more irrevocable. I keep moving, have moved again, taking with me all my passion, all my treasure, not as a bloodless shade but with so green a store of food that I could feed everyone in Hades. Ah, wouldn't he give me a talking-to then, that Pluto.

No, such exchanges are now strictly private, in the sense that today these tongue-tied interlocutors are more likely to belong to that subterranean, scattered, isolated diaspora of poets and readers for which this book is intended. I can only hope that they find it, and that it finds them.

Having spoken of the difficulties, I return as promised to the essential simplicity of the translator's task. It is the transcendent simplicity of the act of creation felt by those who abscond with nature's hoard. The effortless simplicity of a miracle. What miracle? The one Pasternak wrote about in 1919, in an essay upon the truth of which, he swore to Tsvetayeva seven years later, he would 'stake his life'. It came as he was translating Swinburne in obscure, snowy Elabuga.

What is the miracle? The miracle is that once there lived a seventeen-year-old girl called Mary Stuart who sat by the window, as the Puritans jeered outside, and wrote a French verse that ended:

> Car mon pis et mon mieux
> Sont les plus déserts lieux.

It is, secondly, that once in his youth, as October fumed and feasted outside his window, the English poet Algernon Charles Swinburne finished his *Chastelard*, in which the quiet plaint of Mary's five stanzas swelled with the awesome roar of five tragic acts.

It is, thirdly, that once, about five years ago, a translator looked out of the window and wondered which was the odder thing.

Was it that the Elabuga blizzard, still troubled by the fate of the seventeen-year-old girl, spoke Scotch, or that the girl and the English bard who lamented her could both speak to him, in such clear and soulful Russian, about what still troubled them?

What can this mean, the translator asked. What is happening? Why is it so quiet out there, if the blizzard is raging? What we send forth should bleed. Instead, it smiles.

Therein the miracle. In the equality and oneness of those three, and of many others – participants and eyewitnesses of three epochs, characters, readers – before a known October of an unknown year that roars, losing its voice and sight, out there, at the foot of a mountain, in . . . well, in art.

That is the miracle.

In 1941, to the three epochs was added a fourth: Tsvetayeva hanged herself in Elabuga.

In conclusion, an autobiographical paraphrase. The paternal advice I received long before Pasternak became second nature to me was *Idealist unósit kássu* ('The idealist makes off with the cash-box'). By this advice I have lived, and by it this book has lived in me.

> Would that not imply lilacs made into garlands,
> The splendour of daisies crushed by the dew,
> Lips squandered like mad on celestial parlance?
> Would that not imply embracing the vault,
> Entwining the hands round the hero's collar,
> Would that not imply spending ages of malt
> To brew heady evenings of nightingale dolour?

Such questions were never meant to be rhetorical. To recognize this is to understand the essential simplicity of the task.

Andrei Navrozov

From *A Twin in the Clouds*

February, let ink and tears flow,
Explain February is come,
While the roaring slush below
Burns with the spring it blackens numb!

Then get a cab, in just one moment,
Through evensong and carriage clink,
Transported where the rain's omen
Looms darker still than tears and ink;

Where like pears charred to ashes,
A hundred rooks just off the tree
Appal grey sleet in sudden freshets
Of sorrow from a single stream;

Beneath them, furrows lie blackened,
Bird cries scar the silence numb,
And the more certain the less reckoned
Like sobs the lines then become.

Like brazen ashes off a brazier
Drop beetles in the drowsy garden;
Against my candle, in the azure,
The blooming worlds continue ardent.

And as if to a faith unfathomed
Into the night I am conveyed,
Where shadows of decrepit almond
Veil moonlight bounds newly made.

Where ponds are mysteries apparent,
Where apple tide blossoms high,
And the suspended orchard's derrick
Of plain wood holds up the sky.

Träumerei

I dreamt of autumn in the dim glass light,
Of friends, with you, in their motley love,
And like a falcon, tasting blood in flight,
The swooping heart alighted on your glove.

But time would grow old, and deaf, and pass,
And, lightly touching frames with webs of amber,
Dawns from the garden veined the terrace glass
With sanguine tears of September.

But time would grow old, and pass. And pliant,
Like ice, armchair silk would melt and swell,
First audible, you stumbled and grew quiet,
The dream grew silent like the echo of a bell.

And I awoke: was, like the autumn, raw
The sunrise, and the wind drew into distance,
Chasing the sled, a running rain of straw,
The running birches chasing leaden instants.

Feasts

The bitterness of rose and autumn sky,
And in it your betrayal's burning ray,
The bitterness of faces, evening light,
Wet bitterness in every line I drain.

To workshop fiends, sobriety is blind.
On rainy days we have declared war:
Four winds may be the bearers of the wine
At trysts that our future holds in store.

Heredity and death at these feasts are guests.
A quiet dawn sets tops of trees on fire,
Like bread-box mice now rustle anapests,
And rushing Cinderella changes her attire.

Floors have been swept, the table has no crumbs.
Like child kisses, verse begins to breathe.
And Cinderella hurries: carriage to the dance,
Her own two feet when everybody leaves.

Winter

My cheek is against the whorled part
Of winter, in coils like a shell.
'Places, all! We are ready to start!'
Cries, whispers and silence pell-mell.

'We play "Stormy Sea" then? That fable,
Spinning, like rope in the pail,
Where players take turns when unable?
Then – life? Then the fabulous tale

Of how sudden the end? Of death laughing,
Of crowding and clearing the way?
Then truly the sea has stopped bluffing
And the storm starts its fiery play?'

Is it the hum of the sea-shell gyre?
Is it the gossip of rooms in dead earnest?
Or, fighting with shadows, is it the fire
That rattles the door of the furnace?

So the air gusts in the vent,
Looks about, then sighs out loud,
The sound of carriages, echo, and then
The trotter is splitting a cloud . . .

As unweeded snowdrifts crawl
Right on the window frieze.
Beyond these cups of blue vitriol
Nothing has been, nor is.

From *Over the Barriers*

The Soul

O manumitted – if memory can embalm her,
O if oblivion can – committed to time,
They're holding – a soul and a palmer,
An illegible shadow – I am . . .

O when immersed even – still stone soundless,
On the tablets of verse – even when arisen,
You thrash as once did the treasonous countess,
When February came to flood the prison.

O ingrafted – appealing for your reprieve,
Cursing the times, as one does – sentries,
Like leaves, fallen years will interweave
Through the calendar garden entries.

Spring

The buds burnt to butts their unctuous essence
To lighten and lessen the burden of kindling
April. The parks grew redolent of adolescence
And forest replies redounded, dwindling.

The throat of the forest is smalted by sounds
From feathery gullets as if by a gorgon;
Then, cracking the smalt with sonatas, resounds
Some gladiator of a steel organ.

O poetry, turn into spongy Greek fossils
With suckers! Amid sticky sward then
I'd set you to rest on the slippery mosses
Of this wooden bench in this garden.

Grow yourself ruffles and frills on trees,
Swell on clouds, like a wet wafer;
And at night I shall wring you, poetry,
To benefit thirsty paper.

Swifts

The swifts of the evening are breathless with pain
Containing the coldness of sapphire.
It bursts, and subduing their breasts' throaty strain,
Comes gushing, remaining entire.

The swifts of the evening have nothing to cry of
If something up there can quench with entreaty
Their jubilant claim, exulting – O triumph,
Just look, down there, the earth is retreating!

As a pot bubbles over with fine white lace,
The quarrelsome moisture is gone;
Look there, look there! The earth has no place
From the dell to the edges of dawn.

Improvisation

I was feeding a flock of black piano keys
To the sound of splashing, of wings and of leaves.
With outstretched hands I stood on my knees;
The night grasped my elbow, clawed at the sleeve.

And there was autumn. And there was a lake
And waves. – And birds of the love breed were there,
Prepared to slay sooner than to be slain
By darkness, black hardened beaks in the air.

And there was a lake. And there was autumn.
Tar barrels of midnight were flaring and lighting
The waves that gnawed at the boat from the bottom;
And just by my elbow birds were fighting.

And darkness was stuck in the throat of the weir.
It seemed that the nestlings had tasted first blood!
Prepared to die before others could hear
From those deep gorges a throttled roulade.

From *My Sister Life*

To the Memory of the Demon

Es braust der Wald, am Himmel zieh'n
Der Sturmes Donnerflüge
Da mal' ich in die Wetter hin,
O Mädchen, deine Züge.

Nic. Lenau

He came at night
From Tamára, in the blinding blue,
Ruled with his flight
For the dream to burn and conclude.

Never wept. Never wrung, nor entwined
Bare, lashed and scarred hands.
The old stone was confined
By the fence of Georgian gardens.

As the ancient hunchback entered
On the wall tall shadows clowned like fire.
The *zurná*, by the light of the lantern,
Of the princess, barely breathing, inquired.

But the lightning raged
And contracted, the hair a phosphorous edifice.
The colossus then heard how the Caucasus aged,
Growing grey by the edge of the precipice.

Just a foot from the window-pane,
Stroking the wool of a cloak he had worn:
'Darling, sleep!' By the ice, by the rain,
'I'll return in a torrent!' he swore.

17

Sorrow

For this book's sombre epigraph
The deserts were rippling
As lions roared, and tigers' wrath
Was reaching out to Kipling.

Here the gaping empty chest
Of woe stood wide open,
And there swayed and caressed
Merino prose, hoping

For a continuous parade
Of rankless verses,
Treading the fog in shades of grey
The Ganges cleanses.

Cold mornings came next, to ease
Entwined instants
Of jungle, moist as ecstasy
Or incense.

My sister – life – is again out flooding,
Smashed, like spring rain, against what is past,
But people with pendants are subtly pedantic,
Attentively stinging, like snakes in the grass.

The elders, no doubt, have reason to wonder.
It's clear, it's clear: your wonder is small,
That lashes and lawns are empurpled with thunder
And wet mignonette spills all over the knoll.

That in May, when the timetable's diptych
Of some local line unfolds in the swarm,
Transcending the Scripture, it looks far more cryptic
Than canopies flapping off dust in a storm.

The brakes, having barked, bump the patience
Of villagers steeped in a warm rural liquor,
To watch off the mattresses for their stations
And mine as the sunset's condolences flicker.

So splashing in third, bells flow through the car
In endless regrets: I am sorry, uncertain.
And threshing the steppe from the step to the star,
The night still aglow is thrust through the curtain.

Now winking, now twinkling, now quietly sleeping!
The beloved, asleep, fairy visions unravels.
Meanwhile the heart, like a coupling, keeps leaping,
Scattering sparks through the plain in its travels.

The Weeping Garden

Horrible! – It drips and listens:
　　Whether it's alone, sighing,
Lays twigs on glass and glistens,
　　Or there's someone spying.

And swallowing drops, swollen
　　Audibly, the porous earth yields:
Now listen how remotely fallen
　　August midnight ripens in the fields.

Not a sound. It's all alone.
　　Its solitude certain and utter.
At it once again – will be blown
　　Over the roof, along the gutter.

Nearing my lips, become all ears:
　　Whether I'm alone, sighing,
Whether I can spill the tears,
　　Or there's someone spying.

Silence. And not a leaf flickers.
　　Signs of vision gone. There intervene
Only gulps and splashes in slippers
　　And sighs and tears in between.

The Girl

Seesaw through the garden, all ready to topple,
    A branch rushes straight at the mirror,
So huge and so near, with stray drops of opal
    Atop its nearing spear.

The garden is flustered, all scattered the islands
    Of lustre long beckoned to near,
So large and so dear, itself a great silence,
    A sister! A second mirror!

But here the branch is brought in, in a phial
    Placed by the frame of the mirror.
What is it, it wonders, that wants to beguile
    My eyes with a lay, gaol fear?

You are in the wind that marks with a green arrow
Whether it is time for the birds to sing:
Soaking, like a sparrow,
Lilac twig!

Drops have the weight of cuff-links,
The blinding garden veers
The sprinklings and the dapplings
In millions of blue tears.

The nurseling of my agonies
That you burst into thorn,
It quickens with the peony,
Exhales and forewarns.

All night it tapped away at glass
So windows had no rest
As qualms of sudden dankness
Overwhelmed her dress.

Awakened by the wondrous roll
Of names and of times,
It holds the present day in thrall
With its anemone eyes.

Rain (An Inscription)

With me at last. Then pour and laugh,
Leak through the twilight pores!
Let flow, let go the epigraph
For such a love as yours!

Go on, bob like a bombyx worm,
Molest the silk like flax!
Entangle, veil, cocoon the storm
To slant the darkness past!

No night at watch – at noon – at all!
The gravel creaks of asthma!
And whole trees are falling tall
At eyes, temples, jasmine!

Hosanna to the hosts of Isis!
Laughter is prone before the breeze!
A spectre of redemption rises
From thousands of infirmaries.

And now – we begin to list,
Like groans plucked off guitars,
Washed in the liquid linden mist,
Those garden Saint Gotthards.

In Superstition

A box with bitter-orange cells:
   My garret.
Oh yes, I could have peeled hotels:
   Bear it!

I move here second time round
   Out of superstition.
The walls are papered oaken brown:
   The door's contrition.

Never let go of the latch:
   You tried to free.
The hair had an iris match,
   The lips a violet spree.

O tender, for the past one's sake,
   Free fate to will
Your dress, as snowdrops ache, to say
   Hello to April.

To think you vestal would be stealth:
   You entered interested,
Then took my life, as from a shelf,
   And dusted it.

Waving a fragrant anther,
  Instilling the excellence darkling,
From blossom to blossom in transfer
  A liquid dews dizzy from sparkling.

Gliding from blossom to blossom,
  Dazzles but those, interlinking,
Twin drops, drawing agaty glosses;
  Hangs timid, flickering, clinquant.

Let the wind, inspiring spirea,
  Flatten and plumb the twin globe
Of these, entire and real,
  Kissing and drinking below.

Filled with laughter, undo the enigma
  Of bondage, to spring up full.
But drops cannot tear the ligament,
  Nor part, even if you pull.

Boating Oars

The boat is athrob in the drowsy breast,
Kissing the clavicles, willows raise
Oarlocks, elbows: please take a rest,
It really happens to everyone, always!

In the ancient songs it would even amuse . . .
Would that not imply lilacs made into garlands,
The splendour of daisies crushed by the dew,
Lips squandered like mad on celestial parlance?

Would that not imply embracing the vault,
Entwining the hands round the hero's collar,
Would that not imply spending ages of malt
To brew heady evenings of nightingale dolour!

English Lessons

And when the songs were Desdemona's,
Little was there to live for.
Not as the starry night, her leman, does:
She weeps for willows more.

And when the songs were Desdemona's,
The voice obscured her features.
Not as the rainy day, her demon, does:
The psalm of weeping reaches.

And when the songs were Ophelia's,
Little was there to live for.
With each breath the soul was kneeling as
When the wind at willows tore.

And when the songs were Ophelia's,
Her tears bittered true.
The water warned with feeling as
With columbines and rue.

And treading daffodils like passion
They entered, their trophies furled,
Into the pool of heaven, splashing
As if to deafen with the world.

A Definition of Poetry

It is a fully ripe whistle,
It is ice, shard on shard,
It is night, chilling thistle
When two nightingales sparred.

It is peas run to seed sweetly raw,
It is tears of the universe, pod-clad;
It's the stands' and the flutes' *Figaró*,
Downpouring hail on the flower-bed.

All the things that night stands upon
Like submerged bathing-boards it embalms,
And a star is transplanted into the pond
On wet trembling palms.

Flatter than planks in the water, so stuffy.
Heaven falls earthward, like an alder.
It would become these stars to be laughing,
But the universe wants a beholder.

A Definition of the Soul

Torn off like a pear come thunder,
With one leaf beyond separation.
How loyal: so willing to sunder!
Insane: into dry suffocation!

A ripe pear aslant from the storm.
How loyal: 'Not people like us!'
Turn round and look: mere form,
Burnt to ashes and fallen to dust.

Our land is all smudged by the glare.
Your nest: do you recognize it, darling?
O nestling! My leaf, are you scared?
Why keep beating, my shy silky starling!

O song grafted on to me, do not fear!
Where else on this earth can we live?
Ah, the deadliest adverb – 'here' –
Cannot quiet the spasm swathed stiff.

A Definition of Creativity

Shirt collar unbuttoned to expose its
Hairy chest, like the Beethoven torso's;
Like draughts under palm – ever posits
Dream, conscience, night and love forces.

And some piece that is barely queened,
With some frenzied sorrow in the opening –
Prepares the world for an end by the fiend,
The cavalier in a foot company.

In the garden, from vaults, ice-cold,
Stars exhale their cellared bane –
Veins athrob like the vines of Isolde,
Tristan stifles a swelling plaint.

And the gardens, the lakes, the fences,
Boiling tears to a white outpour
Of creation – so passion dispenses
What condensed in the human core.

Our Storm

The storm, a priest, has burnt a plant.
The smoke of sacrifice has veiled
Eyelids and clouds. – Rectify,
With lips, an insect's sprained eye.
The bucket clank is smashed aslant.
O why such greed: has heaven failed?
A hundred hearts beat in a ditch.
The storm has burnt the plant to pitch.

Of smalt the lea. What azure frills!
O just a touch, they are so dainty.
The smallest finch is off to find
Some pearly malt to clear the mind.
The storm, which barrel thirst instils,
Continues down from clouds of plenty.
And clovers grow brisk and brown
Under the brushes of renown.

Mosquitoes are thick as crows.
But why the siphon of malaria,
Right here, must you, devil insect,
Where summer luxuries are intact?!
Inflame the skin and strike a pose,
Red ballerina, blithe Ariel!
The goad of mischief makes a channel
Where blood is like the leaves of anil.

O trust my play, and do have trust
In migraine throbbing through the air!
Thus wrath of day is sure to spark,
A scion graft in cherry bark.
Now trustful? Now then, now thrust
Your face still nearer: in the glare
Of this your summer gone insane,
Behold its fires never wane!

I cannot hide this from view:
You hide your lips in jasmine snow,
And on my lips a snow is felt
That in my dreams can never melt.
Where shall I put a joy so new?
In verse? Into the lined flow?
Its mouth is already chapped
From poisons written pages sapped.

In alphabet it strains its sinew
To glow as a blush within you.

Sparrow Hills

Breast under the kisses as under a faucet!
Now or never is the summer's spell.
Every night some sundered doloroso
Drags along a dusty farewell.

I have heard of time: auguries are wicked!
Every ocean wave has a star to heed.
Speech is wind, and speechless is the thicket,
Heartless is the pond, and godless is the field.

Slant my soul empty! Foam it out entire!
Noontime world is here, where your eyes end.
Here thoughts ascend and catch like fire,
Scorching clouds over the pine horizon.

Here cross the rails of suburban lines.
Then there are the pines. There you cannot pass.
Then there is a Sunday. Catching at the vines,
Clearings run wild, sliding on wet grass.

Trinity and strolling through the noonday sieve:
To the groves the world is ever green.
So believes the thicket, so the fields perceive,
So the clouds spill it on the linen screen.

A Sultry Night

It fell, but had the bent restrain
The tempest in a sack of pollen,
While the dust took pills of rain,
The iron powder quietly fallen.

No blain cures saved the tuber!
The poppies swooned up to the ankles.
Rye lay embossed for want of rhubarb,
Quotidian God incised carbuncles.

In the insomniac turned sodden,
The orphaned, universal space,
Each sound had its echo trodden
By gusts of wind upon my face.

In the pursuit that followed on,
Drops ran. Then by the garden gate
The wind filled in the hollow dawn.
I held my breath. I was too late!

It seemed eternity conveyed
Those blind drops with blind force.
Unseen, I felt I could evade
The awesome garden's mad discourse.

If not, it would become eternal!
O it would carry on, infernal.

Summer

It stretched its thirsty spiracles,
Its butterflies so faithful,
Spun memories seemed miracles,
So mintful, meadful, Mayful.

The clock was still, but sound born
Of swipples, as if to sever
And pierce the air with a thorn,
Came to astound the weather.

Away sometimes, gone for hours,
The sunset put a cricket
In every bush, with powers
Over both field and thicket.

Not shadows, beams the crescent laid,
Sometimes very blatant,
And quiet, quiet nights would wade
Through moonlit clouds stately.

Rather asleep than aslope roofs, and more
Prepared to restrain than to refine,
Rain lingered, shuffling by the door,
And smelt like cork, or wine.

So smelt the dust. So smelt the breeze.
And if you want a sequel,
So smelt nobility's decrees
On who's free and equal.

While others knew the squires well,
Some knew them only partly.
Days lingered in the fields and smelt
Like cork, or wine, tartly.

What We Had

And then we had a loft of hay;
It smelt like cork, or wine.
August is gone, and since that day
Unweeded paths entwine.

The tendrils and the lips among,
Hoarse diamonds shivered, drizzling,
In their numbness to the tongue
Remíniscent of Riesling.

September was a small expense
The way we were spending:
It pruned our trees and rimed our fence,
It said the summer's ending.

Diluting wine in puddles, broke the bread
Of glaucous sand baked white,
Syringed from heaven, melting into lead
The latticed glass of light.

Or it would melt light into sand
In flight, igniting trees and eaves,
And then our glass could not withstand
The sight of burning leaves.

For there are brands of joy – the oaths
Vin gai, *vin triste*. Have trust –
These tendrils are but slender growths,
And Riesling – only rust.

Thus we had night. We had the strain
Of lips. Hoarse diamonds sought
The eyes, where the autumn rain
Redounded, unechoed in thought.

It seemed that we so loved to pray,
And kissed as though to miss
The briefest years that take a ray
To reach the glow of bliss.

Like music: years spent in awe,
A song would never holler –
One tremulous, uninterrupted O! –
The trembling pith of coral.

My friend, you ask me: Who will pray
For fire in speeches of a fool?

Let us free words anew,
As our garden lets – its amber rind,
Both careless and kind,
A few, a few, a few.

We must not hold our own
In so much decorous trust
Of madder and of citrus
That sprinkle the bestrewn.

Who let pine tears loose
And poured, self-effacing,
At music, at the casing,
Through the latticed sluice?

Who painted the gate
In quicken miniate,
With minium from the calix
Of trembling italics?

You ask me: Who will pray
When August grows frail,
Who lives in digression,
Who knows how to fashion

Any aspen leaf;
Since Ecclesiastes,
Masters all his grief
Chiselling alabasters?

You ask me: Who will pray
For dahlias' lips and asters',
Septembered by disasters?

For willow leaves in braille,
Leafed by caryatids pale,
Leaving an autumn trail
On the infirmary jaspers?

You ask me: Who will pray?
– Omnific god of love,
The deity of detail,
Jadwíga and Jagiéllo . . .

I do not know if the fiat
Of the beyond remains moot,
But life is rather like the quiet
Autumnal, doubtless minute.

From *Themes & Variations*

Margarita

Tearing twigs on herself like a snare of rays gone awry,
Margarita's tight clench so much more lilac lipped,
So much more hotly white than the white of her eye,
The nightingale shone, and warbled and reigned and clipped.

Exuded by grass like a smell: as quicksilver conglobes
In rains gone insane, it quivered in archil.
It astonished the bark. Out of breath, touched the lobes:
All its tongue. All atremble, continued to sparkle.

When her hand moved aslant to the eyes overwhelmed
By the glow, Margarita attracted to warbling argent
And it seemed, with the rains and branches so helmed,
An amazon, breathless, lay fallen on that forest margin.

And the back of her head with one hand is so held,
And the other is free and behind her back just to try
To unloosen that drowned in shadows helm she beheld
Tearing twigs on herself like a snare of rays gone awry.

At dusk I see you in the schoolgirl light,
A boarder. Winter. Sunlight fells the trees
Of hours in the wood where I lie in wait
For twilight's fall. Here it falls and frees.

The night, the night! A hell, a vicious oval!
Had you but known it has become communal!
It is your step, your marriage, your betrothal,
More grave than an interrogation by tribunal.

Remember life? Remember slow flakes fly,
Like doves of snow, sped abreast of silence?
The wind would quickly whirl them on the sly,
Then quickly hurl them down with such violence.

You changed places! – It placed under us
Carpets of sleds and crystal heirlooms!
For life, like blood, blew venous clouds, thunderous
With fires of flurries, pouring burning blooms!

Remember movement? Time? Merchant rows?
Do you remember tents, and crowds? You recall
The cold of copper coins – how there was
A tumult of church bells for holidays of old?

Ah, love! Alas, depiction is so scant!
What can replace you? Drops? Of bromin?
A stallion's eye, I watch the dark askant
In fear of insomnia's vast omen.

At dusk I see you pass one last examination.
I see you finish. Migraine, maths, canary.
But O at night! How thirsty, O how patient
The eyes of pills, and phials of glass, how arid!

Plait these splashes of elbows into the cold of a wave,
Palms of atlas and lust into lilies in their lithe languor!
Chant your lays, delight! Let loose! Now leash them
    for that loping play
Where forest echoes drowned the hunt in its Calydon
    clangour
And the doe Atalanta in flight from Actaeon dismayed
    at bay,
Where love was the bottomless lapis in each lavished
    neigh,
Where kisses were lapsed in as traps were leapt
    as in anger
And laughter was whole in horns carrying horses away.
– O let loose! Even looser – as they . . .

Disappointed? You thought, here's
A parting, a quiet swan's Requiem Mass?
Weighing grief, with pupils enlarging the tears
Tried on to gauge their total stress?

During such liturgies, frescos chipped off the apsis
Shaking with music, like Johann Sebastian's lip.
From this vesper forward, hatred sees lapses,
Stretches in all things. A pity, no whip.

In the dark, recovering immediately, decides
Without lingering doubts it's for the best.
That – time. That she has no use for suicides.
That even this is a snail's pace.

Just try to prevent me. Just move to extinguish
These torrents of sorrow throbbing like mercury
    in Torricelli's vacuum frame.
Preclude me, insanity – wed me, advance,
Pronounce me still! O timidity, once –
Extinguish, extinguish! Inflame!

My friend my tender O as in the flight at night from
    Bergen to the Pole
By the hot down falling off the feet of ember-geese
    like snow across the land
I swear my tender I swear it is my soul
When I implore forget and sleep my friend.

When like the corpse of the Norwegian
    ice-bound to the top
In visions of the winter that no frozen masts can move
I fuss in the auroral lights of these eyes O please stop
Calm down my friend stop crying sleep will soothe.

When just as does the North beyond the farthest homes
In secret from the arctic watchful floes
Flushing the eyes of blind seals using the midnight domes
I whisper nonsense please forget don't rub them doze.

A trembling clavier wipes off the foam.
Ready to swoon, gripping its fever,
O darling! you will say to meet my No!
In music's presence? How can we be nearer

Than chords, like pages from a journal,
Into the fire's twilight then, agreed?
O wondrous understanding, be informal,
Just nod and be astonished! You are free.

I do not keep you. Go, be good in deed.
Hasten to others. Werther has been written.
One opens windows to let the veins bleed:
These days the very air is death-ridden.

Thus they begin. When they are two,
Into the sonant dark they peer,
They warble, whistle. Words in tune
Around the age of three appear.

Thus they begin to comprehend.
And in the hum of starting engines,
As a beginning see their end,
And as a brother's home, a stranger's.

Among the roses grown wild,
This awful beauty never dies:
It cannot help stealing the child.
And thus suspicions must arise.

Thus fears ripen. Is the chasm
So deep that stars appear thinning?
When he is a Faust and a phasm?
Thus gypsies take their beginning.

Thus there open, in the quotients
Of the horizon, every time,
Like sighs sudden, distant oceans.
Thus there grows a future iamb.

Thus summer evenings can disperse
The rain in just one dream, Inspire!
Whose light their irides may curse:
Thus quarrels with the sun transpire.

Thus they begin to live in verse.

For My Enemies

O childhood, scoop of soulful wealth!
At home in any wooded region,
With roots deep in the love of self,
My inspiration and my regent!

Would tears on glass be so distinguished!
Would dried wasps and roses burn!
Would all this chaos be extinguished
To flourish like a sanguine fern!

What can be said of piano keys:
Even the chords became tribal!
Nomadic, black and phoney ease
Prepares vengeance for the libel.

A lifelike tear slanders,
Proximity to kings,
A closing door slanders,
Gay jingle of key-rings.

The grace of presents given,
The perfume of a pander,
Deceitful handshakes even,
Even magicians slander.

The smallness of the age left us,
O tender ones! And we?
O left ones – and the leftists –
Pink cheeks and ennui?

Sun! Do you hear? – Fill your purses.
Pine, are we dreaming? – Must endure.
O life, our name is – dispersal,
Unknown by sense and to your cure.

O Duncan of grey guesses! – Fate.
O hosts of legions in his omens!
O God, my Lord, what hast thou made
On our sale to the commons!

Could I forget them? My kin?
My seas? To flatter the charter?
For an orgy of feeling – into a gin?
With a storm – a partisan martyr?

To some cellar? Behind a window? In a rail-car?
To get off somewhere? Rent something, settle?
I savour this agony. Scar!
Your claws, O lioness, show your mettle.

The kindred. The seas. The ordeal
Of routine, so absurdly disciplinarian.
Don't take your revenge like this. Heal!
Oh, not you! It is I – proletarian!

It is true. I've fallen. Now don't spare!
Debased to a beast's self-impression,
I have stooped to depression:
I have stooped to despair.

We are few. Perhaps we are three,
From Donétz, from fire, from hell,
Under the grey running bark of the tree
Of clouds, of rains, of soldiers we fell
Amid councils, verses, discussions
Of art and of transport in Russia.

We have been people. Epochs we are.
Knocked down, sped past in a caravan guise,
Like tundra, to sighs of the tender car,
To the flight of the piston and ties.
We shall circle and startle and whirl,
We shall flock in a ravenous whirl –

And pass! You'll take long to abate:
Thus, striking a straw heap by morning,
Traces of wind still live the debate
Adjourned without warning
To an assembly of trees, in the hatching
Of stormy proceedings over the thatching.

Spring, I am from the street where poplars are aghast,
Where distance is appalled, the house afraid to fall,
The air is blue, like clothing bundles passed
To one discharged from hospital.

Where twilight's empty like the stark surmise
A fairy-tale star puts in a sentence
To the bewilderment of countless noisy eyes,
Homeless, and hungry for repentance.

Now shut your eyes. And in the deafest labyrinth
For thirty leagues of silent space askance,
Drip under steam the snorting and the aberrant
Cries, whispers, smiles, insomnia and trance.

Like me, they walk away when the spring barters.
That has been tried by every philistine.
In the cathedral groves, to honour these martyrs,
The engine offers cups of stolid steam.

But was it long, since in the course of service,
Led by capitulas ordained by black pine,
The worldly March filled each clandestine crevice
Along the garden paths with lilac wine?

Atonement for its sins will be my future share.
Uncorking threshing willow casks afresh,
The morning would transport the emptied tare
Into the streams in its translucent mesh.

The twilight hours would begin to harden
Both puddle pearl and river aquarelle,
With dawn as gardener to keep a guard on
First bagatelles and primer nonpareil.

In comfort, and then by banquet,
By way of *le style Jacob*,
Temperament is made languid,
A bee in a crystal globe.

Sparks scatter far and wide:
Letting your fingers roam,
You curb that demon pride
With just a simple comb.

Your pose is one of defiance
And love, and your lips a show
Of mockery, of 'Be quiet,
You are not three, you know!'

O freshness, O droplet of emerald
Teased by the wrist in motion,
O comb of chaos ephemeral,
O heaven's wondrous notion!

Autumn

Those days reached the heart of the park
With the leaves that October saw falling.
Dawns laboured at forging an end to the dark,
The elbows ached and the throat was swollen.

The fog was washed up. The clouds hit bottom.
The dusk took forever. The evening was specked,
And bared its hectic, inflamed and rotten
Horizon for busy front yards to inspect.

Then blood seemed to freeze, but that did not bind
The ponds, and it seemed to the weather apparent
That the days would not heal the unfirm hyaline,
So transparent its heaven, so pale and barren.

Then vision gained much distance, more resolute
Was eyesight, and pulse became quickened, until
A silence was spilled, and how breathlessly desolate,
How breathlessly endless rang out its still!

The Riddle

A mysterious nail left the markings:
Too late to read now, in any event.
But as I lie in the darkness
None can touch you as I did then.

How I touched you! The bronze of my lips
Touched you as tragedy touches a theatre.
The kiss was a summer. It lapsed and eclipsed,
And a storm gathered later.

Drank like birds. Drew until vision would cease.
Stars take years to reach the stomach through sighs,
While nightingales roll their eyes in ecstasy,
Draining by drop the darkling skies.

Poetry

To you, O poetry, I swear,
To you that isn't simply rain,
And not a voice one picks to wear,
But summers with a third-class fare,
But suburbs stifling a refrain,

But stuffy, like a May, environs,
A field of battle in the mist,
Where clouds moan of perseverance,
Where the horizon barks Dismiss!

Where with the rail web entwined,
As it envisions, not ensnares,
Along the lines, far behind,
Not with a song, but unawares,

Rain spouts froth and clusters frosty,
Enthralled forever by the dawn,
In eavesdrip scrawling its acrostic,
With rhyme into bubbles blown:

When, poetry, under the faucet,
Truism, like bucket zinc, lies low,
Then, even then, the stream is glossy,
Some paper underneath, and – flow!

Notes to the Poems

On 29 January 1890, in Moscow, Boris Pasternak was born into an idyll. The first child of loving parents, a painter and a pianist, he would date the beginnings of his conscious life to an evening in November 1894 when he was awakened by the sounds of Tchaikovsky's trio in A minor. His mother, assisted by two of her peers from the Moscow Conservatory, was performing the work for Tolstoy in the next room.

No member of the Pasternak family would ever pursue success for its own sake. The mother, Rosalia, a protégée of Anton Rubinstein and one of the most promising musicians of her generation, sacrificed her career to family life. The father, Leonid, is unquestionably among the most gifted painters Russia has produced, a kind of Impressionist *sui generis*, yet one who lacked the promotional skills of Diaghilev's 'World of Art' luminaries to win for himself some lasting international reputation. The children were brought up to uphold that tradition. The eldest daughter, Josephine, is a supremely talented poet, yet to this day her work remains for the most part unpublished and largely unknown.

It is for this reason that, in biographical terms, the persistent identification of Boris Pasternak with the *succès de scandale* of *Doctor Zhivago* is so contrary to the nature of the Pasternak phenomenon. In literary terms, it is even more misleading.

The year was 1912, *annus mirabilis*: Alexander Blok began the publication of his collected poems and the Silver Age of Russian culture reached its apogee. In that year the genius of young Pasternak burst in. There was no warning, no transition. At twenty-two the poet seemed to have sprung from the godhead of Lermontov. The 'biography' of one so young

could not have been relevant until later, when it became the
stuff of autobiography in his 1931 *Okhrannaya gramota* (Safe
Conduct). Happy childhood at 21 Myasnitsky Street, an
eighteenth-century town house in the heart of Moscow. Fifth
Gymnasium, one of the city's best schools, which he entered at
eleven. A brief encounter with Rainer Maria Rilke at a railway
station in the summer of 1900, as the family was leaving
Moscow to go off on a holiday in the country: 'A silhouette
among bodies'. The summer of 1903 in Obolenskoye, south-
west of Moscow, where the composer Alexander Scriabin,
then at work on his Third Symphony, was the Pasternaks'
neighbour: 'The infatuation struck.' The years 1903–1909
were accordingly devoted to the study of musical composition, under the tutelage of Reinhold Glière, among others.
The family spent 1906 in Berlin, to get away from the previous
year's political turmoil at home. In 1908, admission to the Law
Faculty of Moscow University – and, far more important, the
discovery of a dusty copy of Rilke's *Das Stunden-Buch* in his
father's library. In 1909, an impulsive decision to abandon
music.

After a year at the University, philosophy was the dominant
interest, and Pasternak went to Marburg to study Kant under
Hermann Cohen. There, an unsuccessful courtship and the
sudden realization that, as Lara put it in *Zhivago*, to study only
philosophy 'is as odd as eating nothing but horse-radish' broke
Professor Cohen's spell. Youth was ending. 'How infinite a
thing youth is. . . . That part of our lives which is greater than
the whole.' During his first post-Marburg summer the poems
of *Bliznets v tuchakh* (A Twin in the Clouds) came into
being:

> Thus they begin. When they are two,
> Into the sonant dark they peer,
> They warble, whistle. Words in tune
> Around the age of three appear.

Some of these were later integrated, in revised form, into
the 1917 collection *Poverkh baryerov* (Over the Barriers),

written in 1914–16. In 1922, *Sestra moya zhizn'* (My Sister Life), conceived in 1917, followed. In 1923 came *Temy i varyatsii* (Themes & Variations), written in 1916–22. In 1932, subsequent poems were collected in *Vtoroye rozhdeniye* (Second Birth). Together with the additions and revisions of two decades, and the four long poems – *Vysokaya bolezn'* (High Illness, 1924), *Devyatsot pyatyi god* (The Year 1905, 1926), *Leitenant Schmidt* (Lieutenant Schmidt, 1927), and *Spektorsky* (1931) – the five collections of verse written over a period of twenty years comprise the Pasternak canon in the hearts of those who understand his work and the tragedy of his life.

The first 'words in tune' appeared in print just before the First World War, when the poet's home was still the idyll it had been in his childhood. The events in the autumn of 1917 put an abrupt end to that idyll:

> Our land is all smudged by the glare.
> Your nest: do you recognize it, darling?

Shortly thereafter, the family was scattered, and the last time Boris Pasternak saw his parents was during a visit to Berlin in 1923.

The poet remained in Moscow where, despite increasingly frequent spells of despair, he continued to write and publish poems so fresh, bold and somehow immutable that by the early 1930s his verse came to occupy a place in Russian literature that bears comparison with that of Shakespeare in English.

> Let us free words anew,
> As our garden lets – its amber rind,
> Both careless and kind,
> A few, a few, a few.

Like Shakespeare, Pasternak transformed the existing poetic vocabulary, and with it the very language of Russian poetry, by the elemental force of his genius. Alexander Pushkin is often said to have 'created' the Russian literary language. If the place of the 'Russian Shakespeare' is permanently reserved for Pushkin, it can truly be said that the English equivalent of Pasternak has not yet appeared.

The spiritual world created by Pasternak between 1912 and 1932 is unique. Whether the key analytical 'section' be the sound of the poet's voice (Aseev's 'element of intonation') or the inexorable logic of his 'phantom syntax' (in Tynyanov's phrase), all attempts to dissect it end in critical failure. Significantly, Osip Mandelshtam called Pasternak 'the initiator of a new mode of prosody commensurate with the maturity and virility of the Russian language'. Marina Tsvetayeva, the poet closest to Pasternak personally and spiritually, understood this as soon as she opened a copy of *My Sister Life*. Pasternak, she concluded, was 'a poet more important than any, for most present poets *have been*, some *are*, and he alone *will be*'. Pasternak's world is lyrical. It is closed to critics, pedants and cultural paraphrasts who revel in reinterpreting spiritual realities which they are powerless to create. In this, it is more like Shakespeare than Shakespeare.

The last of the poems in *Second Birth* had been written and published in magazines in 1931. The book appeared in 1932. On 24 April of that year *Postanovleniye TsK VKP(b) o perestroike literaturno-khudozhestvennykh organizatsyi* ('Party Decree on the Restructuring of Literary and Cultural Organizations') was issued, a signal that the totalitarian state was ready to eliminate the last vestiges of independent publishing remaining from the previous decade. The myriad literary 'currents', inherited by the regime from the Silver Age of Russian culture and allowed to flow in the early 1920s, would now be dammed by decree into a single stream of 'Socialist Realism'. Officially this happened in August 1934, when the Union of Soviet Writers was convened in Moscow, but by the spring of 1932 the intention had long been clear.

By that time Pasternak's 'reputation' had been established,

and the State accepted it for what it was. What is remarkable, in fact, is the extent to which the regime's ideologues saw his work as 'constructive'. The child of a family idyll, Pasternak saw ecstasy – and not merely happiness, as the State's propagandists required – in the world around him, a world being plunged into terror and misery. Such was the nature of his joyful genius – in contrast, for instance, to Akhmatova's melancholy and Mandelshtam's wistfulness – and the State chose to interpret his ecstasy as approval of the regime. A more worldly, politically astute writer would not have been able to mistake the emerging totalitarian reality of the 1930s for an organic part of nature's universal flowing, as Pasternak had in *Second Birth*. 'In the days of the congress, six women trod fields', an immortal line in Russian from one of the poems in that collection, encapsulates the time and lives on as an example of this uniquely Pasternakian astigmatism. The regime was inclined to treat it as political vision, and the poet was duly appointed to the governing board of the new Union of Writers.

Despite the regime's benevolence, Pasternak stopped writing. In a private letter he wrote in 1953, he recalled his state of mind at the time:

> I was nineteen years younger, Mayakovsky had not yet been deified, they kept making a fuss over me and sending me on foreign trips, I could have written any filth or trash and they would have published it; I was not in fact suffering from any disease, but I was constantly unhappy and was pining away like a fairy-tale hero under the spell of an evil spirit. I wanted to write something honest and genuine in honour of the society which was so kind to me, but this would have been possible only if I had been willing to write something false. It was an insoluble problem like squaring the circle, and I was thrashing around in an uncertainty of intention which clouded every horizon and blocked every road.

To say that in time the poet's ambiguous perception of the least free political and cultural period in recorded history turned to hatred, or even fear, is to misrepresent him. 'Created before Adam', in Tsvetayeva's phrase, Pasternak was above politics, even the politics of life and death. Genius is above everything, including language.

The spiritual paralysis of the man who described himself in his odd new position as 'thrice-decorated wizard-consultant for poetry' did not, however, pass unnoticed by the regime. The ruler's displeasure was akin to the embarrassment of a host who wants to show off to his guests a prize songbird, which at that moment becomes obstinate in its silence. The suicides of Vladimir Mayakovsky, in 1930, and Tsvetayeva, in 1941, framed that silence, and there was nothing anyone could do about it, not even the poet himself.

Professionally, like many writers in the deadly stillness around him, Pasternak began looking to the art of translation for material as well as spiritual sustenance. Of the translations he was to produce during the next quarter of a century, some fifty poets from a dozen languages, Shakespeare's sonnets and plays and Goethe's *Faust* are best known. The rest was largely *khaltúra*, hack-work, as he often acknowledged. This was inevitable. Temperamentally the poet was still too full of himself, in the best sense, to bow to another's original. So even his early attempts to translate his beloved Rilke into Russian were doomed to failure.

Publicly, in his 'holy idiocy', Pasternak vacillated between curiosity, which he felt for the dictator personally, and revulsion, which he felt for his incarnation in the regime. Even in retrospect it is not clear which was the more dangerous course of behaviour: to attract Stalin's attention and insist on speaking to him 'about life and death' (as Pasternak did in the famous conversation when the dictator telephoned to ask his opinion of Mandelshtam) or to jeer openly at the sycophancy of the new 'Soviet' writers (as he did in a February 1936 speech to the Union of Writers' board meeting in Minsk). When, in 1936, mass terror reached a new height, Pasternak's actions became still more reckless, and he was duly attacked *ex cathedra* by

V. P. Stavsky, Secretary of the Union of Writers, for 'slandering the Soviet people' with a spray of pale poems about Georgia which he had managed to squeeze out of himself that summer. In April 1937 he refused to sign a 'collective letter' against André Gide and, in June, one condemning Marshal Tukhachevsky. Private indiscretions, such as his visit with Nadezhda Mandelshtam after her husband's second arrest in 1938, continued to accumulate as well. Nevertheless, like very few others in his circle, he survived physically. Spiritually, his suffocation was by now total.

The disintegration of his second marriage (his first, to Evgeniya Lurye, had broken up in 1927), to Zinaida Neigauz, did not help matters. The war, part of which Pasternak spent in evacuation in Chistopol, on the Kama River, was something of a welcome diversion. A new collection, *Na rannikh poyezdakh* (On Early Trains), was published in 1943. Its poems read as if they had been translated from the language of Pasternak into a plodding, versified prose. A decade earlier the revellers in *Spektorsky* drank their New Year toast to 'the writer's becoming a poet / And the poet's becoming a demigod'. Now an opposite fate had befallen the poet.

As early as 1936 Pasternak began to think of prose as a way out of his creative stupor. To be sure, he had written prose throughout his life – but, in one critic's apt phrase, it was prose as 'prophecy of the verse to come'. Now prose was becoming its own prophecy.

The muse of the prose to come was Olga Ivinskaya, a junior editor with the magazine *Novy mir*, aged thirty-four when Pasternak, then fifty-six, met her in 1946. The 'Party Decree on the Magazines *Zvezda* and *Leningrad*', with its denunciation of Akhmatova, had just been published, as Stalin unleashed Andrei Zhdanov on what remained of the literary milieu in Russia. It was in this atmosphere that the fourteen-year liaison between the poet and his muse began, and the prose that ensued was *Doctor Zhivago*.

As Zhdanovite denunciations piled up – in March 1947 Pasternak was branded as 'ideologically alien' and 'full of malice' –

Olga Ivinskaya was the ageing poet's only solace, inspiration and hope. By 1948, early chapters of his novel existed in typescript, as did some of the 'Poems of Yuri Zhivago' which the novel would later incorporate. In October 1949 Ivinskaya was arrested. After several months of unsuccessful interrogation, devised to make her 'confess' by implicating her lover in a variety of political crimes, she was sentenced to five years' hard labour.

Despite his infinite grief and a heart attack he had suffered during this ordeal, Pasternak continued his work on the novel. Stalin died in March 1953, and Ivinskaya returned from the camps in the autumn. In April 1954 ten of the 'Poems of Yuri Zhivago' appeared in *Znamya*, accompanied by a note about the prose work in progress: 'The hero is Yuri Andreyevich Zhivago, a doctor, an intellectual. . . . He leaves behind some memoirs and among other papers some . . . verse, part of which is offered here and which, grouped together, will form the novel's final chapter.'

In her journal entry for 4 December 1957, Lydia Chukovskaya, Anna Akhmatova's amanuensis of many years, recorded Akhmatova's reaction to the novel, which she had just finished reading in typescript:

> There are some absolutely unprofessional pages. I suppose Olga [Ivinskaya] wrote them. Don't laugh: I am serious. As you know, I have never had editorial inclinations, but here I wanted to grab a pencil and cross out page after page. And yet the novel has landscapes . . . I would maintain they are unequalled in Russian literature. Not in Turgenev, not in Tolstoy, not in anyone.

Akhmatova's extemporaneous verdict may or may not be taken for a sober analytical assessment of *Doctor Zhivago*. Yet the fact remains that, by 1957, she was one of the few surviving remnants of the cultural milieu which had engendered Pasternak and nurtured others who in some sense could be considered his peers. For this reason, her mixed response to the novel, like her discriminating opinions about Pasternak's work before and after 1932, stands as the only reliable critical judgement by an eyewitness. As for Pasternak's own judgement, he told Chukovskaya that the novel was 'the only worthwhile thing I have ever achieved'. This corresponded with his fitful, savage, tone-deaf revisions of his early verse throughout the *Zhivago* period, which dismayed Akhmatova, and with his new, 'simple' verse, which she abhorred.

The 'Poems of Yuri Zhivago' are the last instalment of the Pasternak of *On Early Trains*, as distant from the Pasternak of *My Sister Life* as *Wellington's Victory* is from the Beethoven we know. Compare Pasternak's lines invoked at the end of my introduction to this collection (p. xxxvi) with the late poem 'In Hospital', both in translations by his sister Lydia:

> This then would mean – the ashes of lilac,
> Richness of dew-drenched and crushed camomile,
> Bartering lips for a star after twilight.
> This is – embracing the firmament; strong
> Hercules holding it, clasping still fonder.
> This then would mean – whole centuries long
> Fortunes for nightingales' singing to squander.

And the first seven lines of the other:

> They stood, almost blocking the pavement,
> As though at a window display;
> The stretcher was pushed in position,
> The ambulance started away.
> Past porches and pavements and people
> It plunged with its powerful light
> Through streets in nocturnal confusion . . .

'Deep into the blackness of night', reads the following line. The banality is unstoppable, mechanical. The 'meaning' is clear. The poet is dead.

Thankfully, in his prose the contrast was less pronounced. As a novel, despite the fundamental weaknesses quickly glimpsed by Akhmatova, *Zhivago* endures, condensing all that had remained of the supreme genius of Russian poetry in his later years into a prose style. Certainly against the backdrop of the cultural wasteland which was Stalin's Russia, this was a remarkable achievement.

The prospects for its publication, whether in a journal like *Novy mir* or by the State publishing house in book form, being quite dim, in May 1956, against the entreaties of both his wife and his mistress, Pasternak, ensconced in his country house in Peredelkino, fifteen miles from Moscow, passed on the type-script of the novel to the Milan publisher Giangiacomo Feltrinelli. Soon thereafter tentative arrangements for its serialized publication collapsed altogether, and – despite persistent attempts by Soviet literary officials to dissuade him – Feltrinelli published the novel in November 1957. The émigré of a novel, the first on record since writers like Pilnyak and Zamyatin were pilloried for publishing abroad some thirty years earlier, became a best-seller and a *succès de scandale*. On 23 October 1958 its author was awarded the Nobel Prize for Literature.

According to Ivinskaya, his love unto the last, the *Zhivago* scandal 'broke and finally killed him'. Pasternak developed lung cancer and died in hospital on 30 May 1960. He was buried in Peredelkino, where his novel was written.

A Twin in the Clouds

It is not in keeping with my views of Pasternak's life and work to cite his own views expressed after the years of silence during which his voice left him for ever – that is, after the publication of his prose autobiography, *Safe Conduct*, in 1931, and of his fifth book of verse, *Second Birth*, in 1932. Yet poets rarely speak of their earliest years until they have completed the process of autobiography by means of which their imaginary career is made. The retroactive action of *Safe Conduct* does not uncover, and often, with a capriciously shifting focus, occludes, the quotidian of circumstances under which

Pasternak's first poems came into being, because the book, like all of Pasternak's writing before 1933, lives for its own pleasure and feels no obligation to relate anything. The direct speech of art is figurative and intransmutable. It is only about Pasternak over the age of forty-three that one can ask, as he was asked by his Marburg professor about Kant, 'Was meint der Alte?' This is what the old man meant at sixty-seven, as he recalled the youth of twenty-three summering in the village of Molodi, where he came with his family in distant 1913 after his last term at Moscow University.

At the bottom of the park a small stream wound its way in whirling pools. Over one of these deep eddies, a large old birch tree broke and continued to grow upturned. The green confusion of its branches created an airborne gazebo overhanging the water. In their sturdy weave one could sit and even recline. This I made my study. In the thick of the tree, during two or three summer months, I wrote the poems of my first book. The book, with pretentiousness bordering on foolishness, was entitled *A Twin in the Clouds*, in homage to the cosmological sophistries for which the titles of books by Symbolists and the names of their publishing ventures were known. To write these poems, to scratch out and restore what had been crossed out, was a profound need and a source of incomparable and verging on tears pleasure.

I tried to avoid romantic excess, impersonal captivation. I had no intention of thundering from the stage to make white-collar employees recoil from these poems, outraged: 'How degenerate! How barbarous!' I had no wish for flies to die from their modest elegance, or for lady professors to say, after hearing them read to a circle of six or seven admirers: 'Allow me to shake your honest hand!' I did not strive for the rhythmic clarity of song or dance which, nearly indifferent to words, quickens hands and feet. I did not relate, reflect, represent, or react to anything. Later, for the sake of unnecessary comparisons between me and Mayakovsky, oratorial and intonational beginnings were diagnosed in me as well. This is wrong. I have them no

more than any man speaking. Quite to the contrary, my
abiding concern was with the content, and my abiding hope
was for the poem to contain something of value, a new
thought or a new image: for it to be etched, in all its
singularity, deep into the book, where it would speak from
the pages with all its silence and all the red letters of its black
and colourless typeface.

All of this may help us to understand why Pasternak has
not left a definitive name by which to call his poems written
before 1914. These earliest poems were collected in *A Twin in
the Clouds*, his first published volume, produced in an edition
of two hundred by The Lyric, an association of young writers,
in January of that year. Only a few of the poems from the book
were retained, revised and made part of the final canon which
he arranged in 1928. In the 1929 edition of *Over the Barriers*
they were grouped under a descriptive heading, 'The Early
Years', but I have chosen to emphasize their provenance.

The reasons for this may not be apparent at this juncture,
but they exist all the same. What is clear is that one must draw a
line between other people's opinion of Pasternak and one's
own, and this is as good a place to start as any: 'You play Bach
your way,' Wanda Landowska was once quoted as quipping,
'I shall play him his way.' That Pasternak, unlike Bach, did
not die shortly after completing his *Art of the Fugue*, compli-
cates matters, but it does not change the essential truth of
Landowska's individualism, or love under another, less
boastful name.

'February . . .': First published 1913. Line 5: The vehicle in
question is of course horse-drawn, a hansom.

'Like brazen ashes . . .': First published 1913. Line 1: Not
necessarily, but possibly, a brazier used to fumigate fruit trees.

'*Träumerei*': First published 1914. The Russian word meaning both 'sleep' and 'dream' is here replaced with the title made
famous by Schumann.

'Feasts': First published 1914. Line 5: The original has

'offspring', but the negative sense of 'spawn' is amplified by the well-established word combination, outside of which it is rarely used, meaning 'fiend'. 'Workshop', as in English, is both an artist's studio and a craftsman's workroom.

'Winter': First published 1914. Line 5: 'Stormy Sea' is a parlour game. Line 27: Cups of vitriol used to be placed between window-frames to prevent condensation. Vitriol, a white powder, absorbs moisture and turns blue.

Over the Barriers

Over the Barriers, originally subtitled 'Second Volume of Verse', was first published in 1917, carrying an epigraph from Swinburne:

> To the soul in my soul that rejoices
> For the song that is over my song.

As with *A Twin in the Clouds*, many of the fifty-odd poems in the book underwent extensive revision, but in the end most became part of the 1928 canon. 'With the passing of years,' Pasternak recalled in 1946, 'the notion of "Over the Barriers" evolved in me. From the title of a book it grew into the name of a period or a manner, and under this heading I would join together things written later, so long as they matched that first book in character.'

Earlier, in *Safe Conduct*, Pasternak tells how he was startled into the manner, and over the barriers, by the spectre of a spiritual dead end he saw in Mayakovsky:

> Had I been younger, I would have quitted literature. But age interfered. After all the metamorphoses, I did not dare to redefine myself for the fourth time.
> Something else happened. Time and a mutualism of influences bound me to Mayakovsky. We had some coincidences in common. I noticed them. I realized that unless I did something with myself, they would become more frequent. I had to protect him from their commonness. Not

knowing how to put it, I decided to break with its cause. I broke with the romantic manner. Thus arose the un-romantic poetics of *Over the Barriers*.

But beneath the romantic manner, henceforth pro-scribed, lay a whole world-view. This was the understand-ing of life as the life of a poet. It came to us from the Symbolists, and the Symbolists had absorbed it from the Romantics, especially the Germans.

This world-view possessed Blok only for a time. In the form that was natural to him, it could never have satisfied him. He either had to intensify it or leave it. He chose to let this world-view go. It was intensified by Mayakovsky and Esenin.

In its symbolism, that is in all that shares a conceptual border with Christianity and Orphism, in the poet who offers himself as a measure of life and pays for it with his own life, the romantic vision is compellingly bright and incontrovertible. In this sense something eternal is em-bodied in Mayakovsky's life and, deaf to epithet, Esenin's destiny, bound on immolation as it begs to be ushered and entering in the fairy-tale.

But without the legend this romantic plan is false. The poet at its foundation is inconceivable in the absence of non-poets, who place him in relief, because this poet is not a living person absorbed in moral study but a visual-biographic emblem, which needs a background to provide it with visible contours. Unlike passion plays which must have a heaven to hear them, this drama must have the evil of mediocrity to be seen, as romanticism must always have philistinism, for with the loss of conformity it loses a good half of its content.

The understanding of biography as a spectacle was a thing of my time. I shared that concept with everyone. I parted with it while it was still undemandingly soft for the Sym-bolists and neither invited heroism nor smelled like blood. First of all, I freed myself from it unconsciously, breaking the romantic devices that held it up. Secondly, I eschewed it consciously as unsuitable glamour, because having limited myself to the craft, I now feared any poeticization that would put me in a false and inappropriate position.

'The Soul': First published 1917. The original title in *Over the Barriers* was 'The Ingrafted One'. Line 7: The treasonous countess named in the poem is Countess Tarakanova, imprisoned in the Peter and Paul Fortress and drowned when it was flooded in 1775.

'Spring': First published 1917. The original title, deleted when the poem was grouped with two others under the title 'Spring' in the 1928 revision, was 'Poetry in Spring'. Line 5: Smalt, here and elsewhere in my versions, is enamel. But here also, as in Dante's *Inferno*, IX: 51: 'Vegna Medusa: sì 'l farem di smalto', when the three furies wish for Medusa to come and turn him to stone.

'Swifts': First published 1917. Swifts rarely alight, and even gather their nesting materials on the wing.

'Improvisation': First published 1915. The title was clarified in 1948: 'An Improvisation for the Piano'. I introduce that clarification in the first line (which has merely 'a flock of keys' in the original).

My Sister Life

My Sister Life was published in Moscow in 1922 and in Berlin the following year. Unlike the poems of *A Twin in the Clouds* and *Over the Barriers*, the poems of this book were not revised and became part of the 1928 canon as first collected. The epigraph from Lenau's 'Das Bild', appropriated here by my version of 'To the Memory of the Demon', appeared on a separate page, following the dedication, 'Dedicated to Lermontov', printed on the title-page beneath the title *My Sister Life* and the subtitle 'Summer 1917'.

In Berlin in 1922 Marina Tsvetayeva recorded her first impressions with these words: 'Before me is Pasternak's book *My Sister Life*.' When the review appeared, it brought the two poets together, and Tsvetayeva did not conceal that she was writing it 'from sheer cupidity: it is a precious thing to become part of such a destiny'. Pasternak, she wrote, 'does not yet know our words; his speech seems to come from a desert island, from childhood, from the Garden of Eden; it does not quite make sense, and it topples you. At three this is common and is called "child". At twenty-three it is uncommon and is called "poet". (Oh, equality, equality! How many did God have to rob, even to the seventh generation, to create one Pasternak like this!)'.

Pasternak was of course a decade older than in Tsvetayeva's example. But she was thinking back on 1912, when his first poems were written, and she was right. When she herself was a decade older, in 1933, she developed that instinctive revelation into a coherent vision of Pasternak under the title 'Poets With and Without History'. There she wrote: 'Boris Pasternak is a poet without development. He began with himself in the beginning and this never changed.' Before her was the first edition of Pasternak's *Collected Poems* of 1933: '1912–1932. Twenty years. Half a thousand pages.' Every one of those twenty years, in short, was a year of *My Sister Life*, as a mountain range may bear the name of one of its highest peaks.

'To the Memory of the Demon': First published 1922. The poem was itself something of an epigraph. It opened the book, prefacing its ten cycles: 'Whether It Is Time for the Birds to Sing', 'The Book of the Steppe', 'Diversions of the Beloved', 'Studies in Metaphysics', 'Song Epistles, so She Would Not Be Sad', 'Romanovka', 'Attempts to Separate the Soul', 'The Return', 'To Helen' and 'Afterword', the last nine parts of this decameron originally called 'The Book of the Steppe'. I apply the epigraph from Lenau to this first poem because I do not wish to delete it altogether, as I do the cycle headings, nor do I want it to overshadow what is, after all, only a selection from the book. 'The Demon' is a poem by Lermontov: a banished angel soars over the Caucasus and appears to Tamára, a Georgian princess, in her dreams. Line 6: 'hands' is implicit, not explicit, in the original, and 'arms' is suggested in Blok's

'Demon' of 1910, but a subject is more necessary here than elsewhere and this one is more pianistic. Line 11: *zurná* is a Caucasian musical instrument akin to the flute, the word itself being of Persian origin (from *sûr*, 'joy', and *nâj*, 'reed').

'Sorrow': First published 1922. Line 1: The book here is probably 'The Book of the Steppe', although in the volume's simplified, post-1928 arrangement the line would refer to *My Sister Life* as a whole.

'My sister – life . . .': First published 1922. The dash between the second and third words of the first line of the poem, and in late variants of the title of the book, is a revisionist scar. It appeared in later editions, and I follow suit, with mixed feelings, hoping that the English language will finally heal the wound. Line 10: 'some local line', in the original, is the Kamyshin branch of the Tsaritsyn railway. Line 17: 'in third', in a third-class compartment. Line 22: The original contains a reference, deleted here, to Fata Morgana, an apparition sometimes seen in the Strait of Messina.

'The Weeping Garden': First published 1922. The slippers undoubtedly belong to the poet, walking up the terrace steps to return inside.

'The Girl': First published 1922. I have deleted a two-line epigraph from Lermontov, as did Pasternak for the 1933 *Collected Poems*. Line 2: The mirror envisioned here is a pier-glass, whose three sections reflect the blossoming branch set before it and the garden beyond.

'You are in the wind . . .': First published 1922. Pasternak tried to identify the metaphysical addressee of the poem in 1945 by supplying it with a title, 'Dawn'. Line 16: 'her' is not in the original, but the 'dress' in this line, in modern Russian usage, is a woman's dress.

'Rain (An Inscription)': First published 1922. The full title is 'Rain: An Inscription on The Book of the Steppe', this being the second cycle of poems, and initially a unifying name for most of the cycles, in *My Sister Life*. It is to 'The Book of the

Steppe', recently completed, that the poem is addressed. As the only poem from this cycle of seven for which I offer a finished version is 'In Superstition', the title is abridged here. Line 5: Bombyx is a genus of moths which includes the silkworm moth. Line 20: 'Saint Gotthards' here, by extension, are the chasms in rain-drenched foliage, listed and mapped like Swiss mountain passes.

'In Superstition': First published 1922. Line 1: The Russian word for the fruit of wild, or bitter, orange used in the original is a borrowing from the German, *Pomeranze*. A picture of the fruit adorned matchboxes popular at the time. In the winter of 1913–14 and again the following autumn Pasternak rented a tiny room in Swan Passage in Moscow.

'Waving a fragrant anther . . .': First published 1920. The poem was entitled 'The Kiss' at the time of its first publication. Line 9: spirea is a common flowering plant, often spelt spiraea, belonging to the family *Rosaceae*. It has dense clusters of small pink or white flowers, like meadowsweet.

'Boating Oars': First published 1918. Line 10: The hero, named in the original, is Heracles (Hercules).

'English Lessons': First published 1922. Line 1: Pasternak fractures the traditional Russian stress of 'Desdemóna' with his English 'Desdémona', adding a stress mark to make this clear here and again in the next stanza.

'A Definition of Poetry': First published 1922. Line 6: Pasternak's 'pod-clad' is a dialectal usage, easily misunderstood as a word meaning 'shoulder-blades', which the poet felt compelled to clarify in a footnote. Line 7: Mozart's *Figaro*, here and in the original, is stressed as indicated by the accent on the last syllable.

'A Definition of the Soul': First published 1922. In the Russian the first stanza, in contrast to the other three, rhymes AABB in the original. In my version, it conforms to the ABAB pattern of the poem.

'A Definition of Creativity': First published 1922. Line 2: It is hardly of any importance that in none of the images of Beethoven we know, such as the paintings by Mähler (1815), Schiman (1818), or Stiler (1820), can his chest be seen. The important thing is his hair. Every contemporary observer felt obliged to remark on what, unbeknown to him, amounted to a visual emblem of Romanticism. 'A truthful eye beamed from under his bushy eyebrows,' Louis Spohr recorded. 'The reception room in which he greeted me', wrote Johann Tomaschek, 'was as disordered as his hair.' 'His hair, which neither comb nor scissors seem to have visited for years, overshadows his broad brow in a quantity and confusion to which only the snakes round a Gorgon's head offer a parallel,' Sir John Russell remembered in *A Tour of Germany* (Edinburgh, 1828). Line 5: In a game of draughts or checkers, a piece that makes it all the way across the board is queened, like a pawn in chess. The term used by Pasternak is obscure, and he added a footnote explaining it. Line 8: Here the scene shifts to the chess-board, with the Devil as a mounted knight among pawns.

'Our Storm': First published 1919. In the first edition of *My Sister Life* this poem was followed by an explanatory note, later deleted: 'These diversions came to an end when she passed her mission on to a substitute.' The next poem in the cycle is entitled 'The Substitute', beginning 'I live with your photograph.' Here, as with nearly all of my versions, I have retained Pasternak's rhyme scheme, although visually the original is divided into ten four-line stanzas and one couplet. Line 1: The plant named in the poem is Pasternak's beloved lilac. Line 22: As Pasternak has it, the mosquito, stinging through the blouse, poses like a 'red ballerina' – that is, a Soviet dancer on a foreign tour, an allusion much too vague for the English reader. Line 24: Anil is a shrub from whose leaves and stalks indigo is made. Line 27: 'wrath of day' – that is, Judgement Day – *Dies Irae*, and by association the Latin hymn included in the Requiem Mass.

'Sparrow Hills': First published 1922. Sparrow Hills, an elevation just outside Moscow which was not unlike old rural Montmartre, has been asphalted over and is now called Lenin Hills. Line 1: I am compelled to use 'faucet' instead of, for instance, 'tap'. Pasternak has something else in mind, thinking instead of a type of metal wash-stand for outdoor use, a savage contraption best rendered by the word used here. It finds its way into my collection once more, albeit for slightly different reasons, in the penultimate line of 'Poetry' (p. 59). Line 15: The Sunday in question may or may not be Trinity, the Sunday following Whit Sunday, in the last stanza.

'A Sultry Night': First published 1922. Line 1: 'It' is the rain, manipulating the reeds. Line 5: The stanza caused a great deal of critical consternation, compelling Pasternak to add a footnote to at least one line and to introduce a bland variant in 1945, replacing the name of an infectious disease, absent here, with 'fever'. My version is true to the original variants. Line 21: The 'it' here refers to the 'discourse' of the garden, which in turn becomes the subject of the final line.

'Summer': First published 1922. The last two stanzas evoke the Great Reforms of the 1860s and 1870s, which created the *zemstvo* as part of a system of local government. The initial mandate, revised in the year of Pasternak's birth, required that 42 per cent of the *zemstvo* deputies came from the gentry and 39 per cent from the peasantry, the rest being merchants, clergymen and the like.

'What We Had': First published 1922. The link to the previous poem justifies its insertion here, although in *My Sister Life* it falls into the subsequent cycle, 'Afterword', coming after the next poem. Line 8: The unorthodox stress, especially in a line containing a proper name and a foreign word, is true Pasternak, like his 'uneducated' stresses in Russian words so natural to Moscow speech. Line 22: *Vin gai, vin triste* would be footnoted by a Russian editor ('Wine of gladness, wine of sadness').

'Let us free words . . .': First published 1922. The epigraph is from another poem in *My Sister Life* for which I do not have a finished version. Here is the concluding stanza of 'Balashov' (a town in the Saratov province), whence it comes:

> My friend, you ask me: Who will pray
> For fire in speeches of a fool?
> By rule of linden, rule of rail,
> By fire summer was to rule.

Line 7: Madder is a herbaceous plant of the genus *Rubia*, especially *Rubia tinctorum*, from which a crimson dye is made. Line 14: Quicken is a name for the rowan-tree, which bears clusters of red berries in autumn, and minium is a name for the red oxide of lead which has given us the word 'miniature'. Line 31: 'the infirmary jaspers', stone floors in hospitals. Line 35: Jadwiga and Jagiello are the Polish queen and the Lithuanian prince whose betrothal united their nations in 1386. The Jagiello dynasty ruled until the sixteenth century.

Themes & Variations

This is a minutes younger twin of *My Sister Life*, a parallel development of words from the same seed: published in January 1923, directly after the Moscow edition of the earlier book and almost simultaneously with the Berlin edition, it contained everything written between 1916 and 1922 that did not fit the overall scheme of Pasternak's lyrical decameron. Like the poems of *My Sister Life*, the poems of *Themes & Variations* became part of the 1928 canon without revisions. Pasternak insisted on using the antiquated spelling *varyatsii* in preference to the modern *variatsii*, and the ampersand in my version of the title pays homage to that quaint singularity.

'Margarita': First published 1920. Pasternak's relationship with Goethe's *Faust*, which he translated into Russian late in his life, may well be a subject of special study. This poem was initially part of a 'Faust' cycle. Margarita is not of course a spelling of the name of Goethe's heroine common in English, but I prefer it to plain Margaret. Line 6: Archil is a kind of lichen.

'At dusk I see you . . .': First published 1922. Line 22: bromin, a variant pronunciation and spelling of bromine, is by popular misconception the substance (actually potassium bromide) prescribed as a sedative.

'Plait these splashes . . .': First published 1922. This and the subsequent four poems are part of a nine-poem cycle entitled 'The Rupture', that is, the lovers' final quarrel, a break-up. The five versions here (Pasternak's numbers 4, 5, 6, 7 and 9) are presented in a slightly different sequence to capture the variation of tone. Line 5: The hunter Actaeon surprised Artemis bathing and the amazon Atalanta was outrun by Milanion, but accounts of the myths vary.

'Disappointed? . . .': First published 1922. Line 6: J. S. Bach (merely 'Sebastian' in the original).

'Just try to prevent me . . .': First published 1922. Line 2: Evangelista Torricelli, Italian physicist and secretary to Galileo, concieved a design for the barometer.

'My friend my tender O . . .': First published 1922. Line 5: The Norwegian is Amundsen and, by extension, his ship. In 1918 Amundsen made headlines when he turned to air exploration (hence the 'flight' in the opening line).

'A trembling clavier . . .': First published 1922. Line 10: Goethe's *The Sorrows of Young Werther* and, by extension, the novel's hero.

'Thus they begin . . .': First published 1923. This and the subsequent three poems are from a five-poem cycle entitled 'I Could Forget Them', here in a different sequence.

'For My Enemies': First published 1923. The title in the original names the enemy as slander, here made more general and 'classical', as in the Russian.

'Could I forget them? . . .': First published 1923. Line 2: Charter in the sense of a train booking. Line 3: Gin in the sense of an instrument of torture.

'We are few . . .': First published 1923. The original manuscript title of the poem was 'The Poets', although it is untitled in *Themes & Variations*, where it first appeared. A presentation copy of the book was inscribed by Pasternak to Tsvetayeva with the words 'To the incomparable poet Marina Tsvetayeva, "from Donetz, from fire, from hell".' Tsvetayeva, for Pasternak, was one of the poets of whom there were 'perhaps only three'.

'Spring, I am from the street . . .': First published 1922. This and the subsequent poem are from a group of five entitled 'Spring'.

'Now shut your eyes . . .': First published 1923. Line 6: 'philistine' should be pronounced, as the rhyme requires, with a long 'i'.

'In comfort . . .': First published 1923. In *Themes & Variations* this preceded the 'Spring' poems and is here out of sequence. In the book it follows the opening poem of the book's final cycle, 'The Unquiet Garden', of which all the poems that follow here are also part. Line 2: Pasternak is more specific: 'By furniture in the Jacob style'. The firms of Georges Jacob and his son François Jacob-Desmalter, Jacob Frères and Jacob Desmalter & Cie, were the leading makers of furniture of all forms in the Empire style, both before and after the Revolution, until the Jacob tradition ended with the sale of the family business in 1847.

'Autumn': First published 1922. This poem opened a group of five entitled 'Autumn', in which the following poem came last.

'The Riddle': First published 1923. This poem, untitled in the original, ends *Themes & Variations*.

'Poetry': First published 1922. This poem is out of sequence. Line 7: The battle alluded to in the original is Borodino.